D0464368

HISTORICAL GEOLOGY

The quality of the materials used in the manufacture of this book is governed by continued postwar shortages.

(*Frontispiece.*)

"Window to the Past." A mural by Constantin Astori in the American Museum of Natural History. The animals were drawn by Alastair Brown. Cliffs of Jurassic and Cretaceous rocks rise from the shores of an inland sea. The large flying reptile in the air above is *Pteranodon;* the smaller one is *Nyctosaurus. Dimorphodon* is shown in the three lower figures. (*Photograph from the American Museum of Natural History.*)

HISTORICAL GEOLOGY

The Geologic History of North America

BY

RUSSELL C. HUSSEY

Professor of Geology, University of Michigan

SECOND EDITION
SECOND IMPRESSION

McGRAW-HILL BOOK COMPANY, INC.

NEW YORK AND LONDON

1947

HISTORICAL GEOLOGY

Copyright, 1944, 1947, by the
McGraw-Hill Book Company, Inc.

PRINTED IN THE UNITED STATES OF AMERICA

*All rights reserved. This book, or
parts thereof, may not be reproduced
in any form without permission of
the publishers.*

THE MAPLE PRESS COMPANY, YORK, PA.

PREFACE TO THE SECOND EDITION

This second edition of "Historical Geology" follows the same general plan of presentation that was used in the first edition, and the author has kept in mind the fact that the book will be used chiefly by students who are interested in the cultural aspect of the subject. It is very encouraging to see the large numbers of students who are studying elementary physical and historical geology, because both subjects contain a great deal of material that is both valuable and interesting. Increasing numbers of Americans are seeing more of our country every summer, and geology is the one subject that will help them to understand the face of the earth with its varied features.

The book has been simplified in several places by the removal of material that the students are seldom required to remember, and some new and better illustrations have been added. A few generic names have been changed, and some paragraphs have been altered to take into account recent changes in the classification of vertebrates.

The author is very grateful to Dr. Howard Meyerhoff for valuable suggestions concerning changes in the new edition. Dr. George Cohee, of the United States Geological Survey, helped revise several old plates, assisted in making some new ones, and gave permission to use one of his recent plates made during his study of the oil fields in Michigan and adjoining states. Dr. Claude Hibbard, vertebrate paleontologist at the University of Michigan, has helped check recent changes in the names of some of the vertebrates. Many letters have been received which contain kindly and valuable comments, and the author is indebted to all these writers for their helpful suggestions.

Everything that we can do to spread the gospel of geology to more people will not only strengthen the position of geology as a science but will also open up many new and delightful vistas for thousands of people.

RUSSELL C. HUSSEY

ANN ARBOR, MICH.,
August, 1947.

v

PREFACE TO THE FIRST EDITION

Anybody who attempts to write the geologic history of the last 2,000,000,000 years and to confine his story within the limits of a single moderate-sized volume, has a difficult task. There is an abundance of material available and the writer must necessarily describe only the most significant events, but there are also long stretches of time for which no record can be found, and it is often difficult or even impossible to bridge over these lost intervals.

Historical geology reaches into many different fields of science. It describes the earth's changing physical features and the development of plants and animals from the time of their earliest appearance down to the present. It seems almost inevitable that nearly everyone should have an interest in the earth on which he lives and that a knowledge of the major events in the history of our unique planet should be a part of every liberal education. A person can hardly step out of doors or look through a window without seeing some aspect of geology, while on his travels geologic history is displayed everywhere. Historical geology is a great book of nature that offers unforgettable knowledge of the past and a vision of the future.

The methods of presenting the geologic history of North America in this book are not radically different from those employed by other authors in similar volumes. Emphasis is placed upon those features of the earth that most people will see some day, and the extinct animals that are described may be found in the natural history museums open to the public in many towns and cities.

A certain number of scientific words and terms must be used in every textbook of science, but the reader should remember that these words are always subordinate to the broad panorama that is being presented. General principles are always important to the student who is beginning the study of geology. Many of these principles are presented in the early part of the book, with more detailed discussions distributed throughout the rest of the text. A mere recital of geologic events may have a certain amount of interest in some cases, but this interest can be greatly increased and the subject matter made far clearer by brief descriptions of some of the methods employed by geologists in deciphering the geologic record.   The student should be given the best answers possible to such questions as "How do you know that this is true?   Where did you get the information upon which this conclusion is based?"   The great majority of students who elect geology in our schools will take only the elementary courses.   Such persons are interested chiefly in the cultural side of the subject.   This phase of geology has much that is of value if it is presented in a manner that can be readily understood and if the student is not confused by too many technical terms, such as are of interest only to the professional geologist.

We are at the beginning of a new era in our educational system. People have a right to know more about the things that scientists have discovered in their laboratories and as a result of field work everywhere.   Geologists can render a valuable service to the cause of education in general by giving to the people of this country a wider knowledge of the great natural science, geology.

Many persons were very helpful to the author during the preparation of the manuscript and the illustrations for this book.   Professor Kenneth Landes read the entire text and helped in securing several excellent pictures.   Professor Armand Eardley helped with those portions of the book that deal with periods of mountain building and furnished an outline history of the Ouachita and Wichita geosynclines.   Professor Eardley also kindly permitted me to use a part of one of his unpublished maps.   Professor George Ehlers helped with several problems of invertebrate paleontology. Other colleagues in the Department of Geology offered many valuable suggestions and criticisms.

The original drawings by John Jesse Hayes were made under the direction of the author.   Miss Dorothy O'Donnell made most of the pen-and-ink sketches as well as some of the maps and charts.   Dr. Glenn Tague, of Williams College, drew the set of diagrams illustrating the history of the Appalachian Mountains.   Mr. M. V. Denny, curator in the Mineralogy Department of the University of Michigan, did most of the photographic work that was involved in making certain illustrations; and Mr. Eck Stanger, photographer for the *Ann Arbor News*, was also very helpful with several problems of photography.

Special thanks for pictures must be given to the New York State Museum, The Carnegie Museum, The American Museum of Natural History, The Chicago Natural History Museum, The Alabama Musum of Natural History, The Canadian Geological Survey, the geological surveys of Kansas and Michigan, The United

States Geological Survey, The Carnegie Institution of Washington and the Geophysical Laboratory, Dr. Carl Dutton, Dr. Walter B. Lang, Dr. Orlo Childs, Dr. M. K. Elias, and Mr. M. V. Denny.

Several of the paleogeographic maps have been modified by permission from "Textbook of Geology," Part II, Historical Geology, by Charles Schuchert and C. O. Dunbar, published by John Wiley & Sons, Inc.; and from "Introduction to Geology," by E. B. Branson and W. A. Tarr, published by McGraw-Hill Book Company, Inc.

RUSSELL C. HUSSEY

ANN ARBOR, MICH.,
August, 1944.

CONTENTS

HISTORICAL GEOLOGY

CHAPTER I

INTRODUCTION

THE ROCKS CAN TELL MANY ROMANTIC STORIES

> He who with pocket-hammer smites the edge
> Of luckless rock or prominent stone, disguised
> In weather-stains or crusted o'er by Nature
> With her first growths, detaching by the stroke
> A chip or splinter, to resolve his doubts;
> And, with that ready answer satisfied,
> The substance classes by some barbarous name,
> And hurries on; or from the fragments picks
> His specimen, if but haply interveined
> With sparkling mineral, or should crystal cube
> Lurk in its cells, and thinks himself enriched,
> Wealthier, and doubtless wiser, than before!
> —WORDSWORTH, "The Excursion"

The greatest and most important historical record ever written is enclosed in the rocks of the earth's crust. This extraordinary document lies all around us. In spite of the fact that many of its pages are missing and that great parts of it lie veiled in the obscurity of the distant past, the main truths may still be read and, when these have been deciphered, they present a series of vast panoramas tremendous in their sweep and intensely dramatic. This great book of geologic history, which has recorded the story of the earth and its inhabitants through nearly two billion years, reveals how many events that occurred millions of years ago have profoundly affected the course of human history and shaped the destinies of nations. It is difficult to conceive of anything that has had a greater influence upon the development of our country than the vast iron and copper deposits in the Lake Superior region; yet these were formed countless ages ago. Many of the things that we regard as essentials today are possible only because of events that occurred in the very distant past, while most of the materials that are neces-

1

sary in this modern age come from the earth. Thus they all represent some phases of geology.

Since it became a planet, our world has passed through a remarkable series of changes. The familiar features of its present time-worn surface have not always existed. Mountain ranges once towered to great heights in regions where seemingly endless plains now stretch to the horizon. Sun-baked deserts have been replaced by well-watered farming lands and great forest areas. Vast shallow seas have invaded the continents from time to time, and their ancient shore lines may still be traced in many places. Tremendous changes such as these seem incredible to most people, but they are no more startling than the spectacular procession of animals that moved across the scene during past ages. Great herds of elephants were formerly as common in North America as they are today in parts of southeastern Asia or Africa. Huge reptiles once flew in the air, swam through the seas, and wandered widely over the lands. Camels, members of the rhinoceros family, lions, true wild horses, and a host of other animals that are utterly foreign to this land today were once natives of what we know as the United States. The whole course of geologic history reveals the constantly changing face of the earth and the development of life upon it, from the forms of primitive creatures to the higher races of mankind. Without the information found in the rocks, this most significant of all historical records would have remained unknown.

Most people are aware that geological science has made important contributions to human welfare, particularly in the development of natural resources; but few stop to think that a little knowledge of geology may give large aesthetic rewards. The works of nature are more inspiring than anything that the art of man has produced. Nothing is more beautiful than the earth upon which we live. To almost everyone mountains and valleys, great canyons, deserts, plains, and rivers are interesting merely as scenery; but the really intelligent observer will want to know more about the origin and the history of such features. The development of a lively curiosity about the innumerable geological features on every hand, together with the study that will gratify that curiosity, cannot fail to make all travel more enjoyable and life far richer for anyone. Every excursion will then become an adventure of the mind, and the great scenic regions of the world will have new and important meaning. Only by knowing the distant past as it is revealed through the medium of historical geology can we understand the present.

CHAPTER II

THE ORIGIN OF THE EARTH

They say
The solid earth whereon we tread

In tracts of fluent heat began,
And grew to seeming-random forms,
The seeming prey of cyclic storms,
Till at the last arose the man.
—TENNYSON, "In Memoriam"

THE SOLAR SYSTEM

The Sun. The sun is the center of our solar system, yet, even though its diameter is 860,000 miles, it is one of the lesser stars in the universe. The temperature of the sun varies from about 6,000°C. at the surface to several million degrees toward the center. This intensely hot body furnishes all the heat and light that are necessary to maintain life upon the earth. Many of the chemical elements that are known to exist in the rocks of the earth's crust and in its atmosphere have been identified upon the sun also, and the two bodies are closely related in chemical composition.

The Planets. The nine planets that have been discovered in our solar system are Mercury, Venus, Earth, Mars, Jupiter, Saturn, Uranus, Neptune, and Pluto. Mercury, which is nearest to the sun, has a diameter of 3,100 miles; while Pluto, farthest from the sun, is about the size of the earth. Jupiter is the giant planet, with a diameter of 88,600 miles. The earth is the densest of the planets, having a specific gravity of 5.5, while the specific gravity of Saturn is only 0.72. The planets revolve about the sun in concentric orbits that are nearly circular. Only the earth is known to be inhabited, although some form of life may exist upon Mars.

Satellites. Satellites, or moons, are associated with all the planets except Mercury, Venus, and possibly Pluto. Our own satellite, the familiar moon (Fig. 1) of our planet, is so close to the earth that it can easily be photographed and many of its topographic features have been mapped in considerable detail. The same side of the moon is always turned toward the earth. The surface is apparently a barren waste, covered by vast lava fields, lofty moun-

3

tains, and thousands of craters, which may be of volcanic origin although some of them might have been produced by the impact of meteors. The gravitational force of the moon is not sufficiently strong to retain an appreciable atmosphere, and the temperature

FIG. 1.—A portion of the moon's surface showing a range of mountains, the Apennines, rising 18,000 feet above the plain. The smooth areas are probably lava flows. Observe the numerous craters. (*Courtesy of Lick Observatory. Negative by J. H. Moore and J. F. Chappell.*)

at the surface varies from 214°F. at noon to −243°F. during the night. These conditions, together with the absence of water in any recognizable form, make it impossible for life as we know it upon the earth to exist at the surface of the moon.

The Asteroids. About 1,200 distinct solid bodies have been discovered revolving about the sun in a belt between Jupiter and

Mars. They are all small objects varying in diameter from about 5 to nearly 500 miles, the origin of which has never been satisfactorily explained. There are probably many asteroids or planetoids still undiscovered.

Comets and Meteors. Comets (Fig. 2), with their luminous heads and tails, are among the most interesting members of our solar system. The heads are probably composed of swarms of meteor-like bodies and the tails consist of tiny particles driven away from the heads by the pressure of light from the sun. Some comets enter our solar system from outer space, move around the sun in great parabolic orbits, and speed away never to return; while others travel in elliptical paths and come back at regular intervals.

Any observer who watches the heavens on a clear night may see many luminous objects, called meteors, flash across the sky. These are mostly small bodies and the majority of them are consumed by friction with our atmosphere. Those that reach the earth are called meteorites (Fig. 3) and they present many unsolved problems. Studies are now being made to determine whether meteorites originate outside or within the limits of our solar system and the results of this interesting research may have important bearings upon the source of the material that makes up the earth.

Fig. 2.—Halley's Comet, May 6, 1910. (*Courtesy of Lick Observatory.*)

The stony meteorites are chiefly complex silicates while the others are composed of iron and nickel (Fig. 4) with a subordinate amount of cobalt.

THEORIES OF THE ORIGIN AND EVOLUTION OF THE SOLAR SYSTEM

The origin and evolution of our solar system is one of the unsolved problems confronting modern science. All attempts at its solution have met with many serious objections. However, in

spite of very great difficulties, some real progress has been made
and the problem is not a hopeless one.

Fig. 3.—Meteor Crater near Winslow, Arizona.   (*Courtesy of Spence Air Photos.*)

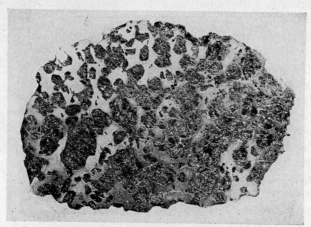

Fig. 4.—Polished surface of a nickel-iron meteorite.   The dark areas are cavities
filled with olivine; the light portions are metallic iron with about 8 per cent of nickel.
(*From University of Michigan collection.*)

The Nebular Hypothesis.   The nebular hypothesis starts with a
vast disk-shaped cloud of hot gaseous material, called a "nebula,"
with a diameter that reached beyond the orbit of our most distant

planet. This mass was rotating very slowly at first, and the gravitational attraction between its particles caused the nebula to shrink. As the shrinking continued, the speed of rotation increased. Finally, the outermost portion of the gaseous mass was rotating so rapidly that centrifugal force was greater than gravitation and a ring of gas separated from the parent body in the equatorial region. Contraction continued, the rotational speed increased, and nine rings were formed one after another. The material that composed each ring gradually condensed into the nine planets and the asteroids. Secondary rings formed around some of the planets and these produced the satellites. The asteroids were formed from a ring that condensed into many bodies instead of one.

Objections to the Nebular Hypothesis. According to this hypothesis the sun should be rotating very rapidly, since it is the last remnant of the original nebula, whose speed of rotation is supposed to have increased gradually as successive rings were formed. Instead of rotating more rapidly than any of the planets, the sun rotates rather slowly. There should also be an appreciable equatorial bulge on the sun, as another ring is formed, but there is no perceptible flattening at the poles. It is also very doubtful whether rings of gaseous matter would separate in the manner assumed by the hypothesis, and it is even more doubtful whether such rings would condense into planets, once they had formed. This hypothesis also encounters great difficulty in explaining the fact that three of Jupiter's satellites and one of those belonging to Saturn move in retrograde orbits.

The nebular hypothesis was originally proposed by the great philosopher, Immanuel Kant, and later elaborated by the French mathematician, Laplace. No modifications of it have been proposed that overcome its fundamental difficulties; therefore, apparently it must be abandoned.

The Planetesimal Hypothesis. The planetesimal hypothesis was developed by T. C. Chamberlin, a geologist, and F. R. Moulton, an astronomer. According to this conception, a star passed close to our sun at some time in the exceedingly remote past. As this star approached, great tidal bulges began to form on opposite sides of the sun and these reached a maximum when the two bodies were closest to each other. At that time our sun was partly disrupted, as great masses of material were violently torn away in a succession of bolts.

This erupted matter cooled to form a vast number of small solid bodies, called "planetesimals." The largest of these acted as nuclei, which attracted to themselves smaller planetesimals, and thus the planets slowly grew to their present size. The five major planets were formed around the largest nuclei on the side next to the passing star, and the minor planets were formed from smaller nuclei on the opposite side. Secondary nuclei acted as centers of accumulation for the satellites. Some of the meteors that may be seen on any clear night are supposed to be planetesimals still being attracted to the earth.

Objections to the Planetesimal Hypothesis. A number of very serious objections have been raised to the planetesimal hypothesis, some of them geological and others astronomical. It is doubtful whether the planetesimals would collect to form the planets, since collisions between the various particles would either reduce them to finer bits or dissipate them as gas. The densities of the major planets are still so low that they must still be largely in a gaseous condition and so they could hardly have been solid originally.

Fig. 5.—Thomas Chrowder Chamberlin (1843–1928). A great geologist, an inspiring leader.

There are excellent reasons for believing that the earth has a very dense metallic core, with the other materials arranged around this core in roughly concentric layers, which become less dense from the center outward. This arrangement of matter according to density requires a molten stage in the history of the earth, yet the planetesimal hypothesis assumes that our planet was originally a solid body.

The Gaseous Hypothesis. The gaseous hypothesis, as developed by Sir James Jeans and Harold Jeffreys, starts with the assumption that our sun was partly disrupted by the gravitational pull of another star as the two bodies passed very close to each other. Some of the material was drawn out from our sun while the other star was approaching, and this disrupted matter increased in quantity up to the time of closest approach and then gradually decreased. A spindle-shaped filament of incandescent gas was thus produced, which extended out into space at least as far as the most distant planet. The instability of this comparatively thin stream of hot gaseous material caused it to break up into a number of parts, which gradually assumed spherical form and slowly cooled to form the planets. In order to account for the great speed with which these present planets rotate, Jeffreys later assumed that the star and our sun actually collided a little off-center, and, as the two bodies pulled apart, a hot gaseous ribbon was drawn out, with its parts in extremely violent rotary motion, caused by the friction of collision.

Objections to the Gaseous Hypothesis. The energy of motion is very unequally distributed among the various members of our solar system. Jupiter possesses nearly 60 per cent of this energy, while the sun, with its vastly greater mass, has less than 3 per cent. This very remarkable distribution of the energy of motion cannot be explained by any of the hypotheses that have been offered. H. N. Russell attempted to overcome the difficulty by assuming that the sun was a double star when the collision occurred and that the smaller of its two components was disrupted to form the planets, asteroids, and satellites. The energy of motion thus came largely from the disrupted star, while the other member became the sun.

In spite of the fact that all the hypotheses thus far advanced have failed to explain the origin of our solar system, the following conclusions are fairly certain. The planets were once extremely hot, with temperatures above the melting point of rock; and they probably developed from the sun or from some other star. The planets grew by a process of condensation that proceeded at a comparatively fast rate and not by a slow process of accretion.

Reading References

JEANS, SIR JAMES: "The Universe around Us," 341 pp., The Macmillan Company, New York, 1929.

RUSSELL, HENRY NORRIS: "The Solar System and Its Origin," 144 pp., The Macmillan Company, New York, 1935.

WATSON, FLETCHER G.: "Between the Planets," 222 pp., The Blakiston Company, Philadelphia, 1941.

WHIPPLE, FRED L.: "Earth, Moon and Planets," 293 pp., The Blakiston Company, Philadelphia, 1941.

CHAPTER III

ORGANIZING THE GEOLOGIC RECORD

THE GEOLOGIC TIME SCALE

Any historical record that covers a considerable stretch of time must have some method of organizing the events with which it is concerned, in order that they may be placed in their proper time relations with respect to each other. Whenever possible, the numerous incidents in human history are referred to certain years, either B.C. or A.D. There are also larger and especially important divisions in the story of mankind, such as the Christian Era, The Dark Ages, and the Renaissance.

Purpose of the Scale. The great number of significant events that have occurred during the vast length of recorded geologic time has made it of particular importance for geologists to devise a system of organizing these events in a systematic way according to their respective time relations. The geologic time scale has been devised for this purpose. Although the divisions are somewhat arbitrary, this scale has proved to be quite satisfactory.

The Fundamental Law of Superposition. If we observe the various undisturbed layers of rock as they are exposed in the face of a limestone quarry or in the walls of a canyon, it is immediately obvious that the bottom strata must have been deposited first (Fig. 7) and that they form, therefore, the oldest part of the section. Hence, the strata must become younger and younger from the base of the outcrop to the top. This law of superposition is the first and most fundamental principle used in classifying the rocks according to their relative age.

A normal sequence of beds is often disturbed in mountain regions where folding has occurred. Thrust faults sometimes move great thicknesses of older rock from their original positions and leave them resting upon much younger formations. The Matterhorn is a famous example of such an overthrust mass, and in Glacier National Park Pre-Cambrian strata that have been pushed eastward several miles now rest upon beds of Cretaceous age (Fig. 215). The many special problems of sequence that exist in regions where

TIME UNITS			OROGENY
CENOZOIC ERA	TERTIARY PERIOD	RECENT EPOCH	
		PLEISTOCENE EPOCH	COAST RANGE REV.
		PLIOCENE EPOCH	
		MIOCENE EPOCH	MID-TERTIARY DIST.
		OLIGOCENE EPOCH	
		EOCENE EPOCH	
		PALEOCENE EPOCH	
MESOZOIC ERA	CRETACEOUS PERIOD		LARAMIDE REV.
	JURASSIC PERIOD		NEVADIAN DIST.
	TRIASSIC PERIOD		PALISADE DIST.
PALEOZOIC ERA	PERMIAN PERIOD		APPALACHIAN REV.
	PENNSYLVANIAN PERIOD	CARBON-IFEROUS	Coal deposits
	MISSISSIPPIAN PERIOD		
	DEVONIAN PERIOD		ACADIAN DIST.
	SILURIAN PERIOD		salt deposits, sediments Red beds Lime Stone
	ORDOVICIAN PERIOD		line Stone TACONIC DIST. Greatest extension of seas
	CAMBRIAN PERIOD		Fossils Shale Conglomerous
PROTERO-ZOIC ERA	KEEWENAWAN PERIOD		no fossils KILLARNEY REV.
	HURONIAN PERIOD		egneseous Lime Stone
ARCHEOZOIC ERA	ALGOMAN PERIOD		ALGOMAN REV.
	TIMISKAMING PERIOD		
	LAURENTIAN PERIOD		LAURENTIAN REV.
	KEEWATIN PERIOD		

FIG. 6.—The geologic time scale.

the crust of the earth has been disturbed can usually be solved by field studies and the original succession discovered.

Eras of Geologic Time.   There have been times in the course of geologic history when over great areas of the earth's surface, mountains were formed on an unusually grand scale.   These tremendous crustal upheavals are called "revolutions."   During such periods

FIG. 7.—The lowest layers in an undisturbed sequence of sedimentary rocks are the oldest because they were deposited first.   Potsdam sandstone of Cambrian age in Ausable Chasm, New York.   (*Courtesy of New York State Museum.*)

of continental elevation the numerous agencies of weathering and erosion were extremely active, especially in mountain areas; and widespread unconformities were produced. These world-wide periods of diastrophism, together with the great unconformities, are used by geologists as natural and convenient points for ending the eras, which thus become the greatest divisions of geologic time. Revolutions are recurring events in the history of the earth, but they have not been evenly spaced in time and, as a consequence, different eras are of very unequal length.

Periods of Geologic Time. The continents have been invaded several times, more or less widely, by bodies of marine water called "epeiric" and "marginal" seas. These invasions have occurred in great cycles, each of which begins with the slow advance of the sea over the continent and ends when the land has once more emerged from the water. The complete withdrawal of a sea at the end of each cycle is caused by a broad continental uplift, which often accompanies a mountain-making disturbance that is less widespread in its effect than are the greater revolutions. The extensive erosion and the resulting unconformity, together with the orogeny, serve as distinctive time markers that enable geologists to separate one period from another.

Effects of Minor Earth Movements. In addition to the great upheavals that result from the revolutions and disturbances there have been many local crustal movements during the past, just as there are today. The region of Florida is still rising, while there has been recent subsidence in the Chesapeake Bay area. These numerous minor upheavals have caused a great many breaks in the geologic record that are entirely local in their effects, although they complicate the general situation and make it difficult to determine the exact relationships between the formations within the area of localized disturbance and those in the surrounding region.

Significance of Faunal Changes. The many epeiric seas that have invaded the different continents since the Paleozoic era have been populated by varied assemblages of animals, known as "faunas." Vast numbers of these organisms died, and their shells and skeletons were buried and fossilized in the slowly accumulating marine sediments. When, at the close of each period, the seas retreated widely from the lands, the animals continued their existence chiefly in the shallow waters that covered the continental shelves, where they slowly changed or evolved during the long emergent interval. When the seas began to encroach upon the continents at the beginning of the next period, or cycle of marine invasion, evolutionary changes had produced new faunal assemblages, which were quite distinct from those of the preceding period. The fossils representing these different faunas have been collected, named, and arranged according to their proper stratigraphic positions. They are called "index" fossils, because each assemblage represents the animals that were characteristic of a certain period of geologic time.

Epochs of Geologic Time.   The periods are divided into epochs, and these comparatively small divisions of geologic time are determined by minor and local breaks within each period, such as might be produced by a temporary withdrawal of the sea from certain areas.

Systems, Series, and Formations.   All the rocks of a geologic period are grouped together under the name of "system," while those of an epoch are called "series."   The rocks representing still smaller time divisions are referred to as "formations."

THE GEOLOGIC RECORD

The readily accessible portion of the geologic record is found in all the rocks that make up the outermost portion of the earth's crust.   Some exceedingly important chapters in this story occur in the great succession of sedimentary formations in which is found the history of plant and animal life through many millions of years. Numerous other events in the geologic history of the earth are clearly recorded in various kinds of rocks.   Gneisses, schists, and truncated folds tell us of incredibly powerful compressive forces that once heaved up the crust of the earth into vast mountain ranges, which were gradually worn away by the slowly acting forces of weathering and erosion.   Heavy beds of conglomerate often reveal the former existence of steep, rocky shores and swiftly flowing streams.   Coralline limestones, even though they occur in high latitudes, are a reminder of clear, warm, and even tropical seas.

The geologic record far surpasses all books in the unlimited variety of information that it contains and in the supreme importance of this information as a matter of recorded history and as a means of understanding the present and of forecasting the future.

Fragmentary Nature of the Record.   There is no place on earth where a complete record of all the events in geologic history has been left, and there is no possibility that more than a small part of the entire story will ever be known.   The information that geologists possess is an assemblage of facts that have been gathered from all parts of the world as a result of studies made by thousands of workers.

Unconformities.   Since the very earliest eras, weathering and erosion have been constantly acting upon the surface of the earth, breaking up rocks and carrying the fragments, large and small, to new places.   Although the agencies usually work very slowly, after they have been operating for millions of years vast mountain ranges may have been removed, and thus a great part of the geologic

record may have been destroyed.   All the destructive forces that
have been active through the ages are responsible for the removal of
thousands of feet of igneous, sedimentary, and metamorphic rocks;
and, although erosional remnants may be left in a few places, those
parts that have been carried away can never be recovered.

When rocks are weathered and transported bit by bit to some
other locality, they are furnishing material with which to write new
chapters in the geologic history.   Nature's forces are thus constantly at work tearing down in one place and building up in
another—processes that have been going on for countless ages.   The

Fig. 8.—Disconformity, caused by erosion, between the Harding series and the
Fremont limestone, both of Ordovician age, northwest of Cañon City, Colorado.

great number of erosional unconformities (Fig. 8) found throughout
the different rock sections in all parts of the world are evidence of
missing pages—sometimes, missing chapters—in the story of the
ages.

Lack of Deposition. Geologists are greatly dependent upon
sedimentary deposits for information about the geologic past; therefore, in regions where no sediments have been deposited, there are
breaks in the record and important parts of the story may be missing.   Large areas in the state of Florida are now only a few feet
above sea level.   These places are neither receiving any important
quantity of sedimentary material nor being subjected to vigorous

erosion. This condition has existed since Florida appeared above the sea, several millions of years ago. Such a lack of deposition is due largely to the fact that there is no source of sediment available.

In Michigan and the neighboring states, no geologic record is known for the entire Mesozoic era or for almost all of the Cenozoic era, probably because no appreciable quantity of sediments representing these eras was ever deposited in the Great Lakes area. It is thus almost impossible to write the Mesozoic and Cenozoic geologic history of Michigan and its neighbor states.

Older Rocks Are Buried beneath Younger Deposits. Wherever sedimentary or igneous rocks accumulate, either on land or beneath the sea, they always cover up some older deposits, which may eventually be deeply buried. In this way a large part of the geologic record is concealed and has become inaccessible. If mine shafts penetrate some of the deeper formations, their presence may be thus revealed; but, under such conditions, a thorough study of the rock is impossible. Drill cores may bring up from thousands of feet below the surface samples of sediments containing identifiable fossils; yet no great amount of information can be obtained from such small quantities of material. Even such deep burial is not necessary in order effectively to conceal the rock, because geologists are usually able to examine only those beds that are actually exposed at the surface.

Many of the best outcrops of rock are found in quarries or along the walls of canyons, where only the edges of the various strata can be studied. A thorough examination of the various beds is obviously impossible under these conditions.

Metamorphism. The powerful forces that cause regional metamorphism may alter the rocks over a large area so profoundly that their nature will be completely changed. While this does not destroy the rock itself, the original record is either obliterated or rendered so obscure that it cannot be read. Fossiliferous shales may be changed into schists, and all traces of the organisms are then destroyed. Many limestones have been altered into marbles, with the result that the fossils they contained are nearly always so distorted as to have lost their value.

Rock Outcrops That Have Not Been Studied. One very obvious reason why knowledge of geologic history is so incomplete lies in the fact that not all the accessible rock outcrops have been studied by geologists and that many of them have been examined only superficially. Time may correct some of this deficiency.

CORRELATION

When a study is being made of the rocks in a certain area, the geologist must determine the particular period during which the beds were deposited and discover just how closely the various outcrops are related one to another. Comparisons will also be made with formations of the same age in other regions. This process of comparing one exposure with another in order to determine their precise relationships, including the age equivalence, is known as "correlation."

The geologic history of North America is made up of information discovered by great numbers of geologists working in many different localities; and all the events in this complex historical record have had to be correlated, or placed in their proper age relations with respect to one another.

It will never be possible to determine the exact years in which the events of the geologic past occurred. It would be highly desirable if geologists were able to do so, but the material with which they are working does not yield such precise information and probably never will. In the case of some rocks, especially those that were deposited before the Cambrian period, correlation is so difficult that authorities differ widely as to their age. Such difficulties may eventually be overcome, at least in part, but geology is not an exact science and many of the correlations that are now accepted will be changed in the future.

Methods of Correlation. *By Lithologic Similarity.* When several rock outcrops within a small area have very similar lithologic characteristics, they are probably of the same age and may properly be correlated. This is sometimes the only method of correlation that can be used, particularly in the case of igneous and metamorphic rocks where no fossils are present. Correlation by means of lithologic similarity has little value where the outcrops are far apart, because rocks belonging to widely separated periods of time are sometimes found to be almost identical lithologically.

By Similarity of Sequence. The following hypothetical case will serve to illustrate correlation by means of similar sequences. Two rock sections, each 100 feet thick, are found in the same region. A comparison of these sections shows that they are very similar throughout. The same kinds of rocks are found in both places and the beds follow each other in the same order from bottom to top. All the peculiarities of lithology in one section are found in the corresponding layers of the other. Such striking similarity is strong proof that the rocks in the two exposures were deposited at the same time.

This method of correlation may be used even though the sequences are not exactly the same. It is possible that certain beds might be missing from one section, either because of erosion or because of lack of deposition, yet the general sequence of strata would be very much alike (Fig. 130).

A certain well-defined layer, with easily recognizable characteristics, is sometimes found in a number of different outcrops, and, wherever this stratum occurs, it always occupies the same position in the section with respect to the other beds. A horizon marker so consistent is often very useful for purposes of correlation.

By Continuity of Outcrop. If a certain outcrop of rock can be traced as a continuous exposure from one place to another, then it is clearly of the same age throughout its entire extent. This is a very exact method of correlation, wherever it can be used. It is sometimes employed in canyons or along river valleys, where exposures may extend for several miles without a break.

By Means of Index Fossils. Each one of the geologic periods above the Pre-Cambrian is characterized by a certain faunal assemblage different from that found in any other period. Such organisms, which—as we have noted—are called "index" fossils, are used for purposes of correlation, especially in formations of marine origin, where the same kind of fossils have a wide distribution. Uniform environmental conditions prevailed throughout several of the epeiric seas that covered North America, and this enabled many of the marine organisms to migrate widely so that they became cosmopolitan types. Such forms permit correlation over distances that are almost continent wide and, in a few cases, even intercontinental.

The task of collecting and identifying the fossils that represent the faunas of the different periods has been accomplished by many geologists, working in all parts of the world.

When this method of correlation is used, it is not necessary that precisely the same species of fossils should occur in all the localities that are being compared. Slightly different environmental conditions might have existed in one of the places while the sediment was accumulating, thus causing minor faunal differences. A small number of fossils that are highly characteristic of a certain formation are better for purposes of correlation than a large number of organisms whose exact positions in the geologic column are not known.

It is possible to establish a relationship between deposits that were laid down upon the land and others that were formed at the same time in the sea, if both contain fossils that are known to be of the same age, even though the organisms in the two places are quite different.

Difficulties of Correlation. *Different Contemporaneous Faunas.* The correlation of continental deposits is sometimes difficult or even impossible, because diverse environmental conditions on the land during the past often gave rise to different contemporaneous faunas in localities that were close together. A plentiful supply of rainfall might produce a heavy forest growth on one side of a mountain range while, at the same time, semiarid conditions on the opposite side would cause the spread of open plains. The kinds of animals found in these two regions should normally be quite different—a fact that might lead to many difficulties in correlation at a later time.

Proof of Contemporaneous Deposits. Outcrops that are said to be of the same age may not be contemporaneous with each other. A certain deposit made during the early part of an epoch might contain a fauna very similar to that of another deposit laid down considerably later, and the two formations would probably be correlated. It is usually very difficult, or even impossible, to prove that two or more formations were deposited at exactly the same time.

PALEOGEOGRAPHY

Very few persons who look at a map of the modern world realize the many remarkable changes that have taken place in the shape and size of the lands and seas during the course of geologic history. There is a general strong belief in terra firma, and the familiar outlines of the continents seem unchanging. However, the surface of the earth is constantly being altered by weathering and erosion, and certain parts of the coastal region of North America are known to be rising while others are sinking. Indeed, not one of the well-known features of the earth's surface today is permanent.

Many of the events that have taken place on our continent during the past are extremely spectacular. A few of them, if they should be repeated, might prove disastrous to many forms of life, including the human race. In one of the remote geologic periods, about half of North America was covered by a shallow sea. During the Cenozoic era, many hundreds of volcanoes were extremely active all over the western part of the United States, while only a few thousand years ago nearly all of Canada and a large area in this country were buried under a great continental glacier.

Paleogeography attempts to restore the lands and seas as they were during past geologic time, and paleogeographic maps have been drawn to show the distribution of land and water for many of the periods and epochs. The approximate positions of major topographic features, such as mountain ranges, are indicated whenever possible. The making of these maps has involved a great deal of field work, as well as laboratory study, so that many geologists have contributed information toward the final results.

A thorough paleogeographic study of any period or portion of a period must include nearly all the different factors, both organic and inorganic, that a modern study of a region would have to consider. The problems involved are often extremely complex, and information must necessarily be obtained from all branches of science during the course of the study. The biological side of the problem itself does not include merely a study of the fossils that are found within the area, but the student must consider the nature of the rocks in which the fossils were originally buried, as well as the physiographic and structural features of the rocks, in order to determine the environmental conditions under which the animals and plants lived.

When a paleogeographic study covers a very large area and when the time unit involved is of vast extent, a number of highly generalized conclusions must necessarily be evolved. For example, the different geologic periods were millions of years long, and during that time many physical changes occurred within the area studied as well as changes in the plants and animals. The climate also changed many times during the period, and any statements that involve these factors must be so generalized that they might give the reader a somewhat false idea of the paleogeography. The best and most accurate paleogeographic studies will therefore include small areas and involve small units of time.

Even though small units are used in the study, a great many difficulties are certain to be encountered. Erosion may remove the rock in certain places while deposition will cover and conceal the beds in other localities. Only a few of the different kinds of animals and plants that may have lived within the region will be preserved as fossils, and a great many events that occurred in all the past geologic periods have left no records of themselves.

When we consider the fact that many of the events that the

geologist is called upon to interpret occurred in the very distant past, even hundreds of millions of years ago in many cases, it might seem that these interpretations would be less and less reliable as we go into the more remote ages of the geologic past. This is not always the case, because many of the forces and processes that were active in the past are still active today and they are still producing the same results at present as they have always produced. Conglomerates and sandstones, of marine origin, have nearly always been deposited within the coastal zone, and they may indicate the presence of some high, rugged neighboring land, with swiftly flowing rivers. Pure limestones are an indication of clear waters and these are usually found a considerable distance from the shore, but in some cases where the neighboring lands are extremely low, limestones may form relatively close to the shore. Beds of coal, such as those that are found in Pennsylvania, Ohio, Illinois, and many parts of the Rocky Mountains region, show where fresh water swamps once existed, and the vegetation out of which the coal was made gives a great deal of information about the climate of the coalforming epochs. Widespread deposits of glacial material called tillite have been found within the present tropics and this tillite is a certain indication of the former presence of continental glaciers.

The person who looks at the rocks merely as inanimate objects, without any knowledge of their origin, is sure to miss many interesting stories that these rocks can tell.

Making a Paleogeographic Map. We will assume that a paleogeographic map is to be drawn for the Upper Ordovician period. It is necessary first to locate accurately, on a special base map, all the places where rocks belonging to this part of the period are known to occur. In many areas there are actual exposures of Upper Ordovician formations, while in other localities the existence of these rocks has been revealed through well logs or by mining operations. The distribution of these known occurrences on the map will give at least an approximation to the size and shape of the sea in which the rocks were deposited.

Such a map cannot be very accurate in details because geologists will never be able to locate all the occurrences of Upper Ordovician formations. Erosion has undoubtedly removed the rocks in many places, while uncertainties as to correlation exist in some instances. It is seldom possible to locate the numerous bays and inlets that doubtless existed along the coasts of these ancient seas. However, it is reasonably certain that the marine waters must at some time have covered those places where Ordovician formations are known to exist.

We should remember that the different epeiric seas of the past were very unstable bodies of water, changing their outlines often during the period or epoch. The entire area known to have been covered by a certain sea during the whole span of its existence may not have been under water at any one time.

The approximate position of the shore line can sometimes be located by noting such features as oscillation ripple marks, which are commonly produced in shallow water, and sun cracks, which

Fig. 9.—Charles Schuchert (1858–1942). A leader in the field of paleogeography.

sometimes form at low tide. In a few cases old sea cliffs, wave-cut terraces, arches, and stacks mark the position of the shore with considerable accuracy.

Paleogeographic maps of the smaller time units are more accurate than those representing whole periods, but in all cases they are only approximately correct. When more information becomes available concerning the distribution and extent of rocks in the different periods, greater accuracy in making the maps will be possible.

MEASURING THE LENGTH OF GEOLOGIC TIME

The concept of time as an important factor in geologic processes did not enter into the work of the older writers on geological subjects because all the rocks were thought to be of the same age. Mountains were supposed to have been formed suddenly by colossal forces that upheaved the crust of the earth. Great masses of rocks were believed to have been torn apart with incredible violence by earthquakes to form canyons and gorges. The idea of forces acting quietly and slowly through long periods of time, in order to produce great changes in the surface of the earth, was first clearly demonstrated by the great geologist, James Hutton. His classical paper entitled "Theory of the Earth" was read before the Royal Society of Edinburgh in 1785. Hutton's conclusions were the result of many observations made in the field during years of research, and much of his work is still considered fundamentally sound.

After scientists had come to appreciate the great length of time involved in many of the geologic processes, they began to develop some means of measuring this time in terms of years. Many different methods have been suggested and tried, but none has resulted in any hope of even a reasonable degree of precision until the discovery of radioactivity. Now, with this force at their command, physicists, chemists, and geologists are working together to perfect a method of measuring geologic time that will be reasonably accurate.

The Lead Method. Uranium is an important radioactive element found in igneous rocks and certain vein minerals, such as pitchblende. This remarkable element has the property of disintegrating at a measurable rate that does not vary, no matter what the conditions may be or how much they change from time to time. Helium atoms are emitted during the transformation, and the final products in the complete decay of uranium are lead and helium. When the age of a rock is being calculated, the amount of undecayed uranium, as well as the quantity of lead present, must be determined with great accuracy. Since the disintegration rate of uranium is known, the ratio of lead present to the uranium gives the age of the rock, or the number of years since the uranium-bearing crystal was formed in the vein or from the molten magma.

The Helium Method. This method involves considerable uncertainty, because helium is a gas and it escapes readily from most rocks. If the helium retentivity of the different rock minerals can be determined, then this means of calculating the age of certain rocks may become reasonably accurate. The lead method is satisfactory only when the age determination is made from a completely unweathered specimen of rock or mineral. If some of the lead has been dissolved and carried away by circulating water, the determined age will be smaller than the actual figure. Ordinary lead may be present in the rock, in addition to that which has been

produced by the disintegration of uranium. This will produce a
false time value unless the proper correction is made. A large
number of age determinations in years have been made by the lead
method, but only a few of them can be assigned to definite horizons
in the geologic time scale. The widely distributed sedimentary
formations that are of such importance in historical geology cannot
by these methods be dated directly, but only indirectly, when they
are found associated with some igneous rock whose age in years is
known.

The following table shows some of the dates in geologic time
that may be considered approximately correct. The determinations were made by the lead method.

Mineral	Locality	Known geologic age	Age, years
Samarskite.....	Glastonbury, Connecticut	Pre-Triassic	270,000,000
Pitchblende.....	Jachymov, Bohemia	Late Paleozoic	220,000,000
Thorite........	Brevig, Norway	Permian (?)	230,000,000
Kolm..........	Güllhögen, Sweden	Latest Cambrian	400,000,000
Bröggerite......	Karlhus, Raade, Norway	Pre-Cambrian	900,000,000
Cleveite........	Aust-Agder, Arendal, Nor- way	Pre-Cambrian	1,000,000,000
Uraninite.......	Sinyaya, Pala, Carelia, Russia	Pre-Cambrian	1,800,000,000

From Goodman, Clark and Robley D. Evans.

Reading References

Goodman, Clark, and Robley D. Evans: Age Measurements by Radioactivity, *Geol. Soc. America Bull.*, vol. 52, No. 4, pp. 491–544, Apr. 1, 1941.

Holmes, Arthur: "The Age of the Earth," 263 pp., Thomas Nelson & Sons,
Ltd., New York, 1937.

Knopf, Alfred, and Others: The Age of the Earth, *Nat. Research Council
Bull.* 80, 487 pp., 1931.

CHAPTER IV

FOSSILS REVEAL THE LIFE OF THE PAST

WHAT FOSSILS ARE

The development of living things through the long geologic ages furnishes some of the most significant chapters in the earth's history. The most important factors in deciphering this part of the story are the remains of plants and animals that have been preserved as fossils in the sedimentary rocks.

How Fossilization Is Possible. Among the countless numbers of organisms that lived in the past, comparatively few have left any evidence of their former existence. This is especially true of soft-bodied animals, which have inhabited the world since very early times. Such forms lack the hard or tough parts that enable them to resist the numerous agents of destruction that are constantly active upon the surface of the earth as well as under the water. Creatures that possess shells or skeletons have the best chance of being preserved as fossils, but even the most durable structures must be buried soon after death in some protective material if they are to escape the powerful forces of disintegration and decomposition that are always acting upon exposed objects everywhere. Oxygen in the air, rain and running water, freezing and thawing, bacteria and predatory animals, the widespread effects of metamorphism— these factors and many others have been responsible for destroying all trace of most of the plants and animals that have lived and died during the long course of geologic time. When we take into account the prevalence and the universal distribution of these destructive agents over the face of the earth and to considerable depths below the surface, it seems remarkable that even a fragmentary record of past life still exists.

The bones and teeth of vertebrates and the shells of invertebrates are the structures that have been most commonly fossilized. Teeth, as a rule, persist long after the rest of the animal has disappeared, because they are composed largely of enamel and dentine—two very durable materials that are only slightly affected by the ordinary agencies of weathering. The skeletons of mastodons are frequently found in Late Pleistocene swamps within the glaciated areas, but the bones are often so poorly preserved that it is difficult to remove them from the surrounding material, while the teeth of the same individuals may be in a practically perfect state of preservation. Bones become quite fragile after their organic content has been lost, and they are often crushed by the weight of overlying sediment. The skeletons of sharks are composed of cartilage and are, therefore, seldom preserved as fossils, but the teeth have been found in vast numbers. The enamel-covered scales of certain primitive fish called "ostracoderms" occur in rocks of the Ordovician age, where they have remained practically unchanged for many millions of years.

Fossils Indicate Life That Is Past. The term "fossil" is properly used only in reference to the remains of animals and plants from the geologic past or to such objects as trails, tracks, or impressions made by these organisms. The word "fossil" is sometimes applied to inorganic objects, but in such cases it is used merely to indicate the great antiquity of the objects and the fact that they have long since disappeared.

Vast numbers of shells that belonged to living animals only a few years ago are found buried in the sands along the shores of the oceans, but such organic structures are not old enough to be called "fossils." It is impossible to distinguish sharply between the geologic and the recent past, but the dividing line is roughly drawn at about the time when the last important remnants of the Pleistocene glacier disappeared from the mainland of North America. This event took place several thousand years ago, but the exact time cannot be determined.

The great majority of fossils belong to genera and species that are extinct; but there are places along the Atlantic coastal region today where a collector could find fossil shells in Tertiary sediments that were deposited millions of years ago, while in the near-by ocean he might find the same species of animals still living.

Living Fossils. The term "living fossil" is sometimes applied to some modern animal that has descended from a very ancient stock with comparatively little change. Such forms give us valuable information about the appearance and structural details of creatures that lived in the extremely remote past. The modern lungfishes (Fig. 119) of Australia, Africa, and South America are the living representatives of a once widely distributed group that had its great development during the Devonian period. The North American opossum—the most primitive of all the living marsupials —is much the same as were its distant ancestors who lived in the Cretaceous period, when reptiles dominated the earth.

HOW ORGANISMS ARE PRESERVED AS FOSSILS

The Preservation of Flesh. Much of the ground in the great tundra region of northern Siberia is permanently frozen to a depth of more than a hundred feet. The surface zone thaws out during the brief summer and is then covered with lichens and grasses. Clusters of low willows are found here and there over the rolling surface, while stunted pines and firs are able to grow in the sheltered valleys. Of the great herds of woolly mammoths that lived in this vast waste-land during the latter part of the Pleistocene, many animals fell into snow-filled crevasses, where they perished and were quickly frozen. Because of the low temperature, bacterial action stopped soon after the animals died, and the flesh has remained in a remark-ably fresh condition for about 20,000 years. A number of these carcasses have been uncovered by rivers that undermined their banks, and the bodies have been discovered by hunters looking for fossil ivory. Some of the mammoths still had considerable quanti-ties of undigested food in their stomachs. These remarkable animals were well protected against the severe winter cold by heavy layers of fat beneath their extremely thick skins and by the dense growth of short, yellowish-brown woolly hair. Additional protec-tion was afforded by the long, coarse hair that covered the entire body and gave the animal a very shaggy appearance. Several skeletons and skulls of the woolly mammoth have been dug from frozen Pleistocene gravels in Alaska, but in these cases only frag-ments of the flesh remain, probably because the bodies were not buried soon enough after death to stop bacterial action.

Skeletons of the woolly rhinoceros have been found in oil-soaked ground in Galicia and Poland, with portions of the flesh and the skin still preserved.

The skull of an extinct ground sloth (Neomylodon), together with large pieces of the skin and the long reddish-brown hair, were discovered in a dry cave on Last Hope Inlet, Patagonia. Some of these animals apparently survived until comparatively recent times.

The natural mummies of ancient Indians, called "cliff dwellers," have been found buried in dry caves in the southwestern part of the United States where the exceedingly dry air inhibits the action of bacteria and retards the decay of the flesh indefinitely.

Slightly Altered Plant Material. In peat and lignite deposits the woody parts of plants frequently occur with very little change from the original state except the loss of some of the volatile con-stituents. Unaltered pieces of wood are often found in glacial deposits, whole logs, even, having been discovered in a perfectly solid condition after several thousand years of burial.

Fig. 10.—Ichthyosaurus, a marine reptile from the Jurassic slates of Holzmaden, Württemburg, Germany. The flesh is preserved as a film of carbon. (*Courtesy of Carnegie Museum of Pittsburgh.*)

Carbonaceous Films. During a portion of the Jurassic period, sheltered coastal lagoons in the region of Solenhofen, Bavaria, received deposits of exceedingly fine-grained mud, in which a great

Fig. 11.—Carbonized plant leaves.

many organisms were buried immediately after death and left undisturbed until the present. Among these are some remarkable specimens of the marine reptile ichthyosaurus (Fig. 10), with a thin film of carbon completely outlining the soft parts of the body. This carbonaceous material is the residue left after the flesh had decayed. Such finds are extremely valuable in making restorations of the animal as it probably appeared while still living. Carbonized mammal hairs have been found in certain lignite deposits of Germany.

Plants that decay slowly under water eventually lose much of their volatile material, leaving a thin carbonaceous residue (Fig. 11), which often shows the original form perfectly. Delicate fern leaves from the Pennsylvanian coal formations are frequently beautifully preserved by this method. They present a striking appearance because of their black color.

Molds or Impressions. If an organism is buried in fine-grained material, an impression of the plant (Fig. 12) or animal will often be recorded on the enclosing sediment after it has hardened. Such impressions are frequently left after the original organic structures have been removed by solution. They are called "molds" (Fig. 13). A cast or replica of the original organism may be obtained by filling one of these molds with some plastic compound, such as gutta percha or dental wax.

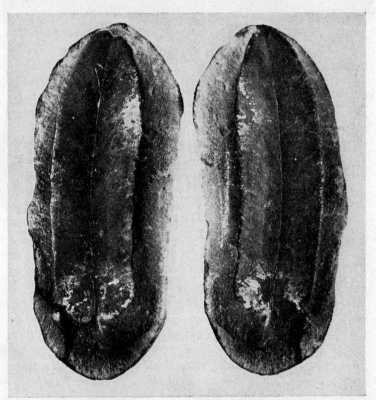

Fig. 12.—Mold (left) and cast (right) of a leaf from Pennsylvanian shales of Mazon Creek, Illinois.

The carcasses of two birds were buried in the mud at the bottom of a lagoon at Solenhofen, Bavaria, during the Jurassic period. When the fossil remains were finally discovered, good impressions of the wing and tail feathers were found upon the rock. These imprints are particularly important because, if only the skeletons had been preserved, the animals would probably have been classed as reptiles and not as birds.

The same sediments have faithfully recorded impressions of the thin skin that formed the wing membranes of flying reptiles (Fig. 14).

The rock is so fine-grained and the fossilization so perfect that delicate wrinkles on the wing surfaces are revealed.

FIG. 13.—Internal and external molds of pelecypods.

FIG. 14.—The flying reptile, *Rhamphorhynchus phyllurus* showing impressions of the delicate wing membranes. Solenhofen limestone, Bavaria. Jurassic period. Specimen in the Yale Peabody Museum.

Great numbers of leaves, the bodies of many insects, the fleshy tentacles of cephalopods, the skin of dinosaurs (Fig. 15), and even such exceedingly fragile creatures as jellyfish have all been recorded as impressions in various rocks.

Fig. 15.—Seven vertebrae of the dinosaur *Trachodon* with impressions of the skin. From Cretaceous rocks of the Red Deer River, Alberta, Canada. (*Courtesy of American Museum of Natural History.*)

Insects in Amber. During the Oligocene epoch extensive forests of conifers were growing along the Baltic coast of Germany, and masses of soft, sticky resin clinging to the bark of the trees

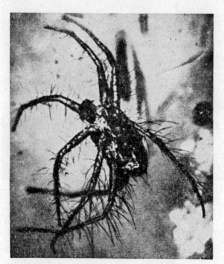

Fig. 16.—A spider preserved in amber.

caught and entombed great numbers of insects (Fig. 16), which are preserved today as extremely lifelike molds in the hardened gum or amber. So perfect is the preservation in some cases that microscopic scales on the wings of butterflies, and many other minute details of insect structure may clearly be seen.   In these pieces of amber, in addition to the numerous insects, several other important finds have been made.   Among them are crustaceans, spiders and their webs, and a tuft of hair from some mammal.

FIG. 17.—Tracks of *Cincosaurus cobbi*, a reptile from the Pennsylvanian of Alabama.   (*Courtesy of Geologival Survey of Alabama and Alabama Museum of Natural History*.)

Footprints and Trails.   When animals walk or crawl over mud and sand that is neither too hard nor too soft, tracks (Fig. 17) and trails will remain, and these have frequently been preserved as fossils.   Such markings can tell us important facts about the animals that made them.   It is possible to determine whether the creatures walked on all fours or on their hind legs.   The length of the stride in bipedal forms gives us some idea of the animal's height.

From a succession of footprints the running and the walking gait can often be distinguished. Sprawling forms such as those of many amphibians and reptiles can usually be distinguished.

Footprints and trails are of particular importance and interest because they reveal the animals in action. Such a fossil record always seems more realistic than any mere shells or skeletons can.

Burrows. Certain animals burrow through mud or sand, and the borings are sometimes preserved after the sediment has solidified. The exact nature of the boring animal can seldom be determined but, in a few cases, external structures on the surface of the organism have left impressions on the inside of the burrow.

Petrifactions. Bones and shells are very porous after their organic content has been removed. Frequently, the pores are filled with some mineral matter, such as lime or silica, that was deposited by water circulating slowly through the sediments in which the organisms were buried. The original material of the shell or bone is not necessarily altered by this method of petrifaction, but the weight and strength of these materials are increased by the additional deposit, and thereby the chance of their being preserved as fossils is greatly improved. This type of fossilization, which is extremely common, is often called "permineralization."

Replacement. Slowly circulating ground waters sometimes dissolve the original material of a buried organism and deposit some other substance in its place. Such replacement may preserve merely the general form of the object, but it may, instead, result in a very perfect reproduction of every minute detail of structure, both internal and external. Silica, calcium carbonate, and pyrite are common replacing substances.

Coprolites and Castings. Coprolites and castings are the undigestible portions of organisms that have been eaten and have passed through the alimentary canal of some animal. They often contain identifiable parts of the animals or plants that served as food. In a few cases entire skeletons have been recovered in an excellent state of preservation. Coprolites are usually associated with fish, amphibia, and reptiles. Worm castings, which resemble tangled masses of coarse string, are very common in some of the early Paleozoic rocks.

WHERE ORGANISMS HAVE BEEN PRESERVED AS FOSSILS

Epeiric Seas. The different continents have occasionally been invaded by more or less extensive bodies of shallow marine water, called "epeiric seas," in which many different kinds of animals and

plants formerly lived.   When these organisms died, vast numbers
of them were buried on the sea bottom (Fig. 18) beneath accumulating sediments, where their shells and skeletons have been preserved for several geologic periods.   Extensive exposures of these
marine deposits, found in all parts of the world, have yielded many
thousands of fossils, which constitute an extremely important
section of the geologic record.

Fig. 18.—Portion of an Ordovician sea bottom with fossil brachiopods, *Dalmanella*,
still in place.   (*Slab collected by W. H. Shideler, Oxford, Ohio.*)

Flood Plains.   Extensive plains areas are often crossed by net-
works of meandering streams that spread widely over the surrounding country, during times of heavy rains, and deposit considerable
quantities of clay and silt over their broad valley flats.   Such
regions as this often support a large and varied animal population,
so that during the course of many thousands of years great numbers
of skeletons become buried in the accumulating sediment and are
preserved as fossils.   The unusually rich grounds for fossil hunting
in Nebraska and the Big Badlands of South Dakota were formed
in this manner.   The present extensive lowland areas along the

lower course of the Mississippi River are favorable places for the burial and fossilization of organisms.

Estuaries. Rivers that flow into the sea at places where the coast line is subsiding will form estuarine deposits near their mouths, and such sediments are likely to be rich in the fossil remains of many different kinds of animals that were carried down by the streams. The faunal assemblage may include marine as well as fresh-water forms and even land animals.

Deltas. Delta deposits that were formed in the sea may contain a particularly varied assortment of animals and plants, which will be very irregularly distributed through the sediment. Marine organisms are quite certain to occur, especially those that lived

Fig. 19.—A water hole in eastern Colorado.

between the mouths of the distributaries, where they would be buried when the river shifted its position. Land and fresh-water animals are often carried downstream, chiefly during flood times, and some of these are sure to reach the delta. As the deposits are gradually built up above the water, extensive swampy flats will develop, where aquatic and semiaquatic animals might live. With the development of drier conditions and a solid footing, rich grass-lands may spread over portions of the old delta area, permitting grazing animals and carnivores to live in the region. Many of these are certain to be preserved as fossils.

Water Holes. In arid regions water is scarce and it is usually localized within certain limited areas. Such places (Fig. 19) are visited by animals, especially during prolonged droughts, when the struggle for water is intensified. All sorts of creatures perish under these conditions—frequently in great numbers. The amazing accumulation of bones near Agate, Nebraska (Fig. 20), represents chiefly a small, active type of rhinoceros called *Diceratherium*. Thousands of these animals perished at this locality and their closely packed bones are distributed throughout the fine-grained sandstone in complete disorder. After the flesh had decayed, movements of the quicksand separated the bones and the tramplings of other animals who were caught in the deathtrap completely disarticulated the skeletons.

Fig. 20.—Loading boxes containing fossilized bones of the rhinoceros, *Diceratherium cooki*, in the famous quarry near Agate, Nebraska. The rock is of Miocene age.

In his classic book, "The Voyage of the Beagle," Darwin describes the great drought in Argentina, which lasted from 1827 until 1832, during which much of the vegetation disappeared and the smaller streams dried up. As hundreds of thousands of cattle perished in the muds of the Paraná River, where they came seeking water, many of their carcasses were carried downstream and buried in the estuary of the Plata. Great numbers of wild horses died in the swamps. Altogether, several million skeletons were left lying around over the drought-stricken surface. A very heavy rain followed these unusually dry years, and undoubtedly thousands of skeletons were buried beneath muds and sands deposited by the

river. Darwin, in closing, pictures the geologist of the future
puzzling over this vast accumulation of bones, all in one horizon,
and finally reaching the conclusion that they had probably been
carried into the region by a disastrous flood.

Bogs and Swamps. Thousands of small lakes were formed
within the glaciated area following the final retreat of the Pleistocene
ice sheet. As these little bodies of water slowly filled with vegetation, they became treacherous swamps and bogs, where many
different kinds of animals were trapped and buried, especially the
heavy-bodied mastodons and elephants. Sometimes an entire
body was buried soon after death, but, in case the carcass lay

Fig. 21.—Excavating one of the asphalt or tar pits near Los Angeles, California.

exposed for a while, the flesh was eaten by predatory animals.
Marks left by the teeth of wolves or other flesh eaters are frequently
found on the bones. The skeletons of the proboscideans are not
petrified, and they have seldom been recovered in a good state of
preservation.

Asphalt Pools. During the Pleistocene epoch, pools of petroleum collected upon the land surface in the Rancho La Brea region
near Los Angeles, California. As the volatile constituents of the oil
gradually evaporated, a very sticky tar or asphalt (Fig. 21)
remained. Thousands of unwary animals who ventured upon
the treacherous surface of this material were entombed, and their
bones are preserved in perfect condition. Unusually large numbers
of predatory forms, such as the saber-toothed tigers and wolves,
are found in these deposits. They were undoubtedly attracted to

the area by the cries of trapped animals and by the unusual opportunity to obtain food.   Many of the flesh eaters were old or crippled individuals, who lacked the strength and agility to extricate themselves from the grip of the tar once they were caught.   No flesh or tendons have ever been found associated with the tar-pit skeletons.

The remarkable faunal assemblage at La Brea (Fig. 274) includes bears, wolves, lions, saber-toothed tigers, camels, horses, ground sloths, elephants, giant bison, deer, antelope, peccaries, and vultures. Some of the pits reach a depth of 40 feet.   One of them, measuring only 30 feet across at the widest part, has yielded the skeletons of 17 elephants.

Fig. 22.—Volcanic ash—bentonite—in the Petrified Forest, Arizona.   (*Courtesy of I. D. Scott.*)

Volcanic Dust and Ash.   When volcanoes erupt with explosive violence, the lava is blown into fine particles, which are often carried hundreds of miles by the wind and distributed over great areas. The ash (Fig. 22) thrown out during a single eruption is often deep enough to bury the carcasses or the skeletons of large animals, and the fact that the deposit settles over forests, plains, and mountains alike indicates that an unusually complete representation of the fauna living within the area may be preserved.

Several thousand inhabitants of Pompeii perished during the great eruption of Mt. Vesuvius in A.D. 79.   Many of them were buried beneath the unusually heavy shower of volcanic ash and the later mud flows.   The flesh and sometimes the skeletons of these unfortunate victims eventually disappeared, leaving molds of their bodies from which a number of very lifelike casts have been obtained. Some of these indicate that the individuals died in a restful attitude, while others are those of persons who were fleeing through the streets and carrying valuable personal possessions.

The Tertiary continental deposits in the western part of North America contain a very large proportion of volcanic ash, and some of the formations are almost exclusively of igneous origin.

Wind-blown Dust and Sand. Winds often carry ordinary dust and sand from arid regions and spread the materials over a wide area. The finer portions of the deposit will form a sediment that makes an excellent medium for the preservation of shells and bones. The Equus beds of the Pleistocene age are made up of fine-grained particles that were deposited by the wind over extensive areas of the Great Plains. The fossils in this deposit are locally very abundant, horse skeletons being especially common.

The Pampas of Argentina are widely covered by a thick deposit of solidified, wind-blown dust, in which collectors have found a great many unusually perfect fossils of Pleistocene mammals.

Fossil hunters occasionally make discoveries that are truly dramatic. One of these finds was made by Professor Williston in loess deposits of northwestern Kansas. He uncovered nine complete skeletons of the Pleistocene peccary *Platygonus* lying close together and all facing in the same direction. It was apparent that they had been caught by a severe storm on the desert and had turned their tails to the wind, exactly as animals do under similar conditions today. After the animals had died, their bodies were buried, where they had fallen, beneath wind-blown sand.

Caves and Fissures. Caverns and fissures—especially common in limestone regions—have proved in many cases to be very rich in fossil remains, especially those of the Pleistocene epoch. Many caves were doubtless formed in earlier geologic periods, and some that probably contained fossils have long since been filled with various deposits, so that very few of them have ever been discovered.

Such beasts of prey as the hyena drag their victims into caves whenever any are available and, after they have devoured the flesh, the bones are left lying upon the floor, where they may eventually accumulate in astonishing numbers.

Open fissures trap many of the animals that fall into such places, and a number of these have yielded valuable Pleistocene fossil material.

Some of the most remarkable chapters in the history of man date from the time when he began to live in the caverns of western

Europe and left there numbers of human skulls and skeletons, together with many paintings and engravings of prehistoric animals. Without this particular part of the human record, the story of man during the latter part of the Ice Age would have remained largely unknown.

RECONSTRUCTING EXTINCT ANIMALS

Shells and skeletons are valuable in themselves, but they acquire an added significance when the animals have been restored as they appeared during life. This often requires the cooperation of the paleontologist, the sculptor, and the painter. The skeleton is the basis upon which reconstructions are made. This is the framework for the entire body. Then, the essential muscles must be placed in position before it is possible to determine the general form of the animal. Fortunately, the basic muscles possessed by many vertebrates have remained quite similar through many geologic periods and, since it is often possible, even after the bones have been fossilized, to see the places where these muscles were attached to them, a reasonably accurate restoration of the muscular systems of extinct animals is quite possible.

The external appearance of an animal depends largely upon its color pattern, whether it be that of the hair, the skin, or the scales; but this particular characteristic is not preserved in the fossil forms except in the case of a few invertebrates. However, even here, some of the restorations are based upon a little information. The color pattern of a young mammal, which is often entirely different from that of the adult, may consist of stripes and spots. These are thought by some scientists to be reminiscent of the ancestral adult forms. The young of the wild boar are prominently marked by longitudinal stripes, while the adults have a uniform coloration. The newborn mule deer is covered by very obvious spots, which are completely absent in the fully grown individuals. Many restorations of extinct mammals, therefore, show the adults with either stripes or spots. It must be remembered that color pattern and coloration are not synonymous and that extinct animals offer no clues as to their actual colors.

It is a mistake to suppose that the paleontologist can restore an entire animal from a single bone or even from a few bones. It is true, however, that a complete skeleton is not necessary, because animals have a certain symmetry. Therefore, the left front leg can be restored if only the right front member is preserved, or the right half of a skull can be reproduced if the left half is known.

Where certain important parts of the skeleton are entirely absent, it is often possible to restore them by studying the corresponding parts in some related form. Where great numbers of bones are available, all belonging to the same species, it is easily possible to assemble a complete skeleton, even though the restoration may be a composite of several individuals.

INTERPRETATIONS OF FOSSILS

Great reliance is placed upon a study of the feet and teeth in determining the habits of extinct animals. In many cases, living representatives of the ancient forms may furnish valuable information. The hoofs of a horse show that the animal would normally live in places where the footing was firm. The long, slender legs, with powerful muscles placed high upon the shoulders and hips, indicate speed; and the long-crowned teeth, which continue to grow out as they are wearing down, are perfectly adapted to a diet of harsh grasses, such as grow upon the open plains in the West.

The long canines and highly specialized slicing teeth of the cats are useful only in a diet of flesh, while other types of teeth show clearly that the animal to which they belonged was omnivorous or herbivorous in its food habits.

Habitat. Certain types of animals, such as the starfishes, corals, and brachiopods, are found today only in marine waters. Apparently they have always lived in such an environment. Wherever an assemblage of these invertebrates is found under conditions indicating that they were buried in their natural environment, geologists know that a sea must have covered the locality at some time in the past, even though it is now thousands of feet above sea level or in the midst of a desert.

The majority of reef-building corals are found living today within the tropics and the subtropics, where the water is clear and not colder than 68°F. Most of the fossil corals that grew in great reefs during some of the past geologic periods probably lived under conditions similar to those required by the modern forms, and the presence of such fossils in high latitudes, even within the Arctic Circle, is evidence that those regions enjoyed milder climates in the past than they have at present.

Reptiles as a group are sensitive to cold. Those that live in places where the temperature drops close to the freezing point or below it during the winter season must seek shelter in protected places, usually underground. Large forms, such as giant snakes, the great turtles, and crocodiles, cannot find such places of refuge because of their size; consequently, they are forced to live in tropical countries through the entire year. The huge dinosaurs (Fig. 197) of the Mesozoic era were doubtless just as sensitive to the cold as any reptiles living today. Therefore, wherever their bones are found in place we may safely assume that the region had a very mild climate. Some of these dinosaurs were more than 60 feet long and could never have found places of retreat during a cold season.

Old Land Bridges. The geographical distribution of land animals in past geologic periods demonstrates the former existence

Fig. 23.—Collecting fossils in the Oligocene (White River) beds of northeastern Colorado. The fossil being taken out here is one of the enteledonts which were curious giant pig-like animals. (*Photograph by Dr. Claude Hibbard, in charge of the expedition.*)

of land connections between the continents where no such connections exist today. The true camel (*Camelus*) lives at the present time in Asia, but numerous fossil forms found in the western part of North America indicate that the family originated there and migrated to Asia by way of some land bridge probably the one that formerly connected Alaska and Siberia. The tapir is found today on the island of Borneo, in the Malay Peninsula, in Central America, and in the tropical portion of South America. Tapirs formerly lived also in Europe and North America. Such a widespread distribution cannot be accounted for except by assuming the existence of old land bridges that are no longer present. The present isthmus that connects North and South America is an excellent example of a land bridge between two continents, but even this land connection has not always been in existence.

Proof of Evolution. Fossils offer especially convincing proof of evolution because they are the actual remains of animals and plants that lived during the course of geologic time. The discussions of several vertebrate groups that appear later in this book will show how fossils are used to demonstrate evolution.

EARLY STUDIES OF FOSSILS

Men of the Old Stone Age who lived in France several thousand years ago occasionally picked up fossils while wandering along the river valleys in search of game. The old cave men probably did not understand the true nature of their finds, and the shells were doubtless kept merely as curiosities or as charms to ward off evil spirits.

A number of writers who lived before the Christian Era observed fossils in the rocks and interpreted them correctly as the remains of organisms that once lived in the sea. The historian Xanthus, who lived in the town of Sardis about 500 B.C., noticed fossil shells in various rock outcrops as he traveled through Phrygia and Lydia in Asia Minor. Although these regions were then far from the sea, he concluded that they had formerly been covered by the ocean and that changes in land and sea were constantly taking place.

Herodotus (b. 484 B.C.) was a keen student of nature. During his journeys across northern Africa, he found some marine mollusk shells in Egypt and near the oasis of Ammon in the Libyan desert. He decided that the sea had once invaded these regions and that the shells had been left after the water receded.

Theophrastus (368–284 B.C.), a brilliant pupil of Aristotle, who lived on the island of Lesbos in the Aegean Sea, devoted much time to the study of biology and was the author of an article on fossils. Although this paper has since been lost, Pliny was familiar with the work and mentions it in his writings.

Leonardo da Vinci (1452–1519) was a good engineer as well as a very great artist. While supervising the construction of some canals in northern Italy, he observed many marine fossils in the rocks. His explanation of the reason why these organisms were found on land is perfectly correct and very clearly stated.

A book written by Conrad Gesner of Zurich and published in 1565 contains the first illustrations of fossils, but the author merely gave descriptions of these organisms without discussing their origin.

Robert Hooke (1635–1703), an English mathematician and physicist, was the first writer to suggest that fossils have played an important part in the earth's history, since they represent animals that lived during the past.

A long series of bitter disputes over the nature of fossils began about the dawn of the fifteenth century and lasted for more than 300 years. Some persons maintained that there was a creative force (*vis plastica*) operating deep within the earth and constantly trying to produce life. This power succeeded in creating fossils, which were objects that had the appearance of living things although they had never been alive. One group taught that fossils were the result of seeds brought in by vapors from the ocean. Many believed that they were merely freaks of nature, while others thought that they were the remains of animals that had been swept inland by the Flood. This last explanation seemed so logical that it was accepted as standard doctrine by nearly everybody during the seventeenth and eighteenth centuries.

Today there is universal recognition of the fact that fossils are the remains of animals and plants that lived in past geologic periods. Our universities and museums hold large collections of these organisms, which not only are valuable to the scientific world but, in many cases, have been arranged in exhibits that are highly interesting to everybody.

Reading References

Scott, William B.: "A History of Land Mammals in the Western Hemisphere," rev. ed., pp. 47–72, The Macmillan Company, New York, 1937.

Shimer, Henry W.: "Introduction to the Study of Fossils," rev. ed., pp. 1–37, The Macmillan Company, New York, 1933.

Von Zittel, Karl Alfred: "History of Geology and Paleontology," pp. 13–23, Charles Scribner's Sons, New York, 1901.

CHAPTER V.

THE CONCEPT OF EVOLUTION

Plants and Animals are Constantly Changing. One of the most obvious facts about the organic world is that no two individuals are ever exactly alike. This is true of animals and plants living today, and, as far as the fossil record shows, it has always been true in the past. Nothing is fixed in nature. Scientists do not know just why this inherent tendency to vary exists among organisms, but it is quite obviously a progressive factor because without change there could be no progress.

Anyone who examines the record of life as it is revealed by fossils through the geologic ages must soon be impressed with the fact that the lower orders of living things appeared first and that progressively higher and higher types developed in succession. There was a time in the history of the earth when invertebrates were the sole representatives of the animal kingdom. Then the fishes appeared and for several geologic ages they were the highest forms of vertebrate life in existence. After these came the amphibians, then the reptiles, and finally the mammals. Each group represented a distinct advance over the one that preceded it. This great procession of life can be followed through many millions of years by means of fossils that are preserved in the rocks. They prove conclusively that the organic world has not remained unchanged. Nevertheless, in spite of profound changes, there is an element of constancy that runs throughout the stream of life. This is revealed in the universal tendency of offspring to resemble their parents and, more broadly, in the numerous basic structural features that so many of the vertebrates have in common. It is as though a certain fundamental plan had been developed early in the history of the group and, with certain modifications, had been followed ever since.

The concept of evolution carries with it no sinister meaning, as some people think. It is simply a belief that the animals and plants of today are the descendants of those that lived in the past; that the whole complex world of life, as it is at present, developed or evolved gradually, by constant changes, from fewer and simpler

forms that lived in the distant past. All the animals and all the
plants are thus bound together by deep-seated relationships that
have persisted from very remote times. The person who finds such
a belief disturbing need only alter his perspective a little in order to
see that this is simply creation working slowly through the years
instead of concentrating its efforts within the space of a few days.
Changes are still going on and the end of progress is not in sight.

The physical laws that produce mountains and valleys, deserts
and plains are relatively unchanging; but with the appearance of
life upon earth there was added the new factor of organic evolution
with its constant changes, and this altered the whole course of
geologic history.

FACTS THAT SUPPORT EVOLUTION

Comparative Anatomy. Among the most significant things
that become apparent when we study and compare the correspond-

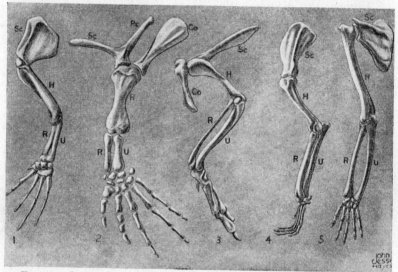

FIG. 24.—Comparative anatomy. The fore limbs of these five vertebrates are
fundamentally alike. 1, amphibian (frog); 2, reptile (turtle); 3, bird; 4, dog; 5, man.
Key: *Sc*, scapula; *H*, humerus; *R*, radius; *U*, ulna. (*Drawn by John Jesse Hayes.*)

ing skeletal parts of many different vertebrates is the fact that
apparently totally unrelated forms have many basic features in
common (Fig. 24). It would be difficult to think of two structures
that are superficially more unlike than the arm of a man and the
wing of a bird. In external appearance they have nothing in common, and they serve quite different purposes; but after feathers

and skin have been removed some surprising relationships are revealed. Both the arm and the wing are found to consist of humerus, radius, and ulna, while the apparent differences are matters merely of degree. Furthermore, comparisons of the arm with the front legs of many other different animals, such as the cat, the wolf, the bat, and the crocodile, show that the same remarkable similarities exist in these widely different creatures.

When the comparison is carried to other corresponding parts, even in the soft anatomy, the evidence of relationship becomes still more striking. Such vital organs as heart, lungs, liver, and stomach are not only structurally similar to the same organs in these diverse forms, but they perform essentially the same functions in them all. The basic anatomical structures that were developed early in the history of the vertebrate line have simply been modified to suit the requirements of various animals as they adapted themselves to many different environmental conditions. It is difficult to escape the conclusion that the presence of so many strikingly similar features in so large a number of different animals means deep-seated relationships.

FIG. 25.—An early stage in the development of the human embryo showing gill slits and limb buds. (*Drawing by John Jesse Hayes.*)

Embryology. The fundamental facts of life cannot be fully appreciated without some knowledge of embryology, or the history of the individual before birth. No matter how many millions of cells the body of an adult animal may possess, each one of these bodies began life as a single cell or egg. This is obviously a highly important sign of relationship.

Every vertebrate, during the earliest stages of its embryonic development, possesses gill slits (Fig. 25). There is no exception to this rule and, since these structures are present because of inheritance, it is natural to conclude that the ancestral lines of the present-day vertebrates extend back into the distant past, through many geologic periods, until they converge in some common group whose members possessed functional gill slits. This points clearly to an aquatic heritage. In a later chapter, in which a remarkable class of fishes will emerge as the probable common ancestral type of all the higher vertebrates, important evidence will be presented.

The Law of Recapitulation. As a result of their extensive researches into embryology, biologists have discovered a great fundamental principle, which has been embodied in the law of recapitulation. This law states that each individual during its embryonic development and early life after birth repeats briefly and imperfectly many of the stages through which the race passed in its evolutionary history. The gill slits mentioned above offer a striking illustration of this law, but there are many others just as important. The geological record shows that the primitive Jurassic

Fig. 26.—Life history of the frog, beginning at left. Eggs are laid in the water; tadpole showing external gills; hind legs appear first; all four legs have developed, tail is gradually disappearing; adult frog. (*Drawing by Priscilla Woodhead.*)

birds had well-developed and completely functional teeth in their jaws. No modern birds possess teeth during their adult lives, but a few forms show the beginnings of such structures before hatching. The bodies of all human beings are completely covered with long, fine hair until a short time before birth, when, ordinarily, it disappears. This is apparently reminiscent of a remote stage in our history when the adults were hairy, like the modern apes. The fetus of the whale shows a similar abundance of hair, which is not present in the adult. A sheep develops a rudimentary collarbone (clavicle) in the embryo, but it is absorbed before birth. The modern squirrels have long incisor teeth in front, separated by a gap from the grinding teeth farther back in the jaws. Before the squirrel is born, this gap is occupied by rudimentary teeth. The same thing is true of other related forms. It seems to show that the ancestral rodents had a more complete dentition than have their modern descendants.

Evolution Demonstrated by the Frog. Nearly everybody is familiar with the remarkable series of changes through which the frog (Fig. 26) passes during its life history from the egg to the adult; yet few persons realize that this is racial history being repeated before their eyes and that it offers a very clear demonstration of the evolutionary process. The eggs of the frog are laid in some pond or in the comparatively still water of a river. When the young tadpoles have hatched they bear no resemblance whatever to the adult frogs. Instead, they are essentially fish-like in appearance and habits, and their breathing is done entirely by means of gills. No traces of lungs or legs exist at first, but these structures develop later, while the gills disappear. The animal then becomes a true amphibian, breathing air for the rest of its life. The frogs, and amphibians in general, thus reveal their relationship to the fish, all showing a decided preference for water or damp places throughout their lives. Every year their eggs are laid in the water and this astonishing metamorphosis takes place.

Vestigial Organs. Many anatomical features possessed by animals during their lifetime are not functional, but are, instead, vestiges or degenerate remnants of structures that served some useful purpose in the past. The appendix is the most familiar example of such a useless organ. This feature of our anatomy is larger and better developed in the embryo than it is in the adult. The caecum, which is the homologue of the appendix, is well developed in many herbivorous mammals and aids in the process of digestion. The human ear (Fig. 27) possesses three muscles that are identical with those used by many other mammals to move their ears. Al-

Fig. 27.— Vestigial muscles of the human ear.

though these muscles are vestigial in man, it is still possible to recover a certain amount of control over them with practice. The little toe and the wisdom teeth are becoming vestigial in man; even now they serve no essential purposes. The Greenland whale still retains remnants of the hind legs in a set of bones that are buried beneath the skin. The adult porpoise has only the front flippers, which are modified fore limbs, but during its embryonic development buds of the hind legs are present.

What is the significance of all these vestigial structures that are present in the anatomy of both man and the lower animals? According to the law of heredity, we must have acquired them from our parents, who in turn inherited them from their forefathers, and so the line might be traced back to some creatures who possessed these organs in a functional condition. Vestigial organs are not just freakish parts of our anatomy that never served a purpose. They are true reminders of the past, and they offer very convincing evidence that animals have evolved by slow changes through a line of ancestral forms, with the result that modern creatures are a composite of many ancestors that have long since disappeared. Man is just as much a product of fundamental biological laws as are any of his fellow creatures; and it is far easier to understand the behavior of modern animals, including man, if we know something of the long and devious paths that they have traveled from the remote past to the present.

Paleontology. The final proof of evolution rests with the fossils that are preserved in the rocks. It is only these organisms that can tell us whether animals have given rise to others through successive modifications.   In order to find this proof and make it effective, it is necessary to discover a succession of sedimentary rocks in which the life history of a certain family of animals has been recorded without any important breaks through a considerable stretch of time.   The fossilized shells or skeletons should then show many of the actual changes that occurred within the group, and this is proof of evolution. Paleontologists have fortunately discovered several localities where the life histories of many groups, especially among the vertebrates, have been recorded in detail through several geologic epochs. The evolutionary histories of such famous families as the horse and the elephant have become veritable monuments along the path that life has followed through the ages—a path whose course is still directed upward.

Another very important and dramatic phase of geologic history recorded by paleontology is the rise and fall of many powerful dynasties of animals that once ruled the world or attained important positions because of their great numbers and varieties. During the Mesozoic era, which is often called the Age of Reptiles, dinosaurs were of world-wide distribution and completely dominated the life of the earth. Nevertheless, in spite of their great superiority in size, strength, and numbers at that time, they have completely disappeared from all the continents. The astonishing history of this remarkable order of reptiles is only one of many that have been recorded with amazing fidelity in the rocks—that has been brought to light by the pick and shovel of the paleontologist.

The Causes of Evolution. The causes of evolution are still only imperfectly understood. This is a phase of the subject that belongs more properly to the field of biology and to the division of genetics. Evolution is possible because variations occur in animals and plants, and much real progress has been made within the last few years toward a solution of the baffling problems of how variations originate. Evolution is undoubtedly going on at the present time, because changes are still continuing in the organic world.

Reading References

LANE, H. H.: "Evolution and Christian Faith," 214 pp., Princeton University Press, Princeton, N.J., 1923.

LULL, R. S.: "Organic Evolution," rev. ed., 743 pp., The Macmillan Company, New York, 1929.

SCOTT, WILLIAM B.: "The Theory of Evolution," 163 pp., The Macmillan Company, New York, 1917.

CHAPTER VI

THE ARCHEOZOIC ERA

The center-fire heaves underneath the earth,
And the earth changes like a human face;
The molten ore bursts up among the rocks,
Winds into the stone's heart, outbranches bright
In hidden mines, spots barren river-beds,
Crumbles into fine sand where sunbeams bask—
—Browning, "Paracelsus"

AN OBSCURE AND CHAOTIC RECORD

There is a great lost interval in the history of the earth between the time that it became a planet and the time that the oldest recognizable rocks belonging to the Pre-Cambrian eon were formed.

The recorded portion of geologic history that precedes the Paleozoic era is usually divided into two eras—the Archeozoic and the Proterozoic—and these together make up Pre-Cambrian time. The difficulties that geologists have encountered in deciphering this part of the earth's history are the result of several factors. The almost complete absence of fossils makes it nearly impossible to correlate the scattered outcrops of rock, even though they are not very far apart. This introduces an element of uncertainty into the results of many Pre-Cambrian studies, and the difficulties will probably never be entirely cleared away. The lack of fossils in the Pre-Cambrian makes it impossible, at this time, to divide this portion of the geologic record into definite periods such as we have in the Paleozoic and succeeding eras. Geologists must use such terms as early Archeozoic or middle Proterozoic or Huronian, divisions that doubtless include within their limits many periods, each one as long as those of the Paleozoic or the Mesozoic. Such time units, which are much too long for the ordinary purposes of historical geology, make it difficult to present the events of geologic history in a connected manner. Another reason for the confusion that exists, especially in the Archeozoic, is the fact that some of the rocks belonging to this era have been so much changed by meta-

52

morphism that their original nature is obscured and in some cases
it cannot be determined.   However, there are many areas where
igneous and sedimentary rocks of the Archeozoic era have not been
altered.   Erosion has removed many thousands of feet of Pre-
Cambrian formations, causing a tremendous loss that can never be

FIG. 28.—Map of North America with outcrops of Pre-Cambrian rocks shown in
black.

replaced.   Furthermore, the rocks of these earliest eras are often
so deeply buried beneath later deposits that they are inaccessible.
This part of the geologic story is just as obscure as are those early
chapters in human history that must be reconstructed from scattered bits of information found here and there over the earth.

It is possible that more than two eras will eventually be recognized in the Pre-Cambrian eon, and some of the obscurity that clouds this portion of geologic history will be clarified by future discoveries; but it is also true that the record of the Archeozoic will always retain some of its present obscurity.

THE CHIEF AREAS OF PRE-CAMBRIAN ROCKS

The Pre-Cambrian rocks are deeply buried beneath younger formations over large areas of the earth's surface, but there are many important exposures on all the continents. Two million square miles of the great Canadian shield region are covered by Pre-Cambrian rocks composed in part of pink granite-gneiss that was originally intruded in the form of batholiths during vast mountain-making upheavals. Some of the lavas and sediments that were involved in these crustal movements are still preserved in certain downfolded areas. The Canadian shield extends from the Great Lakes region northward beyond Hudson Bay, and from the plains of Alberta eastward to Labrador. Greenland is also included within this vast area.

Somewhat smaller shields of Pre-Cambrian rocks are exposed in the Scandinavian region of Europe, in Siberia, the eastern part of Africa, western Australia, and northern and eastern South America.

These remarkable areas are unusually stable portions of the earth's crust and have been very little affected by crustal deformations since the original upheavals during the Pre-Cambrian. All the shields have been subjected to prolonged weathering and erosion, which slowly reduced them to extensive peneplains.

The Grand Canyon Region. The Grand Canyon of the Colorado River, in northern Arizona, is one of the most beautiful and awe-inspiring scenic features in the entire world. Nowhere else can be found rocks of three different geologic eras exposed in a single section and on so tremendous a scale. A vast amount of geologic history has been written in this region, the major events having left an indelible record in the walls of the canyon, where it may still be read.

The Vishnu Series. The Archeozoic era in the Grand Canyon is represented by the *Vishnu* schist (Fig. 29), which is particularly well exposed for about 17 miles in the Granite Gorge along the course of the Colorado River. The rock consists chiefly of several types of quartz, mica, and hornblende schists, with great intrusions of quartz diorite and pegmatite dikes. The almost vertical planes of schistosity have a general trend toward the northeast, and the schist is greatly contorted in many places, showing that the region was subjected to tremendous compressive forces in Pre-Cambrian time.

The Vishnu has been so completely metamorphosed that no very clear evidence of its original nature remains. Nearly all traces of bedding planes have been destroyed, except in a few of the quartz-itic phases; but the great abundance of quartz indicates a sedimentary origin for much of the material. An arkose sandstone or shale, affected by regional metamorphism, would probably produce the conditions existing in much of the Vishnu series today. The hornblende portions of the schist may originally have been some type of basic igneous rock. Many of the great pegmatite dikes were crumpled and distorted at the time when the original

Fig. 29.—The Grand Canyon from the south rim. Looking up Bright Angel Creek, a tributary of the Colorado River, which is here seen running diagonally across the lower right-hand corner of the picture. *V*, Vishnu series, Archeozoic; *G.C.*, Grand Canyon system, Proterozoic; *BA*, Bright Angel shale, Cambrian; *M*, Muav limstone, Cambrian; *R*, Redwall limestone, Mississippian; *S*, Supai formation, Permian; *H*, Hermit shale, Permian; *CC*, Coconino sandstone, Permian; *K*, Kaibab and Toroweap formations. The Toroweap is the dark band at the base of the lighter Kaibab. Permian. (*Courtesy of Spence Air Photos.*)

Vishnu materials were subjected to mountain-making stresses, while the younger dikes cut cleanly across the planes of schistosity and so must have been intruded after the great orogeny.

The base of the Vishnu series has never been seen, and its horizontal extent is unknown. The total thickness of the rocks must be several thousand feet. Their exact position with respect to other Archeozoic formations cannot be determined.

Two major events in the history of the Vishnu series stand out clearly. The first is the great orogeny that folded these ancient materials into a mountain range and metamorphosed them almost beyond recognition, and the second is the long period of erosion that reduced the mountains to a peneplain. The height and the extent of the ranges that were formed in the Grand Canyon region during the Archeozoic era are not known, but they were probably comparable to many of the higher mountains that are in existence today.

The Great Lakes Region. The complicated geology of the ancient Pre-Cambrian rocks has been studied in great detail throughout the Lake Superior region, largely because of the fabulously rich deposits of iron and copper that are found here. Fortunately, the importance of geology to a proper development of the mining industry was realized quite early in the development of the district; therefore, the area has been subjected to an examination so thorough that it has become a center around which Pre-Cambrian studies for the whole country have revolved.

One of the first students of Pre-Cambrian geology in the Great Lakes region was Sir William Logan (1798–1875). The studies of this celebrated geologist proved to be fundamentally so sound that they formed the basis for much of the later work in this field.

The entire Pre-Cambrian section in the Lake Superior region, as it is now known, includes at least 40,000 feet of sediments, representing all the types that are common today, such as conglomerates, sandstones, limestones, and shales. Four major unconformities are recognizable in the sections, and the rocks have been affected by three periods of mountain making, each one of which was accompanied by extensive granitic intrusions in the form of batholiths. The geologic history is very difficult to decipher in the lower part of the section, where the rocks have been profoundly metamorphosed, although studies now being carried on are gradually shedding a little light on these obscure chapters in the earth's history. Much of the story, however, will always remain a mystery. The geology for each of the Lake Superior districts has been fairly well outlined; but it is difficult to correlate these regions with one another and no simple classification of rocks, applicable to the whole area, is possible at present.

The Keewatin System. The *Keewatin* rocks occur extensively throughout the Lake Superior country in both Canada and the United States, where they are the oldest recognizable formations of Archeozoic time. The best exposures are found in the Vermilion Iron District of Minnesota, and in the Lake of the Woods, Rainy Lake, and Michipicoten regions of Canada. The rocks are dominantly of igneous origin, with extensive lava flows that poured out quietly from fissures in the earth's crust and local beds of tuff that indicate explosive eruptions. Sediments are found interbedded with the lavas in a number of places and are locally very important.

Fig. 30.—Pillow lava in the Ely greenstone near Gilbert, Minnesota. (*Photographed by Carl Dutton.*)

The Vermilion District. Some of the greenstones in the Vermilion district were originally a series of basaltic lava flows. They have been metamorphosed to schists in many places, but in the unaltered portions the original character of the rock is clearly shown. An extensive development of amygdaloidal structure is found in the finer grained lavas. It is possible to visualize a long succession of fissure eruptions that spread widely over the surrounding country to form a vast lava plain similar to the Absaroka Plateau, east of Yellowstone Park, or the Columbia Plateau of Washington and Oregon. The former extent of these ancient basaltic flows was far beyond the Vermilion district, but erosion has removed so much of the material that only a few remnants are left. An original thickness of about 20,000 feet is indicated for these lavas in a few places where they are exposed in the truncated folds of the Pre-Cambrian

Laurentian Mountains. The ellipsoidal, or pillow, structure (Fig. 30) that is so characteristic of the greenstone in many places was probably produced when the lava flowed into some body of water, possibly a near-by sea. This theory of underwater origin is further supported by the fact that the surfaces of the flows were apparently never subjected to subaerial weathering and erosion.

FIG. 31.—Crumpled layers in the Soudan iron formation near Soudan, Minnesota. (*Photographed by Carl Dutton.*)

The Soudan Formation. The *Soudan* (Fig. 31) iron-bearing formation in the Vermilion district consists of water-laid sediments that were originally cherty limestones with some shales and sandstones. The source of this sedimentary material was apparently the basalt that had accumulated on land. In several places the sediments are found interbedded with ellipsoidal lavas, but most of the Soudan lies above the greenstone, where it was deposited after the volcanic activity had largely ceased.

The proof of subaerial weathering offered by these ancient sediments is very important, because it seems to indicate that the earth's atmosphere had about the same composition in Pre-Cambrian times that it has today. Rains fell upon the land in Soudan times and running water was a transporting agent then, just as it is at present. The ages-old processes of weathering and erosion have been active since the very earliest part of recorded geologic history.

Michipicoten District. The *Keewatin* system, in the Michipicoten district of Ontario, on the northeastern shore of Lake Superior, includes about 11,000 feet of volcanic ash called the "Wawa tuff." Such great thickness is quite local and was probably not maintained over any extensive area, but the presence of this ash reveals the existence of explosive volcanoes that erupted with great violence, in addition to long fissures from which the quiet flows of basalt issued.

Diamond-drill cores in the Keewatin, from below Michiwakenda Lake in the Sudbury district, show several bands of ash, 20 to 50 feet thick, separated by greenstone flows.

THE LAURENTIAN REVOLUTION

After the accumulation of the Keewatin lavas and sediments, these rocks were affected by disatrophic disturbances accompanied by the intrusion of great batholiths of gray and pink granites (Fig. 32). It is difficult to determine the extent of the mountains that were formed at this time because later orogenies affected portions of the same area and the effects of these disturbances are somewhat confused.

A long period of erosion followed the orogeny, during which the Keewatin rocks were deeply eroded, the mountain folds were truncated, and the deep-seated granite was laid bare. Remnants of the Keewatin formations may be seen today in some of the down-warped areas between the batholiths.

The Grenville Series. The rocks of the *Grenville* series (Fig. 33) are found in a number of places over southeastern Ontario, southern Quebec, and the Adirondack Mountains of northeastern New York. The original sediments of this important series were largely limestones, with subordinate amounts of shale and sandstone. All the beds were altered into marbles, schists, and quartzites at the time of the Laurentian revolution and there is a great deal of contact metamorphism where the Grenville has been intruded by the

Fig. 32.—Laurentian granite gneiss in Admaston Township, Ontario. (*Courtesy Geological Survey of Canada.*)

Fig. 33.—Calcareous beds of the Grenville series near Port Henry, New York. The dark bands of siliceous material show disruption and folding. (*Courtesy of New York State Museum.*)

Laurentian granite. As this great intrusive mass of rock forced its way up into the overlying beds, fragments of the sediments were detached from their original positions and engulfed by the molten magma. The thickness of the entire series has not been accurately determined, because there has been considerable duplication of beds as a result of folding and faulting. In Grenville County, Quebec, where good exposures of the dipping strata have been measured, the thickness is about 10,000 feet.

The rocks of the Grenville series, and especially the schists, contain an enormous amount of graphite, which is of commercial

Fig. 34.—Possible varves in the Knife Lake slates (Timiskaming?) South of Ensign Lake, Minnestoa. (*Photographed by Carl Dutton.*)

importance in a number of places. The graphite is sometimes found interbedded with the other rock and its source may have been carbonaceous shales. The presence of this mineral is indirect evidence that plant life was abundant in Grenville times, since plants are a common source of carbon. The exact age of the Grenville is difficult to determine, but it may be the offshore equivalent of the Keewatin. Some geologists place the Grenville in the Huronian division of the Proterozoic era.

The Timiskaming System. Some of the higher and more resistant parts of the old Laurentian ranges must have persisted for a long time after the other portions in southern Canada had been peneplaned, and these higher areas may have furnished much of the sediments in the *Timiskaming* (Fig. 34) system. These rocks occur in numerous, relatively small, scattered outcrops, from western

Quebec to the region west of Lake Superior.   It has been necessary to use different local names in describing the rocks from a number of these localities because the beds are unfossiliferous and correlations cannot be made with certainty.

The deposits in the Lake Timiskaming area, northeast of Georgian Bay, consist largely of conglomerate (Fig. 35), arkose, and quartzite, with smaller amounts of shale.   The total thickness is about 20,000 feet.   The method of deposition of this great quantity of sediments is still in doubt.   The quartzites are cross-bedded in many places, suggesting the action of running water.

Fig. 35.—Alignment of pebbles in a conglomerate facie of the Knife Lake slate series (Timiskaming?) south of Ensign Lake, Minnesota.   (*Photographed by Carl Dutton.*)

The thickness of the conglomerate varies greatly within short distances, and this condition is frequently found in alluvial fans.

The Timiskaming rocks west of Lake Superior have been described as the *Seine River* series.   In this locality the deposits are lying directly upon the Keewatin lavas and the intrusive granite. The conglomerate that is found at the base of the series contains boulders derived from the granite.

THE ALGOMAN REVOLUTION

This far-flung crustal disturbance folded and faulted the Timiskaming, as well as older rocks, into mountain ranges that must have reached impressive heights.   The intrusion of great batholiths, composed largely of pink granite, was an important part of the orogeny, and the rocks were profoundly metamorphosed.

It is impossible to determine the exact extent of the ranges that were formed during this great revolution, but the vast upheaval must have affected a large portion of the Canadian shield; and the effects extended into northern Minnesota, where there is an extensive development of Algoman granites (Fig. 36). A long period of erosion followed the Algoman revolution; thus, eventually, the lofty ranges were reduced to a peneplain and the deep-seated granites were exposed.

Relative Age of the Granites. The relative age of the granites is revealed in a few places, where the Algoman intrusives are found

Fig. 36.—Dark-colored Knife Lake (Timiskaming?) slates intruded by Giant's Range (Algoman?) granite, north of Virginia, Minnesota. (*Photographed by Carl Dutton.*)

cutting through the Laurentian batholiths as well as the rocks of the Keewatin and Timiskaming systems.

ORE DEPOSITS

The iron ore of the Vermilion range in Minnesota occurs in the highly metamorphosed rocks of the Soudan formation, which belongs to the Keewatin system. The rocks have been closely folded and the iron is found in narrow, steep-walled troughs.

The Porcupine and Kirkland Lake districts of eastern Ontario are among the greatest gold-mining regions in the entire world. The mines in the Porcupine area yielded over $209,000,000 worth of gold from 1910 through 1927 and over $21,000,000 worth in 1936 alone. Most of this vast production came from the famous Hollinger mine.

Fracture lines, which had been formed in the Keewatin and Timiskaming rocks at the time of the Algoman revolution, were filled with quartz porphyry derived from the underlying batholith, and the gold veins were deposited along the same lines of weakness. The discovery of gold in the Porcupine district was made in 1912, and some of the mines have reached a depth of over 4,000 feet.

Kirkland Lake is another of Canada's great gold-mining areas. Production, which began in this region in 1913, has recently forged ahead of the Porcupine district.

In 1930, a tremendous deposit of pitchblende was discovered near Great Bear Lake in the Northwest Territories of Canada. This has since become an important source of uranium, radium, and silver. The ore occurs in Pre-Cambrian sediments and volcanic rocks near their contact with a granite mass.

An exceptionally rich and interesting gold deposit occurs in Pre-Cambrian conglomerates located near Johannesburg in the Transvaal. An old land surface of crystalline schists and intrusive granites is covered with 19,000 feet of slates, quartzites, and conglomerates. The gold is found chiefly in the upper part of this great sedimentary series, where it occurs as a part of the cementing material surrounding the conglomerate pebbles. The deposit may represent a "fossil placer" that was originally a great accumulation of gold-bearing gravel.

The Grenville series contains important deposits of marble which is quarried at Gouverneur, New York, and used for building purposes. The same series contains great quantities of graphite, which in some places is widely disseminated through the rock and in others occurs as veins and irregular masses.

CLIMATE DURING THE ARCHEOZOIC

There is very little evidence upon which to base any specific statements concerning the climate of the Archeozoic era. So vast a stretch of time as this era doubtless represents must have witnessed a variety of climatic conditions that have not recorded themselves very clearly in the rocks. The chief difficulty comes from a lack of fossils, both plants and animals, since organisms give us the most reliable clues to past climates. The thick beds of limestone in the Grenville series strongly suggest deposits made in temperate or warm seas. The fact that land-derived sediments, such as shale and sandstone, were deposited during the Archeozoic, shows that running water was present. The conditions favoring mechanical weathering and erosion appear to have been very much the same then as they are today. There is no indication that the physical conditions of the environment were radically different from those of the present, but the lands undoubtedly presented a very desolate appearance because terrestrial animals and plants were absent.

LIFE DURING THE ARCHEOZOIC ERA

As the discovery of Pre-Cambrian fossils has been a major objective among paleontologists for many years, intensive searches have been carried on wherever there seemed to be any possibility of finding such organisms. The results have been so meager that the task seems almost hopeless; but every discovery, no matter how small, is of importance, so the search still continues.

The great quantity of graphite occurring in the Grenville series is very strong indirect evidence that the sea in which these rocks were deposited contained an abundance of plant and, possibly, animal life. Some of the graphite was probably derived from black, carbonaceous shales that originally contained much organic matter. A considerable portion of the Grenville was originally limestone, which may have been of organic origin. *Eozoön canadense* is the name which was given to a structure found in the Grenville and which was originally supposed to be a deposit made by algae. These objects consist of alternate bands of calcite and serpentine that occur in roughly hemispherical masses, varying from a few inches to several feet in diameter. Excellent examples of *Eozoön* have been found in zones where contact metamorphism is extreme, and it is difficult to see how algae or any organism could have been preserved under these conditions. Serpentine is an alteration product and does not occur in fossils. It seems almost certain that *Eozoön canadense* is of inorganic origin.

Scarcity of Fossils in Archeozoic Rocks. The Archeozoic rocks, as they are known at present, contain a great preponderance of materials that were originally igneous; consequently, they could never have been fossiliferous. The sedimentary deposits belonging to this era are now so completely metamorphosed that any organisms that they might formerly have contained were destroyed long ago.

The earliest forms of animal life almost certainly possessed nothing but soft bodies. Such creatures are seldom preserved except as impressions and, even then, only under the most favorable conditions. Any shells or hard parts that Archeozoic animals might have developed were probably very fragile structures, poorly adapted for preservation as fossils. The deep erosion to which Archeozoic rocks have everywhere been subjected would have removed most of the fossils that might originally have been preserved there. In most places, the rocks of this era are covered by later deposits and so cannot be explored for possible fossil remains. The discovery of fossils, which is partly a matter of chance, often involves a great amount of patient searching. It is possible that Archeozoic organisms are preserved in a few places that have not yet been discovered.

All these reasons make it highly improbable that any great number of Archeozoic fossils will ever be found; thus, our knowledge of this most important time in the evolution of life can never be very satisfactory.

Great Erosion Period. A profound unconformity exists between the rocks of the Archeozoic and those of the Proterozoic wherever the two are found in contact—a great break that indicates an erosion interval of very long duration. The Laurentian and Algoman orogenies had produced mountains of considerable extent in Canada and parts of the United States, but these hills were largely peneplaned before the Proterozoic era. The present flat surface of the Canadian shield is still an excellent example of a peneplain.

Studies in a number of localities show that much of the North American continent stood at a low level during the closing stages of the Archeozoic. Basal sandstones and conglomerates in the Proterozoic contain many angular fragments of rock with fresh feldspar as a common constituent in most localities, and this material was derived from the disintegrated regolith that covered the flat surface of the underlying Archeozoic. Conditions during the latter part of this era apparently favored mechanical weathering and the absence or scarcity of land vegetation must have been an important factor in slowing down the rate of decomposition.

CHAPTER VII

THE PROTEROZOIC ERA

THE GRAND CANYON REGION

The Grand Canyon System. After the Vishnu series had been upheaved into mountains and then slowly reduced to a peneplain, a great period of sedimentation began, which resulted in the deposition of the thick Grand Canyon system (Fig. 37).

Fig. 37.—The Grand Canyon near the Little Colorado River looking north. Navajo Mountain in the distance. *GC*, Grand Canyon system, Proterozoic; *T*, Tapeats sandstone, Cambrian; *BA*, Bright Angel shale, Cambrian; *M*, Muav limestone, Cambrian; *R*, Redwall limestone, Mississippian; *C*, Supai red beds, Permian; *CC*, Coconino sandstone, Permian; *K*, Kaibab formation, Permian.

The basal conglomerate (Hotauta) with which this sedimentary system begins was the first deposit of a shallow sea that advanced across the peneplaned surface of the Vishnu series. This old plain was unusually flat, and the differences in elevation along about 7 miles of its extent in the walls of the Grand Canyon are now less than 20 feet. There is very little evidence of chemical weathering in the Vishnu. The residual mantle of angular rock particles that covered the even Archeozoic surface had been formed by long-continued disintegration, which reduced the fragments to small size, with occasional lenses containing pieces of rock up to a foot in diameter. The minerals in the basal conglomerate were clearly derived from the bedrock directly below. This, together with the decided angularity of the particles, shows that the waves and currents of the advancing Proterozoic sea did not move the debris far from it source. Such a condition might be caused by a very quiet movement of water over a flat land, with comparatively little wave action. This would produce feeble shore currents, which could not move the particles contained in the loose rubble for any great distance, and they would thus retain much of their original angularity. Another theory attempts to account for the lack of rounding by assuming that the Grand Canyon region was slightly below sea level and was shut off from the open ocean by a low barrier. As the land slowly sank, the marine waters rose above the barrier and spread so rapidly over the Vishnu plain that there was no time to produce any appreciable rounding or sorting of the rock fragments that littered the surface.

The Hotauta basal conglomerate is followed by a deposit characterized by innumerable alternations of white limestone and red shale. This part of the section is called the "Bass" limestone. It is difficult to say under what conditions the sediments accumulated. The beds may have been formed during alternate periods of heavy rains and extreme aridity. During a heavy rain the rivers would carry mud into the sea, while the succeeding dry period would permit a temporary clearing of the waters and the deposition of limestone.

A long interval of aridity followed these climatic fluctuations, and during this time a great thickness of red shale (Hakatai) was deposited over extensive valley flats or upon a wide delta plain. The presence of numerous mud cracks at many different levels in the shale shows that the area of deposition was frequently exposed to the air as a broad mud flat, which dried out and formed the cracks. The brilliant red color of the shale suggests an absence of vegetation with which to reduce the iron. Climatic oscillations are again apparent in the upper part of the Hakatai, where beds of sandstone and red shale alternate.

The Shinumo quartzite, which follows next in the section, is 1,500 feet thick. As it consists of very fine, clean sand with well-developed ripple marks and cross-bedding, the rivers that deposited this sediment probably flowed through great stretches of sand dunes or easily eroded sandstone. The fineness of the sand grains and the clean sorting indicate that the material was carried a long distance before its final deposition. Occasional lenses of conglomerate probably mark the positions of ancient stream channels.

The Dox sandstone is found at the top of the Proterozoic section in the Grand Canyon. An unknown quantity of this deposit has been removed by erosion, but the thickness is still more than 2,000 feet. The lower beds of the Dox are greenish gray, while the upper part is bright red. Ripple marks, mud cracks, and cross-bedding occur throughout this section, all indicating deposition in shallow water under climatic conditions of seasonal aridity.

The Grand Canyon Disturbance. Widespread uplifts in the western part of North America brought the long era of Proterozoic sedimentation to a close. In the Grand Canyon area there was some folding of the rocks, and faulting on a grand scale resulted in the formation of block-fault mountains. This orogeny was rather local in its effects, since evidence of the disturbance does not appear in the central and southern parts of Arizona or in the southeastern California area. These Grand Canyon mountains may have been comparable in height to the faulted ranges found in the Great Basin region of Nevada, but nothing is known about their extent.

A prolonged period of erosion followed the making of these mountains, and by the Middle Cambrian period they had been reduced to a peneplain. Remnants of the great tilted earth blocks remain today as wedges in the walls of the Canyon, where the vast unconformity between the Proterozoic and the Cambrian may easily be seen. The contact between the rocks of these two eras is exposed for several miles in the Grand Canyon and some of its tributaries, making possible an examination of the old peneplain surface. In those places where the sediments were easily eroded, the surface of the plain shows gentle slopes, with elevations of less than 50 feet above the general level. In other localities, where more resistant intrusive igneous rocks were exposed, the topography is somewhat rougher. The very hard, tilted Shinumo quartzite, which was uncovered in a number of localities, formed prominent ridges that rose 200 feet and more above the peneplain.

THE NORTHERN ROCKY MOUNTAIN REGION

The Belt System. During the Proterozoic era a great geosyncline developed, extending from Arizona northward through Montana into British Columbia. This slowly subsiding trough received the materials that are found in the Grand Canyon system of rocks and also the tremendous thickness of sediments that make up the Belt system of Montana, Idaho, and British Columbia. The formations of the Belt, which are 50,000 feet thick in places, include sandstone, shale, and nearly 10,000 feet of limestone. Especially fine exposures of these rocks are found in the Cabinet range of western Montana. The formations have a known width of more than 300 miles. If they are traced westward, it can be seen that the

Fig. 38.—Mt. Gould, Grinnell Lake and Glacier in Glacier National Park, Montana. The rocks belong to the Belt System and the dark band near the top is the edge of a great diabase sill. (*Photographed by Hileman. Courtesy of the Great Northern Railway Company.*)

limestones are gradually replaced by shales and sands, which indicates that the source of the material was some highland area to the west. The limestones and most of the shales are of marine origin, but some of the coarser and thicker deposits toward the west were probably formed as alluvial fans upon long piedmont slopes.

This geosyncline can be divided into several more or less independent basins of deposition in which the thickness of the sediments varies greatly. These basins were probably all in existence at the same time, but at present it is impossible accurately to outline their extent.

The rocks of the Belt system itself were not affected by block faulting during the Proterozoic, as were those of the Grand Canyon system, but they were gently warped and uplifted vertically to considerable heights, with the result that about 20,000 feet of the Belt were eroded before Cambrian sedimentation began in the region. As the Cambrian rocks rest upon those of the Belt with an angular unconformity that is not very obvious, the great stratigraphic break that separates the formations of the two eras is difficult to appreciate until the uncomformable contact has been followed in a westerly direction for several miles. All the Beltian areas have suffered great erosion, and in some places the beds were completely removed.

Glacier National Park. A remarkably fine section of Proterozoic rocks belonging to the Belt series (Fig. 38) is found in Glacier Park, Montana. The formations here are 10,000 feet thick and have not been greatly affected by folding or metamorphism. A huge block of these rocks was thrust eastward several miles at the time of the Laramide revolution. It now rests upon Cretaceous sediments.

THE GREAT LAKES REGION

The Huronian System. A long period of erosion greatly reduced the heights of the mountains that were formed during the Algoman revolution, and in many places the ranges were undoubtedly peneplaned. This was especially true of the area extending northeastward across northern Michigan into Ontario. A geosyncline that was formed in this area during Lower Huronian times became a basin of deposition for considerable quantities of sediment. Conditions of sedimentation varied greatly during the long Huronian period. Some of the deposits were laid down in seas, while others were of continental origin. The total thickness of the sediments is between 15,000 and 20,000 feet.

The Lower Huronian. The Lower Huronian, of Michigan and Wisconsin, consists of conglomerates, quartzites, dolomites, and slates. The boulders in the conglomerate have been derived from several different underlying formations; consequently, they vary from place to place. The quartzites are composed of clean, well-sorted sand, and symmetrical types of ripple marks are common. The thick dolomites contain numerous concretionary structures that are believed to be the result of algal growth. The Lower Huronian strata are probably of marine origin.

The Bruce Series. The Bruce series is found in Canada, north of Lake Huron. The rock is composed chiefly of white quartzite,

but conglomerates, slates, and impure dolomites also occur.   The
deposit is much thicker in the southern part of the area than toward
the north, and this is good evidence that the source of the material
was some highland region bordering the geosyncline on the south.
It is uncertain whether the Bruce series is of marine or of continental
origin, but the irregular bedding that characterizes the conglomerates and sandstones is suggestive of torrential stream deposition
on a piedmont slope leading down to the sea in which the shales and
dolomites were formed.

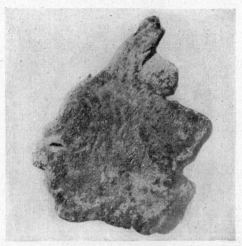

Fig. 39.—A large piece of native copper, weighing 483 pounds, found in the drift
in Houghton County, Michigan.   The piece originally resembled the head of an
Indian, and the Indians apparently improved it by pounding down the edges in a few
places.   (*Photograph courtesy of the Mineralogy Department, University of Michigan,
where the specimen is now displayed.*)

The Middle Huronian.   An interval of uplift and erosion followed the deposition of the Lower Huronian beds.   Then came a
long period of sedimentation, which resulted in the great Cobalt
series of the Middle Huronian.   These rocks include conglomerate
and quartzite, with limestone toward the top of the section.   The
entire thickness is more than 12,000 feet.   The detrital materials
are continental deposits, and the limestone is of marine origin.
The quartzite, which is made of clean, well-assorted sand with an
abundance of ripple marks, is similar to the quartzite of Lower
Huronian times.   The two were probably deposited under very
much the same conditions.   The Cobalt series extends for more
than 160 miles north of Lake Huron.

Glaciation in the Middle Huronian.   The *Gowganda* basal conglomerate of the Cobalt series is, in reality, tillite, or solidified boulder clay. Geologists were skeptical, at first, about the existence of a continental glacier in so early a part of geologic history, but the evidence is now conclusive. The boulders of the tillite, which were derived from the underlying Laurentian and Keewatin rocks, vary in size up to 8 feet in diameter. The stones are irregularly distributed through the matrix, exactly as they occur in the Pleistocene glacial drift. Many of them show facets and striations. Glacial pavements with grooved and striated surfaces have been found directly underlying the conglomerate at Matchewan, Ontario, and near Opasatica Lake in Quebec. The striae run N. 60° E. The tillite here, which is 15 feet thick, contains granite boulders more than 10 feet in diameter, although the nearest source of these rocks is 12 miles distant.

Certain interbedded layers of conglomerate near Cobalt, which are stratified, have been interpreted as interglacial deposits. Slates, showing evidence of seasonal banding, occur above the conglomerate; and these beds contain a few boulders that were probably carried by icebergs and dropped into a lake that formed in front of the glacier. The tillite is 500 feet thick in a few places, but it has suffered greatly from erosion in most localities. The surface over which this continental glacier moved was a peneplain. While the exact extent of the ice is unknown, it apparently spread over several thousand square miles in southern Canada between latitudes 46 and 51°.

The Animikian Series of the Upper Huronian. The Upper Huronian sea spread widely over the low, flat Great Lakes region and advanced northward into Canada somewhat beyond Lake Superior. The Animikian series begins with a widespread but thin basal conglomerate and quartzite, followed by the tremendous iron-ore beds of cherty iron carbonate, and then a considerable thickness of black slates and shales. These upper beds were originally fine-grained muds brought into the sea by rivers flowing southward over the old Pre-Cambrian land surface. The presence of so much carbonaceous material disseminated throughout the black slates and shales is strong evidence that the Upper Huronian sea contained an abundance of plant and animal life, from which the carbon was probably derived.

The Keweenawan Series. The Lower Keweenawan was a time of quiet continental sedimentation; therefore, the rocks of this series consist of thin conglomerates, quartzites, arkoses, and shales. After this there was a long period of igneous activity during which

fissures opened in the crust of the earth, probably near the middle
of the Lake Superior area, and many flows of basaltic lava (Fig. 40)
issued forth until they reached a total thickness of several thousand
feet in the Upper Peninsula of Michigan. The source of this great
quantity of igneous material was probably some deep-seated
batholith. As the molten rock was drawn away from beneath the
Lake Superior region and solidified on the surface, there was a
collapse of the earth's crust and the structural basin now occupied
by the lake was formed.

Fig. 40.—Basaltic lava of Keweenawan age at Houghton, Michigan.

Red sandstones are found interbedded with the trap flows, and
the upper division of the Keweenawan consists largely of red conglomerates, sandstones and shales, having a total thickness of about
15,000 feet. A great part of this sedimentary material was derived
from the exposed surfaces of the various basaltic flows, which broke
up rapidly and furnished the thick beds of conglomerate. Some of
the stones came from Archeozoic granites and some from the iron-
bearing rocks of the Huronian. None of the Upper Keweenawan
sediments show any evidence of having been deposited in marine
water. The extensive development of ripple marks and cross-

Fig. 41.—The Isle Royale copper mine near Houghton, Michigan. The original
Isle Royale Mining Company began operations in 1852.

bedding in the sandstones and of mud cracks in the shales is evidence
of shallow-water deposition. The red color, which extends throughout the entire sedimentary section, is interpreted as a result of
oxidation during the dry seasons, when the materials were exposed
over wide valley flats.

MINERAL DEPOSITS

Iron. The most important iron-ore deposits in the United
States are found in the Huronian rocks lying to the south and west
of Lake Superior in Michigan (Fig. 42), Wisconsin, and Minnesota.

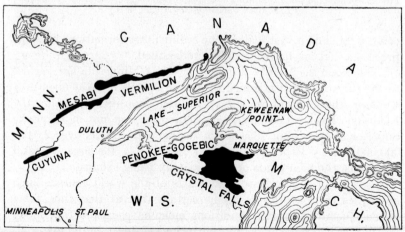

Fig. 42.—Map of the Lake Superior region with the great iron ranges shown in
black.

These three states produce every year about 85 per cent of the iron that is mined in this country.   The value of the ore in 1939 was about $135,000,000.   The occurrence of the ore varies somewhat in the different ranges, but it is usually found in great troughs that were formed as a result of mountain-making stresses.   The iron ranges extend in an east-northeast direction, following very closely the trend of the ancient Killarney Mountains, which were formed in the latter part of the Proterozoic era.

The origin of these great bodies of iron has been a much-discussed problem among geologists for many years.   The ore, which apparently came originally from the greenstone magmas, was later

FIG. 43.—Cleveland Cliffs Iron Mine at Ishpeming, Michigan.   (*Photograph courtesy of L. L. Cook Company, Milwaukee, Wis.*)

concentrated on a vast scale in the sedimentary formations by some processes that are not thoroughly understood.

The ore in the Mesabi Range (Fig. 44) of Minnesota lies so close to the surface that it is mined by power shovels in great open pits, while in other parts of the district the rich deposits occur below the 1,000-foot level.   The entire production of iron ore in the Lake Superior district from 1854 down to the year 1944 is over 2,042,-000,000 tons.   Although the total reserves in the area are still enormous, the high-grade ores are rapidly being exhausted.

Pre-Cambrian rocks in many parts of the world contain huge quantities of iron ore.   It seems certain that at that time some unusual combinations of conditions must have existed that made possible such extraordinary concentrations of this essential material. It is quite certain that the great industrial development of the

Fig. 44.—The Albany open pit iron mine at Hibbing, Minnesota. (*Courtesy of Pickands-Mather Company and M. D. Harbaugh.*)

United States could not have progressed so rapidly without the iron ore from Michigan, Minnesota, and Wisconsin.

Copper. The famous copper deposits of Michigan were first discovered by Indians in prehistoric times. Several of their old mines have been found in the Upper Peninsula of Michigan. A book by Lagarde, published in 1636, mentions the occurrence of pure copper near Lake Superior, and similar discoveries were recorded by missionaries. A huge mass of native copper weighing 6,500 pounds, which was found in 1766 along the Ontonagon River of northern Michigan, was removed to the Smithsonian Institution at Washington in 1843. Stone hammers found near this mass of

Fig. 45.—View from Houghton, Michigan, looking toward Hancock and Quincy Hill. Some of the great Keweenawan copper deposits lie under this ridge, associated with lava flows. (*Photographed by Minnie S. Hussey.*)

copper had been used by the Indians to cut away pieces of the metal. Douglass Houghton, appointed State Geologist of Michigan in 1837, immediately began a survey of the Upper Peninsula. His first report, printed in 1841, contains convincing statements that Michigan held enormous deposits of copper that could be worked without any great difficulty, and this prophecy has been fully justified by subsequent developments.

The native copper is found in conglomerates and basalt flows (Fig. 45) of Keweenawan age. The main producing mines are located within a narrow belt, not more than 4 miles wide, that runs in a northeasterly direction for about 100 miles along the Keweenaw Peninsula. The rocks in this area dip steeply to the northwest. Some of the mines have reached a depth of 10,000 feet along the dip, with plenty of ore still in sight, but the cost of mining at such great depths has become prohibitive. The Calumet and Hecla mine, the most famous one in the district, has had a total output of more than 4,000,000 tons of copper. An immense mass of pure copper from the Minnesota mine measured 46 feet long, 12 feet wide, and 4 feet thick, and weighed 420 tons.

Silver. The Keewatin and Huronian rocks in several localities of southern Canada have been invaded by Keweenawan intrusives containing important quantities of native silver. The ore was probably deposited along fissures by highly heated waters issuing from some magma of diabase. The chief producing area is now around Cobalt, Ontario, where veins of extraordinary richness occur. Native silver is also found associated with the copper deposits of Michigan.

Nickel. The Sudbury district of Ontario produces over 90 per cent of the nickel that is used in the world today. The age of this deposit is Late Proterozoic, probably Keweenawan, and the source of the ore was probably a great sill of gabbro.

CLIMATE OF THE PROTEROZOIC

Many widely different types of climatic conditions must have prevailed during the extremely long Proterozoic era, but very few of these have been clearly recorded in the geologic record. The great scarcity of fossils is especially serious, since plants and animals often afford considerable evidence in a study of past climates. The presence of thick limestones usually indicates warm seas, but this is not always the case. The extensive development of mud cracks in red shales may indicate an alternation between seasons of heavy rain and aridity. It is often difficult to determine the geographic extent of a certain variety of climate, and this is particularly true of Pre-Cambrian times.

Proterozoic Glaciation. It is becoming increasingly evident that extensive continental glaciers were formed in a number of places during the Proterozoic. The *Gowganda* tillite of Huronian age has already been discussed. Two distinct periods of glaciation have been recognized, one in the early part of the era and another toward the close.

Tillite and glacio-fluvial deposits are found in a number of places through northern Utah. These glacial materials occur at several horizons in a great deposit of quartzite, conglomerate, and slate that lies below the Cambrian and is probably of Proterozoic age. Some good exposures of the tillite may be seen between Brigham and Provo, where the thickness is 300 feet or more. The glacial boulders were derived from different kinds of rocks and many of them exhibit distinct striations, as well as characteristic facets. Some of the slates show fine banding and may originally have been varve clays and silts. The pebbles and small boulders occasionally found in these banded slates may have been dropped by floating icebergs. No doubt this ancient drift sheet originally covered a large area, but it has suffered considerable erosion and much of its former extent is concealed by later deposits.

Australia. The Sturtian glacial deposits are exposed in very conspicuous cliffs 600 feet high, along the central part of the Flinders range in south central Australia. Most of the boulders in the tillite are composed of quartzite, but many have been derived from outcrops of granite, schist, gneiss, and quartz porphyry. Most of these stones, which vary in size up to 9 feet in diameter, are well-rounded, while a considerable number show striations and facets. The groundmass is a fine-grained rock flour, reddish in color, which contains numerous angular fragments broken from different kinds of rock. A series of finely laminated slates lying above the tillite may originally have been varve clays. The Sturtian glacial deposits, which occur 1,500 feet below the Cambrian rocks of the region, are very likely of Proterozoic age.

Other Localities. Tillites of both the Early and the Late Proterozoic are found in South Africa, and still others that probably belong to the Proterozoic occur in the Yangtze Valley of China, in East Greenland, Norway, and India. It is impossible to correlate these widely separated tillites and to determine their time relations to one another. A long era like the Proterozoic may have witnessed several glacial periods.

MOUNTAINS OF THE LATE PROTEROZOIC

The Proterozoic era was brought to a close by crustal disturbances of great extent in North America. Lofty mountains were upheaved in three different parts of Canada, as well as in the north central portion of the United States. Huge batholiths of granitic rock accompanied the orogenies. While the ancient grandeur of these ranges has long since disappeared, their worn-down stumps may still be traced for hundreds of miles as visible evidence of their former existence.

The Killarney Mountains. The Killarney ranges have been traced for over 700 miles in a northeasterly direction through Wisconsin and the Upper Peninsula of Michigan, into Ontario to the north of Georgian Bay. As there is no evidence of any decrease in the intensity of the folding at either end, where the folds are now covered by sediments, they must originally have extended a considerable distance beyond their present known limits. The exposed width of the folded belt is more than 100 miles. The hills in the iron and copper districts of Michigan, especially the Porcupine and Huron mountains, are remnants of the ancient Killarneys (Fig. 46). Some of the peaks still rise to elevations of more than 2,000 feet above sea level. The orogeny took place after Keweenawan time, since rocks of that period were involved in the folding (Fig. 47).

The Belcher Mountains. The truncated folds of the Belcher Mountains are especially well shown in the steeply dipping Huronian

FIG. 46.—The ancient Killarney Mountains are now reduced to low, rolling hills. A scene north of Houghton, Michigan. (*Photographed by Minnie S. Hussey.*)

rocks of the Belcher Islands, which lie along the eastern side of Hudson Bay. This long, narrow group of islands runs in a northwesterly direction, following the trend of the original ranges. The Labrador range ran in a northwesterly direction through the center of Labrador.

After the close of sedimentation and the great orogenies of the Late Proterozoic came an extended period of erosion, during which there was extensive peneplanation in many parts of the world. This erosion surface beveled rocks of the Archeozoic and Proterozoic, and its relief was somewhat greater than that of the older peneplain. The Canadian shield (Fig. 48) was finally reduced to a

relatively flat area, while great sections of the earth's surface
became featureless plains. Numerous exposures of the Pro-
terozoic-Cambrian contact enable us to study this old flat land
surface in a number of places.

Physical weathering was apparently still dominant at that time.
There is some evidence that chemical decay had affected rocks of
the Proterozoic surface and the material that is found in the sediments at the base of the Cambrian. That there was little, if any,

Fig. 47.—Proterozoic quartzite (Mesnard) near Negaunee, Michigan, folded during
the Killarney revolution. Many of the surfaces show ripple marks.

land vegetation counted as an important factor in the process of
weathering.

Calcareous deposits of undoubted algal origin (Fig. 49) are very
common in the Proterozoic rocks of several localities. Algae are
primitive types of microscopic plants that grow in colonies and
build up irregular or globular masses of calcium carbonate, sometimes several feet in diameter, often showing a concentric structure.
Such deposits are abundant in certain calcareous beds of the Belt
system in Montana and the Grand Canyon system of Arizona.
Similar structures have been found in Huronian rocks of Michigan

and Minnesota. Algae are very common at present in the oceans as well as in rivers and lakes.

Various kinds of invertebrates have been reported from Proterozoic rocks in different places, but some of these finds are probably not of organic origin. Although *Protaledadia* was described as an arthropod from Pre-Cambrian rocks in southern Australia, it may be nothing more than a concretionary structure and entirely inorganic. *Beltina danae*, from shales in the Grand Canyon system, was supposed to be an arthropod related to the eurypterids

Fig. 48.—The present flat surface of the Canadian shield, called the Laurentian Peneplain, in Dufresnoy Township, Abitibi District, Quebec. (*Courtesy of Geological Survey of Canada.*)

(Fig. 93), but probably it is simply a thin carbonaceous film derived from some marine plants. The sponge spicules, and the impression of a jellyfish from Proterozoic rocks in the Grand Canyon may be actual organisms, although conclusive proof is lacking. In the Belt system rocks of Glacier Park, however, some unknown worm-like animals left trails and burrows that are doubtless of organic origin. A few brachiopods have been reported.

This exceedingly meager record of life in the Proterozoic is astonishing and very difficult to explain. The forces of metamorphism have greatly altered the rocks of this era in many places, but in the Belt series of Montana there has been little or no change in the original nature of the sediment.

Many animals that later developed hard parts might still have been soft-bodied forms through a portion of the Proterozoic. Most of the shells that Pre-Cambrian invertebrates first developed were probably thin, fragile structures that could not easily have been preserved as fossils.

Among the Proterozoic formations there are great thicknesses of black shales and slates that contain enormous quantities of carbon widely disseminated throughout the rock. The most likely source of this carbonaceous material, which must have been deposited along with the sediment, is plant and animal life.

Fig. 49.—Large colonies of calcareous algae in Proterozoic rocks of Grand Canyon National Park, Arizona. (*Courtesy of United States National Park Service.*)

The great abundance of marine invertebrate life in the Cambrian is evidence that the ancestors of these forms must have lived during the Pre-Cambrian times. Life must have been abundant in the Proterozoic seas; but the lands, covered only by a loose mantle of disintegrated rock, were without the forests or grassy plains that are so common today. Animals had not yet emerged from the oceans, and the continents were bare and forbidding places. The larval forms of living marine invertebrates may possibly give us some information concerning the appearance of Pre-Cambrian animal life.

Reading References

COLEMAN, A. P.: "Ice Ages Recent and Ancient," p. 223, The Macmillan Company, New York, 1926.

HINDS, NORMAN E. A.: "Pre-Cambrian Geology," *Carnegie Inst. Washington Publ.* 463, 1936.

SHARP, ROBERT W.: Ep-Archean and Ep-Algonkian Erosion Surfaces, Grand Canyon, Arizona, *Geol. Soc. America Bull.*, vol. 51, No. 8, pp. 1235–1270, Aug. 1, 1940.

CHAPTER VIII

THE PALEOZOIC ERA

THE CAMBRIAN PERIOD

The Geologic Record Growing Clearer. With the dawn of the Cambrian period, much of the vagueness and confusion that have heretofore clouded the geologic record disappears, making it possible to present the rest of the earth's history in a clear and orderly manner that adds greatly to its value and interest. Pre-Cambrian time, with its insurmountable difficulties and fascinating but unsolved problems, will always be contrasted with the succeeding eras, just as the Old Stone Age of human history is contrasted with modern times. One of the main reasons for this great change is the relative abundance of fossils in the rocks of all the periods after the Proterozoic era. From now on it will be possible to determine the time relations between various rock formations and to correlate outcrops over wide areas. The Paleozoic era, with its numerous periods and epochs, marks the beginning of systematic geologic history.

FIG. 50.—Charles Doolittle Walcott (1850–1927). A great student of Cambrian life.

As the reader follows the geological story of our continent during the remaining millions of years, he must remember that the North America of today is not the same as the North America of the past and that the ability to visualize changing lands and seas, as well as the remarkable animals and plants of the organic world, is highly important to a full understanding and enjoyment of the subject. Forget the present while living in the past.

CAMBRIAN LANDS AND SEAS

The history of North America during much of the Paleozoic era was profoundly influenced by two great geosynclines and by two persistent, and often mountainous, land masses, which are clearly outlined for the first time in the Cambrian period.

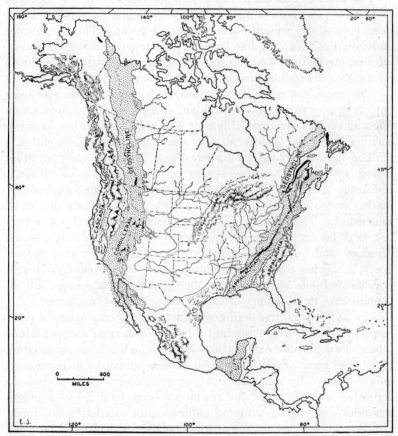

Fig. 51.—North America in Early Cambrian time. The stippled areas show the inferred extent of the seas. Outcrops are in black. White areas are land. The Killarney Mountains were probably still moderately high at this time although their extent to the northeast and southwest is not known. (*Modified from Branson and Tarr.*)

The Land of Appalachia. This ancient land (Fig. 51) was located along the eastern side of North America. Its western edge included the present coastal plain and piedmont regions, and it extended an unknown distance eastward into the Atlantic, probably as far as the outer edge of the continental shelf. Several times during the Paleozoic era, Appalachia was uplifted into mountainous areas, and, just as often, it was low and featureless. These topographic changes are recorded in the sediments that were deposited in the Appalachian geosyncline, which lay along the western side of the old borderland.

The Land of Cascadia. This old Pacific land (Fig. 51) included the area of the coast ranges, while its western margin lay many miles beyond the present border of the continent. The topography and extent of Cascadia, like that of Appalachia, varied greatly during its long history, and it furnished a large quantity of sediment for a series of geosynclines that formed along its eastern edge.

The great central interior region of North America was comparatively low during the Cambrian, except in a few places where remnants of the ancient Killarney Mountains and other Proterozoic highlands rose as monadnocks above the surrounding plains.

The Lands Invaded by Epeiric Seas. Early in the Cambrian period a sea began to move slowly northeastward across southern California into the Cordilleran geosyncline, while another body of marine water entered the northern end of the trough and crept southward. These two epeiric seas eventually crossed a low barrier that lay in the region now occupied by Idaho and western Montana and finally joined their waters during the latter part of Early Cambrian time. The following brief discussion of paleogeographic methods will show how the geologists have been able to demonstrate the existence of these two distinct embayments.

No Early Cambrian sediments have been found within a comparatively small area extending through Idaho and western Montana. Two possible explanations of this condition are considered. Either the rocks might have been there originally and have been removed later by erosion, or no such sediments had ever been deposited there because the region was dry land. The problem was finally solved by studying and carefully comparing the Early Cambrian fossils from the south side of the area in question with those to the north. The two faunas proved to be quite distinct, especially with respect to certain species of invertebrates that would certainly have been found in both places if a land barrier had not prevented them from migrating. These faunal distinctions disappeared later in the period, when the barrier was submerged and the trough was filled with water throughout its entire extent.

The marine invasion of the Appalachian trough was completed by the close of the Early Cambrian. This was followed by a withdrawal of the water from the northern portion of the geosyncline during the middle part of the period, but the sea returned during the Upper Cambrian and once more covered the entire area of the trough.

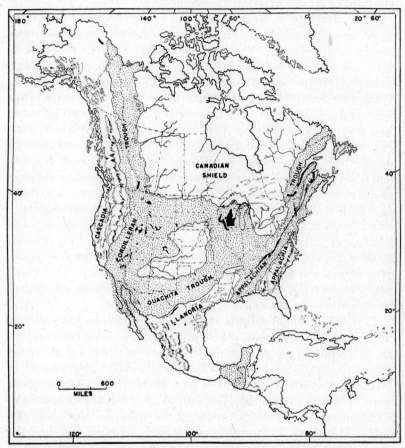

Fig. 52.—North America in Late Cambrian time. The stippled areas show the inferred maximum extent of the seas. Outcrops are in black. White areas are land. The Killarney Mountains had almost disappeared by this time. (*Modified from Branson and Tarr.*)

About the middle of the Cambrian, marine waters began to spread eastward from the Cordilleran trough across the northern part of the United States; and, by the Late Cambrian, the two great geosynclines were joined by a continuous sheet of water.

The Ouachita trough, which came into existence during the latter part of the period, stretched eastward across northern Mexico,

Texas, and Oklahoma.   The borderland of Llanoria lay immediately
to the south of this subsiding area and extended across the present
Gulf of Mexico region.

When the Cambrian seas were at their maximum extent, about
one-third of North America was submerged.

Characteristics of Epeiric Seas.   The invasion of a continent
by an epeiric sea is a far more complex process than these brief
descriptions indicate.   The movements of such vast bodies of
water are not always steady; rather, they advance and retreat,
with many fluctuations of their shore lines in the course of the period.
As the time required for a great inundation to reach its climax may
be several million years, it is impossible to present anything more
than a very general picture of the event.   The rate at which these
seas moved across the land is largely a matter of conjecture.   In
places where the land was very flat and but comparatively few feet
above the sea, a small rise in the water level would rapidly submerge
extensive areas.   The advance of the sea was, in most cases, probably so slow that during the average lifetime of an individual very
little change in the position of the shore line would be noted.   The
slowness of most geological processes is proverbial; yet, if small
changes are continued for many thousands or millions of years,
great effects will finally be produced.   Time is a most important
factor in geologic history—one that must always be considered
when final results are weighed.

If the land should subside at the rate of 1 inch in 100 years, at
the end of 720,000 years the total subsidence would amount to
600 feet, which is the greatest depth of the ocean today at the outer
edge of the continental shelf.   This comparatively small amount of
displacement through the central part of the United States would
cause the sea to invade the Mississippi Valley region as far as Lake
Michigan, while the states bordering the Atlantic Ocean and the
Gulf of Mexico would be widely submerged.   A rapid inrush of the
sea would be possible into regions that are below sea level, such as
the Death Valley area in California.   At present, the ocean is
unable to penetrate into this desert because of mountain barriers,
but these will disappear during the course of time and a sudden
inundation may then become a reality.

Why Seas Invade the Lands.   There are several conditions that
might operate to bring about an invasion of the land by water from
the oceans.   Great mountain ranges have been upheaved at different times during the earth's history, only to be worn away by the

slowly acting forces of weathering and erosion. A great part of this eroded material is carried to the seas, where it eventually displaces a considerable volume of water and causes a gradual rise in the ocean level. With the continents gradually getting lower because of erosion and the water level in the oceans rising because of deposited material, a very considerable part of the land might eventually be covered by a shallow epeiric sea.

There have been undoubted cases where portions of continents that border the oceans have subsided, thus making opportunity for marine waters to cover the lower reaches of the land. After a widespread continental uplift, there is apparently a tendency for the margins of the continents to creep laterally, and such movements would play an important part in marine invasions of the lands.

As the Pleistocene glaciers slowly disappeared from the lands, water from the melting ice returned to the ocean basins, causing a rise in the sea level of more than 100 feet. This resulted in extensive floodings of the continental margins. When all the water now locked up in the existing great ice sheets of Greenland and Antarctica has returned to the seas, there will be a further general rise in the level of the oceans.

Epeiric seas are not permanent features, as are the oceans, and their withdrawal from the land could be caused by an upward movement of the continent or by a deepening of the ocean basins. The fluctuations of these seas during their advances and retreats are due largely to the fact that they are extremely shallow and that the land over which the water flows has very little relief. Under these conditions, a comparatively small upward movement of the land would cause a widespread retreat of the sea, while a downward movement of only a few feet would submerge a large area of the continent. Fluctuations of the shore line often produce a zone of deposition in which alternations of marine and continental sediments appear.

It is impossible to determine accurately what was the average depth of an epeiric sea, but it was not more than a few hundred feet. The water at the outer edge of the continental shelf today is about 600 feet deep. Fossils that occur in the deposits of epeiric seas are, therefore, the remains of organisms that lived only in shallow water.

SEDIMENTATION IN THE CAMBRIAN

The thickest and most important sections of marine sediments that are found in the geologic column were deposited in long, com-

paratively narrow, trough-like areas called "geosynclines." The
total thickness of these deposits of sedimentary material, the origin
of which was chiefly some bordering land mass that was periodically
uplifted to mountainous heights, may amount to many thousands of
feet. As the water in these extraordinary basins of deposition was
never more than a few hundred feet deep, the only way to account
for so tremendous an accumulation of shallow-water sediments is
to assume that there was a more or less continual subsidence of the
trough bottom. Today, there is apparently a geosyncline bordering the eastern coast of Asia and another just south of The
Himalaya, where an excess of deposition over subsidence prevents
the sea from occupying the area.

The Cordilleran Geosyncline. The geologic history of the
Cambrian period as it is recorded in marine deposits of the Cordilleran geosyncline has been divided into three epochs, largely
upon the basis of certain faunal distinctions in which trilobites (Fig.
59) play a dominant part. These trilobites, together with other
genera and species of invertebrates, are typical index fossils, since
they are characteristic of the Cambrian only, and of certain epochs
into which the period has been divided.

The faunal change that marks the boundary between the Waucobian and the Albertan was the result of considerable evolution
that took place during a withdrawal stage of the Lower Cambrian
sea. The waters returned in Albertan time with a new assemblage
of animals. The break between the rocks of the two epochs is
marked in several places by subaerial erosion of the lower formations
and by a great change in the character of the sediments. The
withdrawal of the sea at the close of Middle Cambrian time was
apparently neither complete nor of long duration, as it is difficult to
locate the boundary between the rocks of the Albertan epoch and
those of the Croixian. Under such conditions, the dividing line
between the two epochs must be somewhat artificial and, therefore,
is subject to change if further research makes this seem advisable.
The Upper Cambrian began with the appearance of certain new
elements in the fauna, especially several genera of trilobites.

The greatest section of Cambrian rocks in the entire world was
deposited in the part of the Cordilleran trough that covered Alberta,
Canada (Fig. 53). These formations, which are now exposed in
the Canadian Rockies, have been carved by erosion into some
of the most magnificent scenery on the North American continent.
The southern slopes of Mt. Bosworth exhibit over 12,000 feet of

Cambrian rocks in a single section, and there are other localities in the region where similar exposures occur (Fig. 54).

The Lower Cambrian deposits in the Alberta area are made up largely of quartzites, with some interbedded sandy shales, and near the top of the section the beds are calcareous. The source of this sand was the old land of Cascadia, with its deeply weathered crystalline rocks. The widespread limestones, which are charac-

FIG. 53.—Mt. Assiniboine (right) and adjacent mountains have been eroded from a great block of Lower and Middle Cambrian limestone and quartziferous sandstones. The Lower Cambrian quartzites have been pushed eastward along a great overthrust fault line and now rest upon Devonian limestones. Mt. Assiniboine is 11,870 feet high and is about 22 miles south of Banff, Alberta. (*Courtesy of Canadian Pacific Railway Company.*)

teristic of the Middle Cambrian, indicate that the borderland stood at a low elevation during this epoch and that the sluggish streams were carrying very little detrital material into the sea. These calcareous sediments, ranging in thickness from 2,000 to 5,000 feet, are found distributed all the way from Alberta to Nevada and Utah. The Upper Cambrian deposits are from 3,000 to 4,000 feet thick and consist almost entirely of limestones and dolomites. The conspicuous white cliffs that appear in many parts of the Canadian Rockies are composed of these sediments.

The Mississippi Valley. The absence of Lower and Middle Cambrian sediments from the Mississippi Valley region indicates that this portion of the country was above water during these epochs. In the Upper Cambrian, the sea spread eastward from

Fig. 54.—Mt. Stephen near Field, British Columbia, is composed of Cambrian sediments.   (*Courtesy of Canadian Pacific Railway Company.*)

the Cordilleran trough across the northern part of the United States and finally joined with the marine waters of the Appalachian geosyncline.

The ancient Pre-Cambrian rocks over the northern interior portion of the United States and adjoining parts of Canada had been subjected to subaerial weathering for a great length of time,

until a deep covering of fine material, with considerable quantities
of wind-blown sand, had gradually formed upon the lowlands.
When the Upper Cambrian sea moved slowly eastward across this
region, the waves and currents sorted and redeposited the mantle
rock as shaly formations and sandstones, which now cover a great
area.   The type section is around St. Croix Falls, in Minnesota
and Wisconsin, where the beds are 1,000 feet thick.   Southward,
around the Ozark Mountains in Missouri and Arkansas, the Upper
Cambrian rocks have a sandstone and conglomerate member at the
base, followed by several hundred feet of dolomite with some sandstone and calcareous shale.   The topography in the Ozark region
at the beginning of Upper Cambrian time was quite rough, with a
few old granite hills rising a thousand feet or more above the surrounding country.   The first sediments were deposited around the
hills, but as submergence continued, much of the rough topography
was finally buried beneath the accumulating material and only the
highest peaks remained above the sea.

The Oklahoma and Texas Region. Upper Cambrian sandy
shales are found in the Ouachita Mountains of southeastern Oklahoma, where all the formations have been intensely folded and much
broken by faulting.   The Arbuckle and Wichita Mountains, in
the southern part of the state, exhibit over 4,000 feet of Upper
Cambrian sandstones and limestones.   Similar deposits are found
in central and western Texas.   All the Croixian rocks in these two
states accumulated in the Ouachita trough.

The Appalachian Geosyncline. At the time of its greatest
extent, the Appalachian geosyncline stretched from the Atlantic
Ocean southwestward through the St. Lawrence region and along
the course of the present Appalachian Mountains to the Gulf of
Mexico.   The sediments in this great trough vary in character and
thickness from place to place, reflecting quite accurately the conditions on the neighboring Land of Appalachia, which lay immediately
to the east.

The Lower Cambrian sediments, which are largely clastic in
character, consist chiefly of quartzite, with some conglomerate,
which indicates that the old borderland was high and that the rivers
running down the western slopes had considerable transporting
power.   Many of the present Appalachian ridges, especially those
in Pennsylvania, Virginia, and Maryland, owe their existence to the
extreme hardness of these quartzites, which has enabled them to
resist erosion while the softer limestones and shales have been worn
down into valleys.   There are excellent exposures of this rock at

Harper's Ferry, where the Potomac River cuts through the Blue
Ridge Mountains. A large portion of the coarse detrital material
that is found in the Great Smokies of Tennessee and North Carolina
has proved to be of Pre-Cambrian age instead of Cambrian. Its
present position is the result of an overthrust from the east.

Fig. 55.—Potsdam sandstone of Upper Cambrian age in Ausable Chasm, New York.
(*Courtesy of New York State Museum.*)

Late in Waucobian time, the deposits in the Appalachian trough
changed from coarse sediments to shales and, still later, to dolomites.
This type of deposit, which continued through the Middle Cambrian, gives evidence that Appalachia had been reduced to so low an
elevation that the sluggish streams were unable to carry into the
trough anything except the finer sediments. This condition persisted over a wide area of the geosyncline during Upper Cambrian

time. Thick deposits of limestones and dolomites are especially characteristic of this epoch.

A local highland area in the Adirondack region of northern New York state furnished great quantities of sand for the surrounding sea, and this material is represented today by the Potsdam sandstone, which is well exposed in the picturesque Ausable Chasm (Fig. 55).

CLIMATE OF THE CAMBRIAN

It is impossible to do more than make a number of broad generalizations about the climatic conditions during the Cambrian period. Any division of geologic time that lasted for several millions of years must have witnessed many important variations of climate that are not revealed by the geologic record. The highlands of Cascadia and Appalachia must have been much colder than the low, flat interior of North America. Oceanic climates are more uniform than are continental types; therefore, when widespread epeiric seas invaded the lands, the temperatures must have been milder and more equable than during the times when the continents were elevated and free from marine waters. Many species of invertebrates that lived in the Cambrian seas had a wide distribution through low as well as high latitudes. This is considered good evidence that zones of climate were poorly defined, and that the temperature of the seas was higher and more uniform over greater distances north and south of the equator than it is today. The high-grade limestones and dolomites that were deposited widely in the Upper Cambrian seas in regions as far north as Greenland are strong indications of warm, temperate waters.

LIFE IN THE CAMBRIAN PERIOD

Plants. Calcareous algae existed in great numbers during the Cambrian, and reefs built by these primitive, microscopic plants have been found widely distributed through the rocks. The particular type called *Cryptozoön* built up irregular or hemispherical colonies with a concentric structure, which preserves the general form of the entire colony but not the details of each individual plant. The scouring action of the Pleistocene glacier produced cross sections through several colonies of *Cryptozoön proliferum* (Fig. 56) at Saratoga, New York, where they may still be seen in place. Lichens may possibly have lived in certain moist places upon the Cambrian lands, but the continents were probably almost as barren as they were during the Archeozoic and Proterozoic eras.

Animals. Of the many different kinds of fossil invertebrates that have been found in the Cambrian rocks, all belong to animals

Fig. 56.—*Cryptozoön proliferum* (calcareous algae) in Cambrian limestone near Saratoga Springs, New York. This rock was smoothed off by the Pleistocene glacier during the Wisconsin stage of glaciation. (*Photograph by H. P. Cushing, New York State Museum.*)

that lived in the seas. Protozoa are uncommon as fossils, but certain beds in Shropshire, England, have yielded some Foraminifera. Considerable numbers of siliceous sponges are found in a few locali-

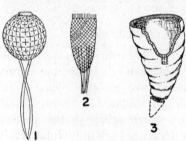

Fig. 57.—1, 2, *Protospongia* from the Upper Cambrian; 3, *Archaeocyathus profundus* from the Lower Cambrian of Labrador. (*From Twenhofel and Shrock.*)

ties, and all belong to the simpler forms of which *Protospongia* (Fig. 57) is typical. The Cambrian formations in a number of places contain extensive reefs built up largely by animals belonging to a group called the *Archaeocyathinae* (Fig. 57). The exact position of these organisms among the invertebrates is uncertain, since they have characteristics in common with both the sponges and the corals, but their place is probably with the former group. The horn-shaped, calcareous skeletons of these peculiar forms have been found in the Lower Cambrian rocks

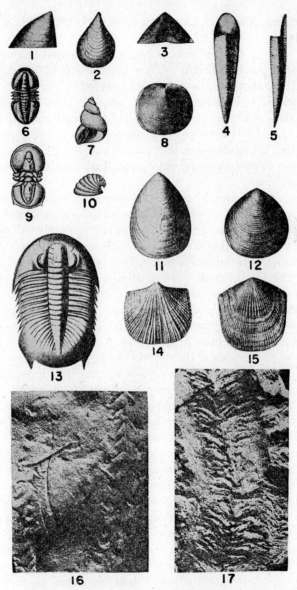

FIG. 58.—Cambrian fossils. 1, 3, 8, *Acrotreta attenuata*, side, ventral, top; 2, *Lingulepis pinnaformis*, ventral; 4, 5, *Hyolithes princeps*, dorsal and lateral; 6, *Eodiscus speciosus;* 7, *Matherella saratogensis;* 9, *Agnostus interstrictus;* 10, *Helcionella rugosa;* 11, *Lingulella granvillensis*, ventral; 12, *Dicellomus politus*, ventral; 13, *Dikelocephalus minnesotensis;* 14, *Eoorthis wichitaensis*, ventral; 15, *Billingsella coloradoensis*, ventral; 16, a trilobite trail on Middle Cambrian sandstone. Only the ends of the legs were touching the sand. 17, a trilobite trail on Middle Cambrian sandstone. (*From C. D. Walcott.*)

of Antarctica, Australia, Labrador, New York, California, and many
other places.

The phylum Coelenterata is poorly represented among the fossil forms of the Cambrian. A few impressions of jellyfish, and a
doubtful sea anemone, have been discovered. The great group of
corals, which is so conspicuous in later periods, had either not
evolved or was represented by soft-bodied creatures that have not
been preserved in the rocks. The cystoids are the only representatives of the Echinodermata that have been found in the Cambrian.
This group is probably the oldest and least specialized member of
the phylum.

Brachiopods. Brachiopods were extremely common during the
Cambrian; all the known orders except one were present in the
lower part of the period. The earliest forms were small, primitive
animals, with phosphatic shells that were not articulated with each
other; but later in the period higher types evolved having calcareous
shells. The brachiopods were so abundant at this time that they
make up about 30 per cent of the faunas. Many of the species
with phosphatic shells that have been preserved in argillaceous
rocks show very little alteration from their original condition. The
mollusks are represented in the Lower Cambrian by a few simple
varieties of gastropods. By the end of the period they were important faunal elements, holding a position that they have kept down
to the present time. The pteropods *Hyolithes* (Fig. 58) and *Hyo-
lithellus* are exceedingly abundant in some of the rocks. These
highly specialized mollusks probably belong to the class of gastropods. The existence of pelecypods in the Cambrian is a debatable
question. A few doubtful forms, such as *Glyptarca*, may be members of this class. The absence of this group may have been due to
the fact that shells of these early forms were made of aragonite,
which is not well adapted to preservation. It is a significant fact
that the great majority of pelecypods from early Paleozoic strata
are preserved as molds or fillings of the interior.

Certain very small conical shells from the Lower Cambrian
may be cephalopods, but their identity has not been definitely
established. A few undoubted fossils belonging to this class of
mollusks are known from the upper part of the period.

Trilobites. The trilobites (Fig. 59) were the most representative
animals of the Cambrian seas. These crustaceans, which existed
in enormous numbers, developed so many different genera and
species that they comprise over half of the Cambrian fauna as it is
known at present. These curious creatures swam through the

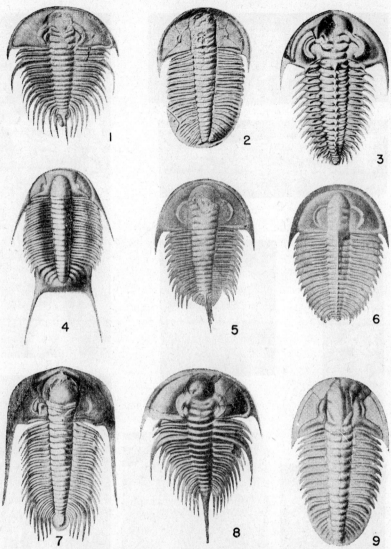

Fig. 59.—Cambrian trilobites. 1, *Poedeumias transitans*, Lower Cambrian; 2. *Ogygopsis klotzi*, Middle Cambrian; 3, *Holmia kjerulfi*, Lower Cambrian; 4, *Crepicephalus iowensis*, Upper Cambrian; 5, *Elliptocephala asaphoides*, Lower Cambrian; 6, *Callavia bröggeri*, Lower Cambrian; 7, *Paradoxides harlani*, Middle Cambrian; 8, *Olenellus thompsoni*, Lower Cambrian; 9, *Bathyuriscus rotundatus*, Middle Cambrian. (*After Walcott*.)

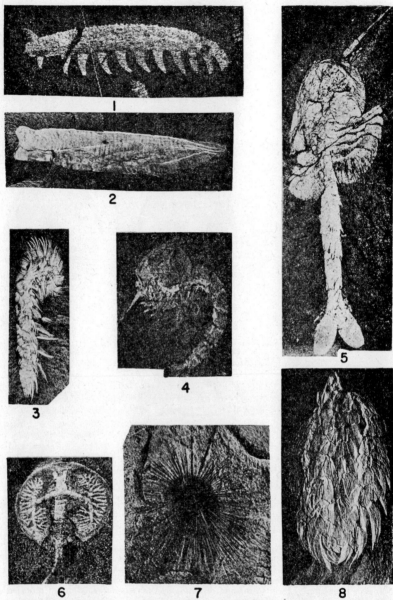

FIG. 60.—Fossils from the Burgess shale of Middle Cambrian age, found near Field, British Columbia. 1, *Aysheaia pedunculata*, an onychophoroid; 2, *Miskoia placida*, an annelid; 3, *Canadia spinosa*, an annelid worm; 4, 5, *Waptia fieldensis*, a shrimp-like crustacean; 6, *Burgessia bella*, a crustacean showing a large part of the digestive system; 7, *Choia carteri*, a siliceous sponge; 8, *Wiwaxia corrugata*, a scaled annelid worm. (*After C. D. Walcott.*)

waters, or crawled over the sea bottoms, and some probably burrowed in the mud.   Many of them were predatory animals who, having developed the habits of scavengers, helped to keep the sea floors free from an excess of decaying organic matter.   Trilobites average between 2 and 3 inches in length, but Paradoxides, from the Middle Cambrian, was a real giant who had reached a length of about 18 inches.   More than 100 genera and 1,000 species of these crustaceans from the rocks of this period have been described.

FIG. 61.—The Burgess shale of Middle Cambrian age exposed on the southwestern slope of Mt. Wapta near Field, British Columbia.   This is the famous locality where Charles D. Walcott discovered the remarkable fauna which contains so many well-preserved soft-bodied forms.   (*Photograph by C. D. Walcott.*)

The group reached its climax in numbers and varieties during the Upper Cambrian and Ordovician times.

The Remarkable Fauna of the Burgess Shale.   Incredible numbers of animals without hard parts have doubtless inhabited the earth since Pre-Cambrian times, but very few of these are preserved as fossils.   This condition, which is responsible for many lost pages in the evolutionary history of life, leaves little hope that any considerable numbers of these missing sections will ever be filled in.

The discovery by Charles Walcott in 1910 of an astonishing softbodied fauna (Fig. 60) in the Middle Cambrian rocks has furnished an important insight into the life of this period.   The site of his discovery is the southwestern slope of Mt. Wapta (Fig. 61) near

the town of Field in British Columbia. The organisms are preserved as flattened carbonaceous films in an exceedingly fine-
grained black shale. Anatomical details, such as fine, hair-like
appendages, intestinal tracts, and scales, are revealed in remarkable perfection. Walcott described 70 genera and 130 species of
invertebrates from this locality, nearly all new. These include
jellyfish, holothurians, siliceous sponges, annelid worms, and
crustaceans. The fact that the 11 genera of annelids found at
Mt. Wapta belong to different families shows that this group had

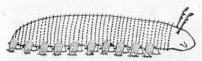

FIG. 62.—Restoration of *Aysheaia*
pedunculata, a Middle Cambrian onycho-
phoran from the Burgess shale. (*After
G. E. Hutchinson.*)

already undergone considerable
evolution before the Middle
Cambrian. Trilobites have long
been considered the rulers of the
Cambrian seas, but this position
may have been vigorously dis-
puted by an arthropod from the
Burgess shale. This animal not
only possessed efficient defensive armor, but, in addition, was
supplied with powerful claws, which must have made the creature
a formidable antagonist in battle.

The Onychophora are a very ancient class of invertebrates that
were probably abundant during the late Proterozoic and early
Paleozoic eras. The genus *Peripatus* is the only representative of
this group that still survives. The discovery of a fossil onychophoroid, *Aysheaia* (Fig. 62), in the Burgess shale was a very
important event. Like the modern forms, their Cambrian
ancestors had unsegmented bodies, somewhat like that of a
caterpillar. The Cambrian *Aysheaia* was a marine animal, but
the living relatives of this form are all found in damp places on
the land.

The conditions under which so many soft-bodied animals were
preserved in an almost undisturbed condition must have been somewhat unusual. In an ordinary marine environment the flesh of a
dead creature is soon eaten by some scavenger, or else it decom-
poses because of bacterial action. The bodies of the invertebrates
from the Mt. Wapta locality were not torn apart by predatory
animals, and decomposing bacteria must have been completely
inactive. We may assume that this particular locality represents an
area on the bottom of the Middle Cambrian sea where the water
was foul with hydrogen sulphide and little oxygen was available
for breathing purposes. The place was evidently a protected spot
far enough from the land so that no currents or waves disturbed its

completely stagnant condition. This portion of the sea floor was practically lifeless, and the animals that came into the area, either crawling or swimming, were immediately asphyxiated and buried rapidly in the slimy mud, where they have remained undisturbed until the present. There are many animals of today that burrow through the soft sediment on the sea bottom looking for organic material, but even such forms as these were not active when the Burgess shale invertebrates were buried.

Invertebrates in Great Abundance. There is a very striking contrast between the Proterozoic rocks, which are almost devoid of invertebrate fossils, and the Cambrian formations directly above, which contain a great abundance of well-preserved organisms. This apparently sudden appearance of abundant organic life merely calls attention to the deficiencies in the existing geologic record. The richness of life in the Cambrian seas and the advanced stage of evolution represented by these invertebrates prove that many different varieties of animals lived in the Proterozoic era. A number of theories have been proposed to account for the lack of fossils in Pre-Cambrian rocks in contrast with the great numbers of fossils that are preserved in the Cambrian.

Soft-tissued animals must have preceded by many millions of years those having shells and skeletons. The power to build hard parts was only gradually acquired. This shell-building habit, which was well developed in the Cambrian, clearly appeared before the beginning of the Paleozoic, but the record of this great event was erased during the long erosion interval that everywhere separates the rocks of the Proterozoic from those of the Cambrian period. It is likely that in the course of this lost portion of geologic history some fundamental change occurred among the invertebrates that caused them to develop shells from chitinous material and calcium carbonate. Just what this change was or what brought it about had not been determined.

W. K. Brooks assumed Pre-Cambrian animals to have been mostly small forms that floated or swam freely in the surface waters of the oceans. Under these conditions, shells would hinder rather than help the organisms, since they would merely add weight to the various invertebrates without performing any essential function. Toward the close of the Proterozoic era these soft-bodied animals gradually adjusted themselves to life on the sea bottom, where they grew larger and more numerous. As the struggle for existence continued to become keener, shells were evolved as protective structures, and this made possible the preservation of many organisms as fossils. Raymond, who has modified the ideas of Brooks in certain details, suggests that, when the active, free-swimming life at the surface was forsaken in favor of a relatively sluggish existence on the ocean bottoms, the animals found it more difficult to get rid of excess calcium carbonate that they had taken into their systems, and the lime was built into skeletons or shells.

It is difficult to explain just why the invertebrates sought the ocean bottom as a living place. Pressure of increasing numbers at the surface or scarcity of food may have been factors in the change. Some of the weaker and less active individuals probably found the environment of the bottom zone more desirable than that of the upper levels and so followed the line of least resistance.

Whatever may have been the causes, the occupation of the ocean bottoms by hosts of invertebrates and the development of skeletons and shells were occurrences of great significance, because they led eventually to the evolution of all higher forms of life.

Reading References

BROOKS, W. K.: The Origin of the Oldest Fossils and the Discovery of the Bottom of the Ocean, *Jour. Geology*, vol. 2, pp. 455–479, 1894.

DALY, R. A.: The Limeless Ocean of Pre-Cambrian Time, *Am. Jour. Sci.*, 4th ser., vol. 23, pp. 93–115, 1907.

HUTCHINSON, G. E.: Restudy of some Burgess Shale Fossils, *U.S. Nat. Mus., Proc.*, vol. 78, Art. 11, 1930.

WALCOTT, CHARLES D.: A Geologist's Paradise, *Nat. Geog. Mag.*, vol. 22, pp. 509–521, 1911.

CHAPTER IX

THE PALEOZOIC ERA

THE ORDOVICIAN PERIOD

LANDS AND SEAS

After the Cambrian seas had withdrawn, North America was left low and comparatively flat. Because of this, there was very little erosion during the emergent period, and the disconformity that separates Ordovician rocks from those of the Cambrian is so poorly defined that in a number of places it is difficult to establish a boundary between the two periods.

Epochs of Inundation and Emergence. Early Ordovician seas first occupied both the Cordilleran and Appalachian geosynclines and then spread widely over the low interior of the United States. This is the Canadian epoch, which ended with a complete withdrawal of marine waters from the continent. The emergence was not of long duration, however. The Middle Ordovician, or Champlainian, sea was confined chiefly to the eastern half of the country and to the Appalachian trough. A temporary emergence of the land followed this epoch before the greatest epeiric sea of all times came, in the Upper Ordovician, or Cincinnatian, epoch. This tremendous inundation proceeded slowly and with many fluctuations until the climax was reached in the great Richmond sea, which covered at least half of the continent. When this vast body of water had attained its maximum extent, North America presented a strange contrast to its present appearance. Instead of an unbroken land mass, the continent consisted chiefly of the old, stable borderlands of Cascadia, Appalachia, and Llanoria, with several low islands rising above the interior sea.

The Cincinnati Arch. This long, narrow land extended from Nashville, Tennessee, northward through western Ohio into Ontario. Large portions of it remained persistently above all the Paleozoic seas, in spite of the fact that it was always low and featureless. The southern end of this structure is called the Nashville dome. There is nothing in the present topography to indicate the existence of such an arch, but where a transverse section is exposed the rocks may be seen dipping gently away from the central area.

The Cincinnati arch was an effective barrier that served to separate several seas in the Appalachian region from those to the west. It also marks the westward limit of considerable sediment derived from the Land of Appalachia.

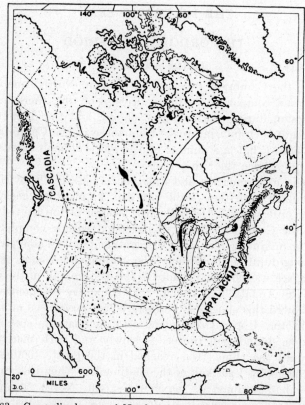

FIG. 63.—Generalized map of North America in Late Ordovician time. The stippled areas show the inferred maximum extent of the seas although all the regions may not have been submerged at the same time. Outcrops are in black. White areas are land. The exact extent of the Taconic Mountains, in the northeastern part of the United States and southeastern Canada, is not known. (*Modified from Schuchert and Dunbar.*)

The Ozark Dome. This persistent land mass, which was located in southern Missouri and Northern Arkansas, was formed of Pre-Cambrian granites. Early Paleozoic sediments dip away to all sides from the central area. These deposits, which apparently never extended over the highest parts of the dome, thin out by overlap upon the flanks.

Other Areas. The Adirondack dome, in northeastern New York, and the highlands of Wisconsin were other very persistent positive areas during the Paleozoic.

SIGNIFICANT ORDOVICIAN DEPOSITS

Lower Ordovician, or Canadian. As rivers in the northern part of Appalachia were rejuvenated, during the Lower Ordovician, considerable quantities of black mud were carried into the nearby trough and deposited along the eastern side as a belt of black shale, which extends from the tip of Gaspé southward through eastern New York as far as New Jersey. The original position of this sediment was several miles farther east, and its present location is the result of an overthrust toward the west. This deposit, which is called the Deepkill shale, in New York, and the Levis formation, in Canada, is noted for the large number of graptolites that are found in certain layers. Some very close relatives of these graptolites are found in western Europe, indicating a free connection between the seas that covered the two regions.

The Cow Head Breccia. The Ordovician system in Newfoundland and Quebec contains some very unusual breccias (Fig. 64), whose origin has been a puzzle for many years, although recent work by several geologists has done much to solve the difficulties. The breccias are composed largely of limestone pieces that vary greatly in size, from small particles to huge boulders several hundred feet long. The calcareous fragments, both large and small, are angular or subangular, and, while many of them have been rolled around to some extent, they probably have not been transported for any great distance. The conglomerate is not continuous over great areas but is local in its distribution. The thickness varies greatly within short distances. In southeastern Quebec this remarkable deposit is found, at several horizons in the section, interbedded with Levis shales. Lower and Upper Cambrian fossils are found in some of the limestone pieces, but Lower Ordovician invertebrates are particularly common.

The origin of the breccia was not precisely the same throughout its entire extent. In some places it represents talus material that accumulated at the base of fault scarps, from which it was dislodged by earthquakes or by various weathering processes. In certain localities the thrust sheet was advancing over the Ordovician sea bottom and the fallen blocks of limestone were enclosed in the accumulating marine shale. A large portion of the breccia is of tectonic origin and, in some places, it is probably the actual material of a thrust-fault crush zone.

Dolomites.   While black shales were being deposited along the eastern side of the Appalachian trough, heavy-bedded gray dolomites were forming in the clearer waters farther west. This dolomite is the Beekmantown formation, which is found from Vermont southward into Alabama and has an average thickness of about 2,000 feet through the central and southern Appalachians. This dolomite was deposited in unusually shallow water, and great stretches of the sediment were frequently exposed to the dry air

Fig. 64.—Cow Head breccia sheet at St. Paul's Inlet, Newfoundland. (*Photographed by Helgi Johnson.*)

before consolidation. Mud cracks were formed over extensive areas. Some of the dried plates, with their turned-up edges, were loosened and redeposited in the Beekmantown as edgewise conglomerate. *Cryptozoön* reefs are altogether characteristic of this formation wherever it is found. Favorable conditions for the deposition of dolomite were widespread during Lower Ordovician time, since rock of this character is found in Oklahoma, New Mexico, Texas, and the Ozark Mountains region. It is also found in high bluffs along the Mississippi River from Minneapolis to Iowa.

An Interval of Erosion.   A disconformity separating the Lower and Middle Ordovician formations, wherever they are found in contact, indicates an erosion period following a complete withdrawal of the sea. The interval was sufficiently long for important faunal changes to take place, for the Canadian and the Champlainian

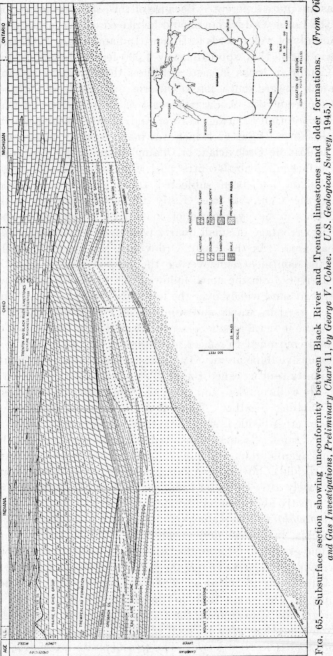

FIG. 65.—Subsurface section showing unconformity between Black River and Trenton limestones and older formations. (*From Oil and Gas Investigations, Preliminary Chart 11, by George V. Cohee. U.S. Geological Survey, 1945.*)

faunas are quite different.   Because of this, some geologists believe
that the Lower Ordovician should be placed in a separate period.

A study of well records in Illinois, Indiana, Ohio, Michigan, and
Ontario shows that approximately 4,000 feet of Lower Ordovician
and Cambrian rocks in eastern Illinois thin out and are truncated
eastward, toward southeastern Ontario.   Black River rocks rest on
Pre-Cambrian rocks a few miles east of Detroit River in Ontario.
The unconformity between Lower and Middle Ordovician formations is shown in Fig. 65, which was made from subsurface studies.

The Middle Ordovician, or Champlainian.   The Pre-Cambrian
land surface in the north central part of the United States and southern Canada had been subjected to long-continued weathering
during the Cambrian and Early Ordovician periods, with the
result that a heavy mantle of loose rock fragments containing
a large percentage of small quartz particles had accumulated over
a great area.   As the Early Ordovician sea gradually withdrew
from the continent, uncovering the central part of the United
States, rivers from the north followed the retreating marine waters
and spread sand widely over the lowlands along the coast, where it
was reworked by waves and winds as an ever-widening sand belt.
During the interval of emergence following Lower Ordovician times,
the sand continued to collect, doubtless being blown by the wind
into extensive dune areas.   This great accumulation of remarkably
pure quartz sand is called the St. Peter sandstone (Fig. 66).   The
grains are well rounded, and many of them are frosted as a result of
much rubbing together.   The St. Peter shows very little of the
intricate cross-bedded structure that is associated with wind-
deposited sand.   Instead, most of the bedding is quite regular, so
the final agents of deposition were probably the waves and currents
of the Middle Ordovician sea as it advanced across the sandy wastes.
Immediately after St. Peter time, heavy beds of dolomite were laid
down directly above the sandstone.

Champlainian Formations in the East.   Another uplift of
Appalachia, in Middle Ordovician time, rejuvenated the streams.
Then fine-grained mud from the land was carried into the Appalachian trough and deposited along the eastern side in a belt that extends
from Quebec city to Alabama.   Extensive deposits of limestone were
forming at the same time in the clearer waters farther west,
and a gradual change from the Canajoharie black shales into the
Trenton limestone may be seen along the Mohawk Valley from
Albany to Utica, New York.   The two deposits interfinger within
the transition zone, and their age equivalence is clearly established.

slowly widening and gently sloping plain, over which the lengthening rivers meandered, building up alluvial deposits that eventually reached beyond the region of Niagara Falls (Fig. 69). The land-laid sediments were subjected to periods of seasonal dryness, during which they were thoroughly oxidized and red color developed, while the materials that were deposited at the same time in the sea farther west retained their gray color. There is an area of considerable width in Ontario where these Queenston deposits may be seen interfingering with Upper Ordovician Richmond formations, indi-

Fig. 68.—Shale of Upper Ordovician (Richmond) age exposed along the eastern side of Little Bay de Noc, east of Escanaba, Michigan.

cating wide fluctuations of the shore line as the conditions of deposition varied. At certain times of the year, probably when rains in the highlands of Appalachia were heaviest, deposition over the swampy lowlands along the sea and in the sea itself was so heavy that the shore line moved to the west. During dry periods, when the sedimentation was comparatively slight in amount, subsidence along the shore area permitted the marine waters to advance eastward. A more rapid sinking than usual might overbalance even heavy deposition, and the shore line would change its position temporarily.

Upper Ordovician Rocks in the West. The Land of Cascadia remained at a low elevation during the Upper Ordovician epoch, and the deposits throughout the Cordilleran trough are largely massive dolomites. Wherever in the Rocky Mountains of Canada and the United States these rocks outcrop, they form bold cliffs because of their resistance to weathering. In the northern states this widespread deposit is called the "Bighorn dolomite," and in the southern Rockies—especially, at its type locality along the

FIG. 69.—Dark red Queenston shale of Upper Ordovician age exposed in the gorge at Niagara Falls. The light-colored rock above is the basal Medina (Whirlpool) sandstone. (*Photographed by Robert H. Thompson.*)

Front range, west of Cañon City, Colorado—it is known as the "Fremont limestone" (Fig. 70). Here the Fremont contains many typical Richmond species of invertebrates that are identical with others found in the Upper Ordovician rocks of southwestern Ohio and the Upper Peninsula of Michigan. The thickness of this widespread dolomite formation is seldom more than 300 feet.

Volcanoes in the Eastern United States. There have been few periods in the history of the earth that were entirely free from volcanic activity. After the intense volcanism in the latter part of the Proterozoic era, the Cambrian period in the United States

FIG. 70.—The cliff-forming Fremont limestone of Upper Ordovician age exposed in Priest Canyon, northwest of Cañon City, Colorado.

FIG. 71.—A layer of altered volcanic ash, interbedded with Middle Ordovician (Trenton) limestone, is seen just above the center of the picture. Exposed along the Escanaba River, Northern Michigan.

was comparatively quiet.   The first signs of renewed igneous action
came with the appearance of widespread deposits of volcanic ash
interbedded with Middle Ordovician marine sediments.   This
material, now altered to bentonite, is found in many places throughout the area of the Appalachian geosyncline from New York to
Alabama, and as far west as Michigan (Fig. 71), Iowa, and Minnesota.   The eruptions recurred over a considerable period of time,
since the bentonite is found at different levels in the Black River
and Trenton groups.   The thickness of the ash beds varies from
less than 1 inch to about 10 feet, and the variation is often considerable within short distances.   Near Jamestown, in southeastern
Pennsylvania, a lava flow is associated with Ordovician shale.
Other lava flows of Ordovician age are found in northeastern
Quebec and on the western coast of Newfoundland.

Some of the ash beds are lenticular in shape, but a single deposit
in the Black River rocks of central Pennsylvania has been found
over an area that measures about 70 by 20 miles.   Its original
extent was doubtless much greater.   Although the volcanoes that
produced this ash and lava have never been seen, they were probably
active along the western side of Appalachia during the Lower and
the Middle Ordovician.

PRODUCTS OF ECONOMIC IMPORTANCE

Petroleum.   The discovery well that opened up the famous oil
field in the Devonian rocks of Pennsylvania, in the year 1859, was
the beginning of an industry that has since reached into every
corner of the globe and that today profoundly affects the lives of
millions of people and the destinies of many nations.   The oil and
gas in the Lima-Indiana field are found in the Trenton dolomite,
where they have been trapped by structures on the northern flank
of the Cincinnati arch.   The producing horizon has an average
depth below the surface of about 1,000 feet.   The first well in this
field, which was drilled in 1883, produced a large quantity of gas.
Production of oil began in 1885, and the maximum yield was reached
about 1896, when over 23,000,000 barrels of petroleum were produced in Ohio.   A maximum of 11,300,000 barrels for Indiana was
reached in 1904.   The output from this field has been declining for
many years, although a few wells are still being operated.

Ordovician rocks in the Mid-Continent field have been tremendous producers of oil.   Production is chiefly from the Simpson
sand, the greatest areas of which are the Seminole and Oklahoma
City, in Oklahoma.

Petroleum is derived from marine organisms, both plants and animals, and is stored in the pore spaces of sedimentary rocks. Oil may migrate considerable distances through the rocks, finally

Fig. 72.—The Pittsford Valley marble quarry, Vermont. The working floor of this quarry is 325 feet below the surface of the earth and concrete piers have been constructed to brace the walls. (*Courtesy of Vermont Marble Company, Proctor, Vermont.*)

accumulating in some favorable geologic structure, such as an anticline, where it is permanently trapped.

Limestone and Marble. Ordovician limestones and dolomites from the Applachian Valley region are crushed and used extensively for road metal. They form an essential constituent in the manufacture of Portland cement, and great quantities of this rock are used by the iron industry for a flux in smelting the ore. The limestone, when burned, is used as lime, as a fertilizer for certain kinds of soils, and as whitewash.

Ordovician limestones have been metamorphosed into very high-grade marbles (Fig. 72), which are extensively employed by the building trades. The most famous quarries are found near Rutland, Vermont, where immense quantities of the stone are produced from vast underground workings. Certain Middle Ordovician limestones, in Tennessee, that have not been completely altered into marble are widely used for decorative purposes on account of their beautiful red and pink colors. The total value of Ordovician marbles produced in the United States is over $5,000,000 annually.

Slate. Fine-grained Ordovician muds, eroded from the Land of Appalachia and deposited in the trough as shales, were later metamorphosed into slates of various colors. This material is used by the building trade for roofing and in various other ways. Most of the slate is quarried in the states of New York, Pennsylvania, Vermont, and Virginia.

Other Materials of Economic Importance. Lime phosphate, which is used as a fertilizer, is found in the Ordovician rocks of central Tennessee. The lack of impurities in St. Peter sandstone, which is composed of nearly pure quartz sand, makes it especially suitable for the manufacture of plate and optical glass.

Important deposits of iron ore have been concentrated in Lower Ordovician sandstones and shales on the north shore of Belle Isle in Conception Bay, Newfoundland. This ore was probably weathered from crystalline rocks on the land and carried into the sea, where it was precipitated. The ripple-marked surfaces of the bedded ore show that it was deposited in shallow water. This important deposit of iron is being worked in great mines, which now extend out beneath the ocean.

CLIMATE OF THE ORDOVICIAN

Most of our information about the climate of the Ordovician period comes from a study of the sediments that were deposited during this time and the fossils that are found in the various formations. The greatly expanded seas and the restricted land areas doubtless caused an oceanic type of climate, with its milder and more uniform temperature conditions, over large portions of the globe. Many of the same species of fossils have been found distributed from northern Greenland and the Mackenzie River Valley region to the central part of the United States. This is evidence that climatic barriers were not present, as they are today; and the existence of compound corals within the Arctic is a good indication that the climate of the far northern regions was mild. Widespread deposits of limestone and dolomite such as characterize the Ordovician are more likely to form in warm than in cold water; therefore, the distribution of these sediments over many degrees of latitude is considered good evidence of uniform temperature conditions throughout the areas of deposition.

The remarkable effects of the Gulf Stream in modifying the climate of Great Britain and of Norway suggest that similar warm oceanic currents may have flowed from the tropical regions northward through the Middle and Upper Ordovician seas into the Arctic, causing far more genial climatic conditions than exist there today. The absence of greatly extended mountain barriers during this period probably resulted in wind systems unlike those of the present, with the result that there was a more even distribution of heat from the tropics to the high latitudes. Such evidence as it is possible to gather from the past, together with our knowledge of present conditions, has led to the broad generalization that diversified climates are characteristic of those times when high mountain ranges exist over great areas of the earth's surface and when the continents stand well above the sea, while milder and more uniform climates are found when the lands are low and epeiric seas are widespread.

THE TACONIC DISTURBANCE

During the Cambrian and Ordovician periods several thousand feet of sediments had accumulated in the part of the Appalachian trough that extended from Quebec southward, through New York and Pennsylvania, to Virginia. At the beginning of Upper Ordovician time, compressive stresses from the southeast were brought to bear upon these sediments and they were uplifted into a range of mountains. This orogeny is called the "Taconic disturbance." The older rocks were thrust several miles westward, where they may be seen today along the southeastern side of the St. Lawrence River and the Hudson Valley.

The formation of a mountain range is a very slow process, extending through several million years. The folding and faulting do not proceed at the same rate throughout the entire area of disturbance, and the orogenic movements may begin earlier in some parts than in others. Long periods of comparative quiet are

followed by times of intense activity. Earthquakes are frequent
and volcanoes are usually active within the uplifted region. The
limestone conglomerates and breccias in southeastern Quebec, which
have been mentioned before, have been explained as the result of
faulting and landslides on the floor of the Ordovician sea during
the Taconic disturbance. The mountain-making forces reached
their climax in the Late Ordovician, but it is impossible to determine the height of the ranges that were produced.

It is the fate of every mountain range to disappear eventually
before the slowly acting forces of weathering and erosion. Considerable areas of the Taconic Mountains were peneplaned by the
Late Silurian, permitting the sea to advance over the old truncated
folds and deposit typical marine sediments. Still later, the entire
Taconic region was uplifted, without renewal of the folding. The

Fig. 73.—*Orthoceras duseri*, a common straight cephalopod from the Richmond of
southwestern Ohio.   (*From Ohio Geological Survey report.*)

present Green Mountains of Vermont have been dissected out of
this uplifted plain.   Such a regional uplift might result in mountains
that are higher than the original ranges.

The beginnings of the orogenic movements that in the course of
time produce a mountain system are sometimes revealed by a widespread change in the character of the sediment that is being
deposited in the sea outside the disturbed area.   The change from
extensive limestones and dolomites of the Middle Ordovician to
great mud deposits early in the upper part of the period, indicate
that uplifts were taking place on the land toward the east and that
these movements were associated with the rising Taconic highlands.

Along the eastern side of the Hudson River, near Becraft
Mountain, nearly horizontal beds of Late Silurian (Manlius) limestone may be seen resting upon the steeply dipping truncated folds
of Middle Ordovician sandstones and shales.   Near Otisville, in
eastern New York, Early Silurian (Shawangunk) sandstones rest
with an angular unconformity upon Middle Ordovician (Martins-
burg) shale, and at Port Clinton (Fig. 74), Pennsylvania, there is a
strong angular unconformity between Ordovician and Silurian
rocks.

Fig. 74.—Unconformity at Port Clinton, Pennsylvania, between Ordovician rocks on the left and Silurian rocks on the right.   (*Photographed by Dean B. McLaughlin.*)

INVERTEBRATE LIFE OF THE ORDOVICIAN

The Ordovician seas were inhabited by an amazing variety of invertebrates, of which the well-preserved fossil remains are found in enormous numbers throughout the calcareous formations in the middle and upper parts of the period.   Over 2,600 species from the Champlainian of North America, have been described, while the Cincinnatian rocks in southwestern Ohio have long been wonderful collecting places for fossil hunters, both professionals and amateurs.

Habitats of Marine Animals.   The ocean bottom has been divided into several life zones (Fig. 75), in each of which certain types of animals are living.

The Littoral Zone.   The littoral, or tidal, zone is a comparatively narrow area between high and low tides.   Living conditions there are unusually difficult, because the ebbing tide lays bare the sea bottom and animals must either find refuge in tidal pools or develop certain specializations that enable them to survive periods of exposure to the air.   Constant movements of the water in the tidal zone, especially during storms, add to the difficulties of living there and make it an unfavorable place for the preservation of organisms as fossils.

The Neritic Zone.   The neritic zone extends from the lowest tide line to the outer edge of the continental shelf, where the water is about 600 feet deep.   Most of this area is lighted, food is abundant,

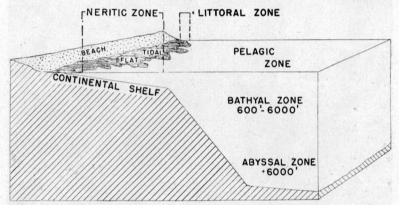

Fig. 75.—Diagram to show life zones in the ocean.   (*Modified from Twenhofel and Shrock.*)

and vast numbers of organisms are able to live there under the generally favorable conditions that prevail.   Most of the invertebrates of past geologic periods have lived in the environment of the neritic zone, and many phases of evolution have taken place there.   As competition among the various forms of life is keen, the struggle for existence is often very severe.   Conditions in the ancient, shallow epeiric seas were similar, in many respects, to those upon the continental shelf.

The Bathyal Zone.   The bathyal zone extends from the outer edge of the continental shelf to the 6,000-foot line.   Only the top of this zone receives light, and even there plant life is rare.   Many different kinds of animals are able to live in this area, but no sediments from the bathyal zone have been recognized in the geologic column.

The Pelagic Zone.   The pelagic zone includes the great open ocean that lies beyond the littoral zone.   The animals that live there are floating and swimming forms and are found from the surface down to the depths. Sediments, such as black shales that are deposited on lifeless ocean bottoms and are normally unfossiliferous, sometimes contain the remains of floating organisms.

The Abyssal Zone. This zone includes that portion of the ocean below a depth of 6,000 feet. The water in this environment is cold and dark, the pressures are enormous; consequently, only highly specialized creatures are able to live in these depths. Some Mesozoic deposits that are probably of deep-sea origin, from the islands of Borneo, Rotti, and Timor in the East Indies, have been described.

Types of Marine Animal Life. The dolomites that were formed so widely during the Lower and Upper Ordovician seldom contain fossils in a good state of preservation, and it is probable that any

Fig. 76.—Restoration of a graptolite colony showing the floating disk and reproductive pouches. The genus illustrated is *Diplograptus*. (*After Ruedemann.*)

organisms that these rocks originally held were destroyed during the change from calcium to magnesium carbonate. Black shales of the Ordovician are generally not fossiliferous, except for occasional layers that may contain the remains of floating organisms, such as graptolites, or certain varieties of ostracods and brachiopods.

The Richmond sea of the Cincinnatian epoch was of such extent that marine animals were able to migrate more widely than usual and there was a mingling of forms from many different localities, which gives the faunas a cosmopolitan aspect.

Graptolites. The graptolites (Fig. 76) reached the climax of their development in the Ordovician. As these floating, colonial animals had no structures that enabled them to move about through the seas, their world-wide distribution must have been accomplished largely by winds and ocean currents. Certain genera of graptolites are so widely distributed over the earth that they can be used for purposes of intercontinental correlation.

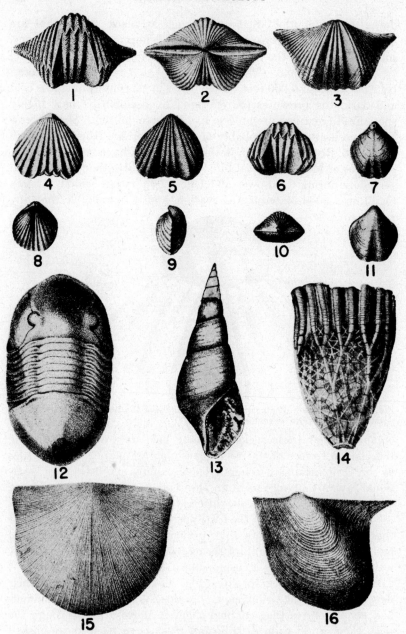

Fig. 77.—Ordovician fossils. 1–3, *Platystrophia acutilirata;* 4–6, *Rhynchotrema capax;* 7, 11, *Cyclospira bisulcata;* 8–10, *Zygospira recurvirostris;* 12, *Isotelus gigas;* 13, *Fusispira nobilis;* 14, *Glyptocrinus decadactylus;* 15, *Rafinesquina alternata;* 16, *Pterinea demissa.*

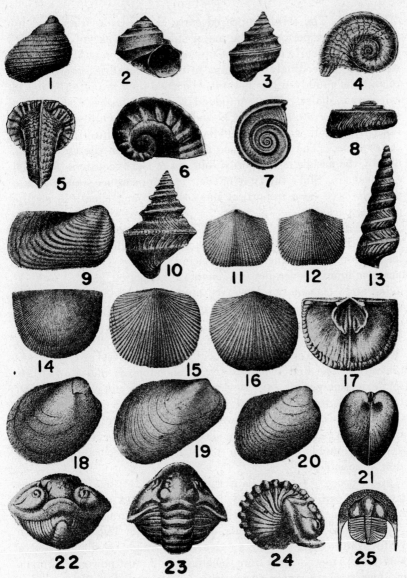

FIG. 78.—Ordovician fossils. 1, *Cyclonema bilix;* 2, *Trochonema umbilicatum;* 3, *Lophospira quadrisulcata;* 4, 5, *Phragmolites fimbriata;* 6, *Cyrtolites ornatus;* 7, 8, *Helicotoma tennesseensis;* 9, *Cuneamya oblonga;* 10, *Lophospira saffordi;* 11, 12, *Hebertella insculpta;* 13, *Hormotoma salteri;* 14, 17, *Strophomena planumbona,* exterior and interior; 15, 16, *Dinorthis subquadrata;* 18, *Cyrtodonta billingsi;* 19, *Modiolopsis similis;* 20, 21, *Whitella ventricosa,* side and end views; 22–24, *Calymene meeki,* front, dorsal, and side views of an enrolled specimen. 25, *Cryptolithus concentricus.* (*From Minnesota and Ohio Geological Survey reports.*)

Corals. The corals appeared early in the Ordovician, and by the end of the period all the major subdivisions except the Hexacoralla were clearly defined. Cup corals of the genus *Streptelasma*, which are exceedingly abundant in certain localities, were rather tolerant of muddy-water habitats, because they are often found in calcareous shales. The compound corals, *Halysites, Columnaria*, and *Paleofavosites*, are locally abundant in Upper Ordovician rocks, but there was no extensive building of coral reefs until the Silurian.

Bryozoa. The first bryozoa appeared early in the Ordovician, and by the middle of the period four out of the five orders were well established. Since the time of their first appearance, these minute animals have been important limestone-forming agents in all the geologic periods.

Brachiopods. The primitive Cambrian types of brachiopods, with their shells built of horny and phosphatic materials, were largely replaced during the Ordovician by forms with strong shells made of lime. Several of the genera in this period, such as *Rafinesquina* and *Strophomena*, preferred muddy bottoms, and their shells are found in vast numbers throughout the Richmond formations, especially in southwestern Ohio.

Cystoids. The cystoids were represented by 21 genera, but their remains are common only locally and well-preserved specimens are rare. The first blastoids (Proteroblastoidea) and starfish are found in this period, but they were apparently not very common. Crinoids are found in considerable numbers.

Pelecypods. Pelecypods were not abundant until the Upper Ordovician. Nearly all of the specimens are preserved as external or internal molds—a condition that often makes accurate identification impossible.

Gastropods. Gastropods were very abundant, but, as comparatively few are well preserved, it is thought that their shells were made of some easily destroyed substance, like aragonite.

Cephalopods. Many kinds of cephalopods lived during the Ordovician. Some of the species with straight shells reached a length of 15 feet. They were the largest and most powerful animals of their time. Certain forms with loosely coiled shells appeared during the period.

Trilobites. Trilobites were just as common at this time as they had been in the Cambrian. From the rocks of this period, 125 genera, representing 1,200 species, have been described. *Isotelus gigas* was a giant creature that reached a length of about 18 inches. Some Ordovician trilobites developed the habit of rolling up, after the fashion of an armadillo, and many of their exoskeletons are found preserved in that position.   This was probably a protective measure.

Ostracods.   The first appearance of the small, bivalved crustaceans called "ostracods" occurred in the Lower Ordovician.   Their shells are very abundant at certain horizons.

THE FIRST PRIMITIVE VERTEBRATES

For many millions of years nowhere on earth were there any forms of life higher than the invertebrates.   By the Ordovician

FIG. 79.—The Harding sandstone and shale exposed west of Cañon City, Colorado. Note the reverse fault.

period, this group had developed an amazing number of different forms, and many of them showed signs of high specialization, which indicates that they had undergone a long evolutionary development extending far back into Pre-Cambrian times.   Something higher than the invertebrates was developing, however.   The first indication of this new form of life appeared during the Ordovician; for in 1891 Walcott announced that evidence of primitive vertebrates had been found in the Harding sandstone (Fig. 79) just west of Cañon City, Colorado.   These fossil remains consist of many broken plates and scales that once covered the bodies of primitive fish belonging to a very ancient group called "Ostracodermi."   The scales are not like those of most modern fish but are made of a very

hard and durable enamel-like substance.   Two other localities in
the Cordilleran region, one in the Black Hills and another in the
Big Horn Mountains, have yielded ostracoderm scales similar to
those found at Cañon City.   A few scales of those primitive fish
have recently been found in rocks of Middle Ordovician age near
Escanaba, Michigan (Fig. 80).

The age of the Harding formation is still in doubt.   The rocks,
which consist of shales and sandstones, are exposed particularly well
along the eastern front of the Rocky Mountains.   The many ripple

Fig. 80.—An Ostracoderm scale from the Middle Ordovician (Black River) rocks of
Michigan.   ×5.

marks, and the red color that is common to the Harding, indicate
that the sediment was deposited in shallow water along the fluctuating shore of a sea where the muds and sands were oxidized
during long exposure to a climate that was marked by periods of
seasonal dryness.

It is impossible to restore any of the Ordovician ostracoderms
from the material that is available; yet, by studying the well-preserved remains of other ostracoderms, of the Late Silurian and the
Devonian period, it is possible to gain some conception of what this
very ancient order of vertebrates was like.

Some authors believe that the ostracoderms in the Cañon City
locality lived in rivers that flowed into the sea, and that the bodies
were carried downstream after death and buried in the muds and

sands along the shore. There is also the possibility that these creatures lived in lagoons along the low, swampy coast, or even in the sea itself. The scales from Michigan were found in marine sediments that contain numerous specimens of ostracods, brachiopods, and parts of trilobites.

The appearance of the vertebrates is one of the most significant events in the evolution of animal life. These primitive fishes from the Ordovician were the vanguard of a group that today includes all the highest forms of life inhabiting the earth.

Reading References

BAILEY, E. B., L. W. COLLET, and R. M. FIELD: Paleozoic Submarine Landslips near Quebec City, *Jour. Geology*, vol. 36, pp. 577–614, 1928.

COHEE, GEORGE V.: Geology and Oil and Gas Possibilities of the Trenton and Black River Limestones of the Michigan Basin, Michigan and Adjacent Areas, *U.S. Geol. Survey*, 1945.

KAY, G. MARSHALL: Distribution of Ordovician Altered Volcanic Materials and Related Clays, *Geol. Soc. American Bull.*, vol. 46, pp. 225–244, Feb. 28, 1935.

SCHUCHERT, CHARLES, and CARL O. DUNBAR: Stratigraphy of Western Newfoundland, *Geol. Soc. America Mem.* 1, pp. 73–86, 1934.

STOSE, G. W., and ANNA I. JONAS: Ordovician Shale and Associated Lava in Southeastern Pennsylvania, *Geol. Soc. America Bull.*, vol. 38, pp. 505–536, 1927.

CHAPTER X

THE PALEOZOIC ERA

THE SILURIAN PERIOD

LANDS AND SEAS

Nearly all of North America except the mountainous borderland of Appalachia was a featureless lowland at the beginning of the Silurian. This condition made it possible for marine waters to spread widely over the interior of the continent, especially during the lower and middle parts of the period. Two widespread withdrawals of the sea, together with important faunal changes, form natural breaks serving to divide the period into three epochs: the Early Silurian or Alexandrian, the Middle Silurian or Niagaran, and the Late Silurian or Cayugan.

Lower Silurian Deposits. The highlands on Appalachia must have been quite high in the Early Silurian, because the basal deposits of this epoch in the Appalachian trough consist of conglomerates and sandstones, from 500 to 1,000 feet thick, which extend in an almost unbroken belt from New York to Alabama. This is the Medina sandstone and, because of its superior hardness, it is responsible for some of the most prominent ridges in the modern Appalachians. When the Medina is traced westward, it shows a gradation through marine shales into limestones within a distance of about 300 miles. These limestones were deposited in the clearer waters that lay west of the Cincinnati arch, and the formations are separated by a number of unconformities that indicate widespread withdrawals of the fluctuating shallow seas.

Middle Silurian Deposits. The deposits of the Middle Silurian, or Niagaran, epoch are largely shales in the Appalachian trough and limestones farther west, where the water was clear. Such sediments indicate that the Land of Appalachia was reduced to a low elevation and that the sluggish rivers were carrying only fine materials into the sea. The Clinton group is a very persistent deposit over the Appalachian region, where it consists largely of shales with some sandstone and limestone members. This widespread group is an important source of iron ore in a number of places, notably at Birmingham, Alabama.

The Arctic embayment spread gradually southward and westward until it covered a great area in Canada and the United States forming an extensive interior sea that was clear throughout most of its extent, because the sluggish streams, flowing from low bordering lands, were carrying very little sediment.   This is the sea in

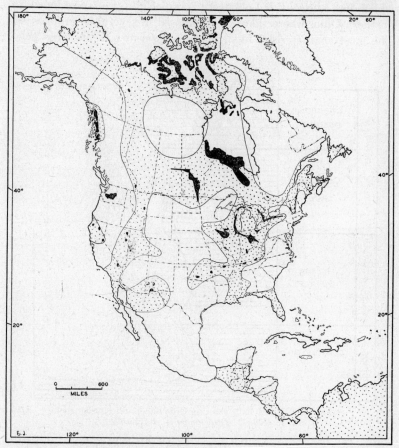

Fig. 81.—North America in Niagaran time.   The stippled areas show the inferred extent of the seas.   Outcrops are in black.   White areas are land.   (*After J. Harlan Bretz in "Geology of the Chicago Region," Illinois Geological Survey.*)

which the far-extending limestones and dolomites of the Niagaran series were deposited.

A very fine section of Middle Silurian rocks is exposed in the gorge at Niagara Falls (Fig. 82), the Lockport dolomite (Niagaran) forming the very top of the section.   The hardness of this rock, together with the presence of soft underlying beds, is responsible

for maintaining the long Niagara cuesta, which extends westward
from the Niagara Falls region, across Ontario and northern Michigan into Wisconsin. The original distribution of the Lockport
must have been very wide. There are still extensive remnants to
the west of Hudson Bay. The Guelph dolomite (Niagaran),
which lies above the Lockport, is especially well developed in
northern Ohio, where the rock is exposed in several large quarries.
The most characteristic fossil in these exposures is the large pele-

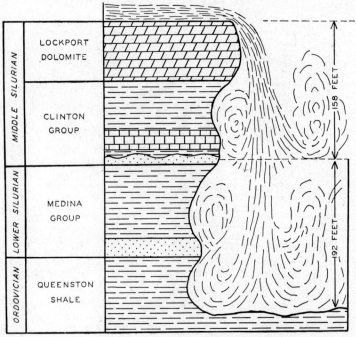

Fig. 82.—Section at Niagara Falls showing Ordovician and Silurian rocks.   (After
G. K. Gilbert.   Drawing by W. P. Staebler.)

cypod, *Megalomus* (Fig. 83), which occurs in great numbers and is
almost invariably preserved in the form of fillings or molds of the
interior. Farther west, through Illinois and into Wisconsin, the
Lockport is called the "Racine" dolomite. Westward from Iowa
the Racine, which extends at least as far as Nebraska and Kansas,
is covered by younger formations.

The Niagaran dolomites (Fig. 84) and limestones (Fig. 85) were
originally widespread through the central and eastern parts of the
United States and over Canada west of Hudson Bay. The rocks

are known from northern Texas and Oklahoma through the Great Lakes region and across Canada to the Arctic. The sea in which these beds were deposited covered about 40 per cent of North America and was comparable to the great Richmond invasion of the Upper Ordovician.

Dolomites of Silurian age occur widely throughout the west, especially in Canada and Alaska, but they are not well known in comparison with rocks of the same age farther east.

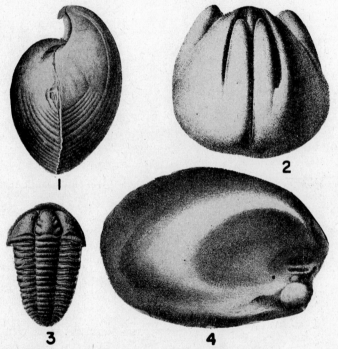

Fig. 83.—Silurian (Niagaran) fossils. 1, *Conchidium laqueatum;* 2, *Trimerella ohioensis;* 3, *Calymene niagarensis;* 4, *Megalomus canadensis.*

Coral Reefs and Bioherms. Corals are common wherever limestones and dolomites of the Niagaran series occur. In many places they are so numerous that small reefs or bioherms have been formed. Such assemblages may be seen especially through Indiana, Illinois, southern Wisconsin, the Upper Peninsula of Michigan, and southern Ontario. These bioherms are not comparable to the Great Barrier Reef of Australia as it is today, but represent areas on the floor of the shallow Niagaran sea that were particularly favorable to the growth of corals and stromatoporoids, as well as many other kinds of invertebrates.

Such comparatively local concentrations of organisms, which are properly called "bioherms," may be only a few yards across, while others extend for a mile or more. The thickness varies from a few feet to more than 70 feet. The rock in the bioherm is not stratified, but consists of a great mass of coral skeletons, many of them in a perfect state of preservation, while others have been

Fig. 84.—Middle Silurian (Niagaran) dolomite exposed near Rockford, Ohio, on the farm of Carl Stallter.

reduced to a fine mud, which has filled up most of the open spaces in the reef and produced a more or less solid deposit. When one of these structureless masses can be seen in cross section and traced laterally to its edge, there is often a gradation into bedded limestone. Some unusually fine Niagaran bioherms may be seen in northern Michigan around the villages of Engadine, Trout Lake, and Gould

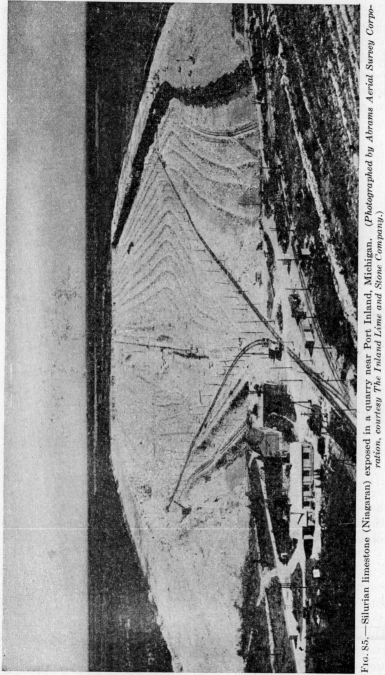

Fig. 85.—Silurian limestone (Niagaran) exposed in a quarry near Port Inland, Michigan. (Photographed by Abrams Aerial Survey Corporation, courtesy The Inland Lime and Stone Company.)

City. The bioherm belt is 50 miles wide in a few places through northern Indiana.

Upper Silurian Deposits. Upper Silurian formations are poorly developed in the southern Appalachians, but they thicken gradually northward. In New York, the Salina, with its extraordinary salt deposits, is over 1,000 feet thick. Rocks of the Cayugan series are found farther west, in Ohio, Michigan, and northwestward in the valley of the Mackenzie River. The lower part of the Salina

Fig. 86.—Manitoulin dolomite (Silurian) resting upon Queenston (Ordovician). East edge of Owen Sound, Ontario.

through central New York consists of red and green shales (Vernon). These grade westward into the upper part of the group, which is composed of gray shales and salt beds (Camillus).

The Upper Silurian Desert and Its Salt Deposits. As arid conditions had gradually developed over a considerable area in the eastern part of the United States during the Upper Silurian, deserts spread to the west across New York, northern Pennsylvania and Ohio, southern Ontario, and all of southern Michigan (Fig. 87). The sea that occupied that region grew so salty, because of the excessive evaporation, that salt and gypsum were deposited over an area of about 100,000 square miles. The salt beds of New York occur as great lens-shaped masses interbedded with soft, gray shales of the Salina. At Ithaca there are seven distinct beds of salt, which begin at a depth of 2,244 feet. Near Tully, New York, one well penetrated 325 feet of salt. Some of the individual salt beds in the Salina of southern Michigan are more than 600 feet thick. Rock salt is being mined near Detroit (Fig. 88), while in other localities, such as Wyandotte and Manistee, water is forced down through wells, the salt is dissolved, the brine is pumped to the surface, and the salt is recovered by evaporation.

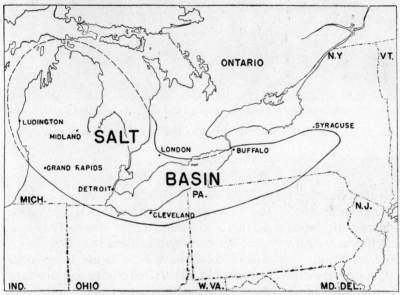

Fig. 87.—Map showing the approximate extent of the Silurian salt basin. (*After I. D. Scott and R. C. Moore.*)

Several theories have been advanced to explain the extraordinary thicknesses of salt that are found in the Salina. One very plausible idea assumes that a Dead Sea covered a portion of the great Silurian desert. Excessive evaporation finally caused the precipitation of salt, while an occasional inflow of sea water through some restricted channel leading in from the ocean renewed the supply of brine and made possible the enormous thicknesses of rock salt existing in many places.

Water Limes. Late in the Silurian period there was a readvance of the sea over a portion of the former desert area in New York State and thin deposits of water limes and dolomites were formed. Water lime is a calcareous material containing a large amount of

Fig. 88.—Rock salt being mined from Silurian (Salina) rocks near Detroit, Michigan.

silt that was probably carried into the sea from the surrounding arid regions.

CLIMATE OF THE SILURIAN

Reef-building types of corals were able to grow widely over the Niagaran sea floor, and their presence within the Arctic regions shows that, during a portion of the Silurian, the climate of the far north was considerably milder and more uniform than it is today. Several identical species of corals have been found in such far separated areas as the interior of the United States and northern Greenland, and a number of other invertebrates from the Niagaran have a similar wide distribution from north to south. The limestones and dolomites, because of their great spread from low to high latitudes, show a uniformity of climatic conditions during the Middle Silurian.

Just because corals have been found widely distributed through certain formations, it should not be assumed that the climate was mild throughout the entire Silurian period. The Niagaran sea was a vast body of water that must have greatly tempered the climate of the coastal lands; but, during the rest of the period, the seas were smaller and land areas more extensive—a condition that made possible greater climatic variations of the continental type. Twice during the period marine water withdrew from most of the continent, and in these times of emergence there may have been wide variations in temperature conditions, even though the change from tropics to polar regions may not have been so great as it is today. The geologic record gives us practically no information on this phase of the subject.

Silurian Volcanoes. Volcanoes were active in the northern part of the Appalachian region in the Silurian, but they were not widespread. In the Gaspé Peninsula, along the north shore of Chaleurs Bay, there are more than 4,000 feet of lavas interbedded with Middle Silurian limestones. In the southern part of Maine and adjoining areas of New Brunswick, there are many beds of volcanic ash and lava flows, with occasional interbedded sediments that contain Silurian marine fossils. The total thickness of this series is about 10,000 feet.

PRODUCTS OF ECONOMIC SIGNIFICANCE

Iron Ore. The Clinton group contains important deposits of iron ore, which is mined in a number of places. The iron near Clinton, New York, was worked before the Civil War, but the area around Birmingham, Alabama (Fig. 89), is second only to the Lake Superior region in the production of iron. Over 600,000,000 tons of ore are still available in this southern Appalachian area. The Birmingham field owes its significance partly to the fact that limestone for flux and coal for fuel are both found within the district.

The Clinton iron ore occurs as beds and lenses, which are interstratified with shales and sandstones. The thickness of the beds varies from a few inches up to 40 feet. Great numbers of marine fossils are found locally in the Clinton ore, but many of the shells are broken and most of them have been replaced by iron.

Salt. Great quantities of salt are obtained every year from the Salina group in New York and Michigan; the supply is inexhaustible. The total production of salt in the United States during 1942 was 12,720,629 short tons, 3,283,063 tons of which came from the Silurian rocks of Michigan.

CLOSE OF THE SILURIAN

In North America the Silurian period closed with a quiet retreat of the sea. There is no evidence of any mountain-making disturbance upon this continent. Wherever the rocks of the Silurian and Devonian are found in contact, the two periods are separated by a disconformity and the hiatus is revealed only by the erosion surface and the faunal change.

The Caledonian Disturbance. The Caledonian mountain system (Fig. 90), which was formed during the latter part of the

FIG. 89.—Rocks of the Clinton group exposed near Birmingham, Alabama. The Irondale seam and Big seam are the most important iron-producing beds. (*Courtesy of Tennessee Coal, Iron & Railroad Company. Stratigraphic divisions by Arthur J. Blair.*)

and the decline is shown in decreasing numbers and varieties. Other lines were progressing and spreading, as new genera and species appeared.

Sponges and Corals. Several kinds of sponges became prominent. Such forms as the concavo-convex *Astraeospongia* and the spherical *Astylospongia* were abundant in certain localities. Graptolites belong chiefly to the *Monograptus* type with the cups arranged along one side of the supporting axis. Corals (Fig. 91) expanded enormously in the warm, clear seas of the Niagaran epoch. The chain coral *Halysites*, the honeycomb variety *Favosites*, and the tube coral *Syringopora*, are prevalent forms.

Bryozoa. These were still abundant and very important limestone builders, especially in the upper Mississippi Valley region.

Brachiopods. The brachiopods not only maintained their important position but developed many new types. Smooth-shelled forms and those with short hinge lines were common. *Pentamerus* and *Conchidium* lived in such vast numbers on certain favorable parts of the sea bottom that they built up extensive deposits of limestone.

Cystoids and Crinoids. Cystoids were locally abundant, while blastoids remained unimportant. Crinoids found the clear seas so much to their liking that they flourished in large numbers in several localities, where their skeletal parts are important constituents of certain limestone formations. Crinoid remains are especially common in the Silurian rocks near Racine, Wisconsin, and Port Byron, Illinois.

Pelecypods, Gastropods, and Cephalopods. Pelecypods are not distinctive of this period, but the large clam *Megalomus* is exceedingly common in the Guelph dolomite of the Niagaran series at several localities, especially in northwestern Ohio. Gastropods were particularly abundant in the Upper Silurian. High- and low-spired shells were common and some were highly ornamented. Although cephalopods both with straight and with coiled shells lived at this time, they were not important members of the fauna.

Trilobites. While trilobites were still abundant, the group had passed the peak of its evolution and specialized forms with spines were beginning to appear.

Ostracods. Ostracods flourished in the genial climate of the Silurian, and some individuals reached the relatively great length of 1 inch.

Eurypterids. The eurypterids (Fig. 93) are first known from the Upper Cambrian, a few have been found in the Late Ordovician,

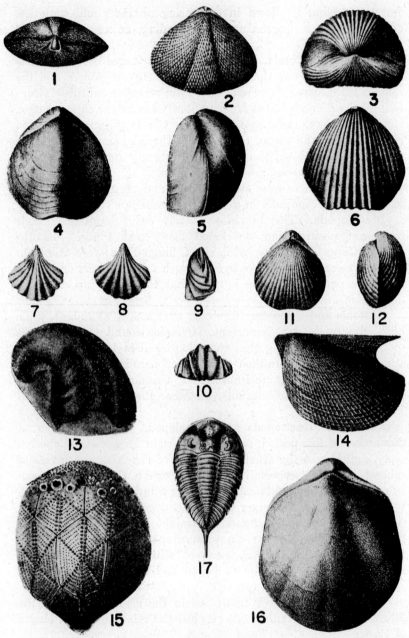

FIG. 92.—Silurian fossils. 1, 2, *Dictyonella reticulata;* 3, 6, *Uncinulus stricklandi;* 4, 5, *Meristina maria;* 7–10, *Rhynchotreta cuneata americana;* 11, 12, *Homeospira evax;* 13, *Platyceras niagarense;* 14, *Pterinea emacerata;* 15, *Caryocrinus ornatus;* 16. *Pentamerus oblongus;* 17, *Dalmanites limulurus.* (*From Ohio Geological Survey.*)

and the group reached its climax during the Silurian. Although these remarkable invertebrates are not found in wide distribution through the rocks, certain horizons and localities have yielded their remains in considerable numbers. The average length was less than a foot, but the gigantic *Pterypotus* and *Stylonurus* were between 6 and 9 feet long. The extremely localized occurrences of these

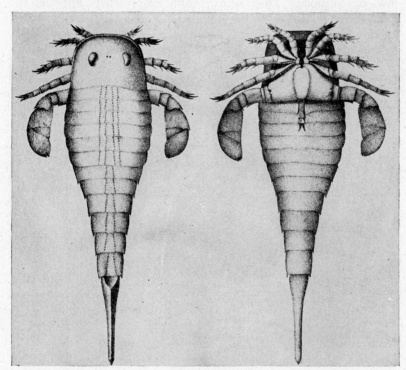

FIG. 93.—The upper and lower (left and right) surfaces of a typical eurypterid, *Eurypteris remipes*, from the Upper Silurian of New York. (*After Hall.*)

animals has led some authorities to the conclusion that they lived not in the seas, but rather in rivers and lakes, or possibly in lagoons and estuaries along the coast.

THE FIRST TERRESTRIAL LIFE

Land Plants. There is scarcely any direct evidence of land plants in the Silurian. A few broken pieces of stems with leaves attached have been found in rocks of Silurian age in Australia, England, and Gotland. These plants were probably terrestrial, but the evidence is not at all conclusive. However, the great abundance of well-developed land vegetation in the Devonian period makes it seem probable that their ancestral forms evolved during the Silurian.

Air-breathing Animals. *Palaeophonus* (Fig. 94), from the Silurian of Europe, and *Proscorpius*, from the Silurian of New York State, were the first known land-going animals. These creatures, which resembled eurypterids in several respects, looked a little like modern scorpions. They were probably air-breathers, although the fossil forms do not show the stegmata, or openings, through which air would be admitted into the trachea. Some paleontologists believe that these ancient scorpion-like invertebrates were aquatic

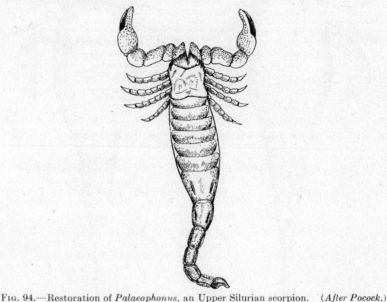

FIG. 94.—Restoration of *Palaeophonus*, an Upper Silurian scorpion. (*After Pocock.*)

in habit, but this is not at all certain. It may be that their adaptation to land conditions was only partial, and they might still have had to breathe air by means of their water-breathing organs, which could function only so long as they remained moist. This would mean frequent returns to the water, unless these creatures were able to live also in damp places.

The millepedes from the Silurian of Wales have been found associated with eurypterid remains, and there is some uncertainty as to whether they were land-living forms.

FISHES

Comparatively few fish remains have been found in Silurian rocks, but primitive members of the group must have existed during the period. The scarcity of fossils may be accounted for by assuming that most of the forms lived in streams, where their chances of being fossilized were not very good.

Certain rocks in Norway that are placed in the Upper Silurian have yielded the remains of ostracoderms (Fig. 95), but the age of these beds may actually be Devonian. These old vertebrates, like

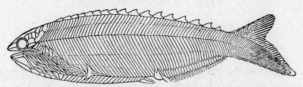

Fig. 95.—*Rhyncholepis parvulus*, a primitive fish (ostracoderm) from the Upper Silurian (Downtonian beds) of Norway. (*From Kiaer.*)

the modern cyclostomes, lacked true jaws, the mouth being a hole or transverse slit, while typical paired fins were absent.

Reading References

Alling, H. L.: The Geology and Origin of the Silurian Salt of New York, *New York State Mus. Bull.* 275, 139 pp., 1928.

Grabau, A. W.: Guide to the Geology and Paleontology of Niagara Falls and Vicinity, *New York State Mus. Bull.* 45, 284, pp., 1901.

Ulrich, E. O., and R. S. Bassler: "American Silurian Formations," pp. 233–270, Maryland Geological Survey, Silurian, 1923, The Johns Hopkins Press, Baltimore, Md.

CHAPTER XI

THE PALEOZOIC ERA

THE DEVONIAN PERIOD

DEVONIAN SEAS

During the early part of the Devonian, no highlands relieved the generally flat surface of North America. The first advance of the sea, at the beginning of the period, was along the Appalachian trough. The Cordilleran geosyncline and the interior of the continent remained dry land during most of this first epoch.

Early in the Middle Devonian, a broad sea spread southward from the Alaska and Mackenzie River region, joining a narrower embayment that had moved from southern California northeastward across Nevada and Utah. When a connection had been established across the northern part of the United States between this great western sea and the marine water in the Appalachian trough, nearly 40 per cent of the continent was submerged. This Middle Devonian epeiric sea, like all the others, must have varied in size during its existence as the shore lines advanced and retreated in response to relatively small vertical movements of the land. The general submergence pattern established by this sea remained very much the same until late in the period, when the waters gradually withdrew and the continent was once more entirely emergent.

SEDIMENTATION DURING THE DEVONIAN

Deposits in Eastern North America. The geologic history of the Devonian period in New York State has been so completely recorded by deposits in the Appalachian trough that hardly any important phase of the record is missing. The various sections in this area have become the standard to which many other Devonian formations in the United States are referred. The rocks of this period outcrop in numerous places across the entire southern part of the state (Fig. 100), and the great abundance of fossils has made it possible to establish unusually complete stratigraphic sequences.

The Helderberg Group. The borderland of Appalachia was so low and featureless at the beginning of the Devonian period that it was not an important source of detrital sediment; consequently,

150

the Helderberg consists almost entirely of limestone, with a very subordinate amount of shale. The group attains its maximum thickness along the central area of the trough and thins out westward. The limestone, which is thick-bedded, forms the prominent Helderberg escarpment near Albany, New York.

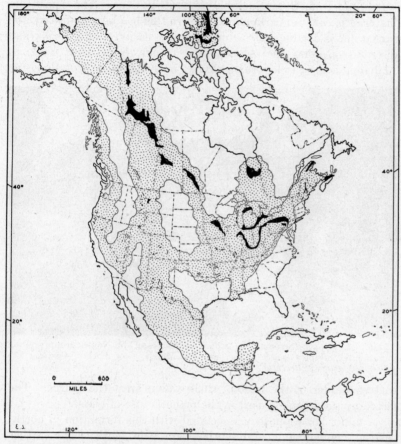

FIG. 96.—Generalized map of North America during the Devonian period. The stippled areas were probably covered by seas, at some time during the period, but all the regions were not covered at the same time. Outcrops are in black. White areas are land. (*Modified from Branson and Tarr, Schuchert and Dunbar.*)

The Oriskany Sandstone. During the Late Silurian and Early Devonian, a residual mantle of very sandy material had gradually formed over the old Adirondack dome and the lowlands of Appalachia. The sand, probably derived from the weathering of some older sandstone deposit, had been widely distributed by winds and running water. A gradual uplift of the land, following Helderberg time, rejuvenated the rivers that were running across this old land surface and gave them renewed transporting power sufficient to carry the sandy material into the sea, where it was reworked and deposited as the Oriskany sandstone. The purity of the sand and the rounding of the grains result from thorough sorting by running water and from a considerable amount of wear. The cementing material is calcium carbonate. Where this has been removed, the sandstone is friable and crumbles very easily. This formation, distributed along the Appalachian trough from New York to Alabama, is usually less than 100 feet in thickness, except along the

Fig. 97.—Upper Devonian sandstones and shales of the Naples group exposed in the gorge of the Genesee River near Mt. Morris, New York. (*Courtesy The Albertype Company, Brooklyn, New York.*)

eastern border of the region, which was nearest the source. The Oriskany sandstone is used in the manufacture of glass.

A minor shale phase is associated with this formation in northeastern Pennsylvania and southeastern New York; while farther west, in Oklahoma and Missouri, the sandstone gives way to limestone.

Deposits during the Middle Devonian. *The Onondaga Group.* The widespread sea and the low neighboring lands of the Middle Devonian were favorable to the formation of calcareous sediments. The Onondaga group consists largely of coralline limestone, which originally formed a continuous sheet stretching from Hudson Bay southward to Tennessee and Oklahoma. Corals, which are widely distributed throughout the rock, are so numerous in places that large reefs have been formed.   One of these reefs, in which the corals are silicified, crosses the Ohio River near Louisville, Kentucky, and forms a small rapids, called the "Falls of the Ohio."   Over 200 species of *corals* (Fig. 110) have been found at this locality, and many have been collected from the Onondaga at Port Colborne, Ontario, as well.

The *Hamilton Group.*   The Hamilton group begins with a deposit of exceedingly fine-grained black mud, called the "Marcellus shale." It spread slowly westward over the sea floor, which became so foul

FIG. 98.—Devonian limestone in the Sibley Quarry at Trenton, Michigan.   (*Photographed by Robert H. Thompson.*)

that all the bottom-inhabiting animals were killed within the area of mud deposition.   The only organisms found in this extensive deposit are the remains of invertebrates that floated in the clearer waters near the surface and were buried in the mud after death. This sediment, which was derived from the eastern land of Appalachia, was carried into the trough by rivers that were rejuvenated as the old land began to rise.   This uplift was the beginning of a great series of orogenic movements that culminated in the upheaval of the Acadian Mountains later in the period.

As the rise of Appalachia continued and the supply of mud

from the land was gradually exhausted, the waters became clearer and sandy deposits were spread over the sea bottom. Under these improved living conditions the invertebrates that had been living in the relatively clear waters outside the zone of shale deposition returned and formed the remarkable Hamilton fauna, in which brachiopods and pelecypods were exceedingly abundant. As the waters continued to grow clearer, calcareous deposits began to appear in the western part of the Hamilton area and, in a few places, descendants of the old Onondaga forms of corals were able to establish themselves, building coral reefs.

FIG. 99.—Disconformable contact between the Onondaga limestone, above, and the Akron dolomite (Upper Silurian), below. The Oriskany sandstone has been eroded here but is present in another part of the quarry only a short distance away. Quarry at Ridgemount, Ontario. (*Photographed by G. M. Ehlers.*)

Fine-grained black shales of Upper Devonian age are found extensively through Ohio, Kentucky, and Indiana. The Middle and Upper Devonian formations in the northern part of the Lower Peninsula of Michigan, although they contain some shales, consist mostly of limestones in which many remarkably well-preserved corals are found.

Deposits of the Catskill Alluvial Plain and Delta. The orogenic movements that began in the northern part of Appalachia about Hamilton time continued with gradually increasing intensity until the close of the period. The old Taconic Range, lying along the eastern border of New York, was reelevated at this time, and materials derived from this rising highland area were partly responsible for building the northern part of a great series of deposits that is commonly called the "Catskill delta." These sediments are

continued southward from eastern New York into Pennsylvania—
a portion of the deposit that was built by materials derived from
some highland area that lay immediately to the east.

The Catskill deposits of Middle and Upper Devonian age in
New York consist largely of graywackes, red shales (Fig. 100), and

Fig. 100.—Kiskatom red beds (Hamilton) in the Catskill delta near Palen-
ville, New York. (*Photographed by W. T. Schoenmaker, courtesy the New York
State Museum.*)

sandstones, together with dark-gray shales and conglomerates.
The earliest phase of the sedimentation began in Hamilton time,
the shales being deposited in a body of water that lay just west
of the Taconic highlands. As the reelevation of this old mountain
area proceeded, the quantity of land-derived material increased and
deposition in the sea was so heavy that the shore line retreated

westward, forming a constantly widening alluvial plain over which
the meandering rivers ran.   Coarser sediments were deposited
toward the eastern side of the plain, where they gradually increased
in thickness and lapped up against the rising highlands to form an
extensive piedmont slope.   The finer materials were carried farther
west, and, where the alluvial plain flattened out toward the sea, a
great coastal flood-plain area developed, over which streams deposited finer sands and shales, especially during times of heavy rains.
In this fluctuating zone of deposition most of the red beds were
formed.   The Catskill sediments vary from 4,000 to 13,000 feet

Fig. 101.—Irregular contact between the gray Kaaterskill sandstone above and
thin shales of the Catskill red beds below, at Kaaterskill Falls, New York.   (*Courtesy New York State Museum.*)

in thickness—an indication that the area of deposition subsided
gradually.   The thickest part of the section is found in Pennsylvania near Harrisburg, where the beds are exposed along the Susquehanna River Valley.

    In order to account for the red beds, it is not necessary to assume
that the climate was arid and hot.   There was doubtless considerable rainfall over most of the Catskill region, but it was probably
seasonal, and continental portions of the sediments may have been
subjected to intensely hot, dry periods, during which the material
was oxidized and the red color developed.

    The continental portions of the Catskill were clearly deposited
by torrential streams, with their rapidly changing velocities.   The
sediments vary extremely in coarseness and kinds of material, the

changes occurring both laterally and vertically within short distances.   The grains of the graywackes are invariably angular, while the conglomerate pebbles are all rounded.   Angularity proves that the source of the material was near at hand; even the rounding of the pebbles does not necessarily indicate transportation for very great distances.

Out of this great body of comparatively flat-lying sediments the modern Catskill Mountains have been carved by the ordinary forces of weathering and erosion.

Deposits during the Devonian in the West.   During the Middle and Upper Devonian epochs, extensive seas occupied the western part of North America, especially Canada, and here the deposits are largely limestones and calcareous shales.   These formations have not been studied so thoroughly as those in the east, but they constitute a very important part of the geologic record.   Extensive outcrops are found also in the lower Mackenzie River Valley.

Great thicknesses of coarse detrital material that has been correlated with the Devonian are found in Ellesmere Land, off the northwest coast of Greenland.   More than 3,000 feet of Devonian conglomerates, sandstones, and shales, all deposited under continental conditions, occur along the eastern side of Greenland, and these have yielded the remains of land plants, fresh-water fishes, and the oldest amphibian remains.   The thickness and coarseness of the conglomerate, as well as the nature of the other materials in the section, indicate the presence of some highland area not far away.

In the Eureka mining district of eastern Nevada, where there is a section of Paleozoic rocks about 30,000 feet thick, from 4,000 to 6,000 feet of this material consists of limestones and shales of Middle Devonian age.

The Old Red Sandstone.   The materials eroded from the lofty Caledonian Mountains were deposited in five great basins that lay between the ranges during the Devonian period.   These areas of deposition continued to subside as the sediments accumulated, and in some places the total thickness is more than 30,000 feet.   This "Old Red Sandstone" (Fig. 102) series in the British Isles, entirely continental in origin, consists of conglomerates, sandstones, shales, and siltstones, which grade rapidly into one another both vertically and horizontally.   The coarser deposits were apparently laid down as alluvial fans by streams that poured swiftly down steep gulches into the valleys.   The sandstones, which are usually cross-bedded, may represent the stream channels themselves.   The shales and the siltstones were deposited over broad flood plains at times of

high water, and many of the layers show mud cracks and a few
raindrop impressions.

The red color that is characteristic of these sediments may have
been developed in places where the deposits were exposed to oxidation during periods of seasonal aridity.   The gray shales and sandstones were deposited in moist places along the valleys where there
were permanent lakes or where the ground-water level was close
to the surface.

The fossil remains of plants are locally common in the Old Red
Sandstone.   Considerable numbers of eurypterids have been

Fig. 102.—A stack of Upper Old Red Sandstone, 450 feet high, resting unconformably upon a base of igneous rock.   This stack is called "The Old Man of Hoy"
and is found in the Orkney Islands off the north coast of Scotland.   (*Photographed
by Geological Survey of Great Britain.*)

found in the lowest part of the section and fresh-water fish are
abundant.

This great series of deposits has been made famous by the classic
writings of Hugh Miller, who worked in the stone quarries around
Cromarty, Scotland.   He wrote a number of books on various
phases of geology, one of which is entitled "The Old Red Sandstone."

THE NORTH ATLANTIC CONTINENT

During the Devonian period an old land mass lay in the North
Atlantic, forming a bridge between North America and Europe.
This land is called "Eria."   The evidence for its existence, while
indirect, is, nevertheless, practically conclusive.

The truncated folds of the Acadian Mountains can be traced across Nova Scotia and Newfoundland to the coast, where they end suddenly as though a fault had broken across them. In a similar manner, the Caledonian folds end sharply at the western coast of Ireland. These two great ranges, which trend toward each other, must both have originally extended much farther out into the North Atlantic, across some land that has long since disappeared beneath the waters of the ocean. The present sea between the British Isles-Scandinavian region and North America is very shallow. This was probably a part of Eria. Iceland and Greenland are remnants of this land that still persist.

Fig. 103.—Hugh Miller (1802–1856), a famous Scottish geologist and author of "The Old Red Sandstone."

Certain Devonian fresh-water animals and land plants from the British Isles and the Acadian region are so similar that there must have been a land connection, free from barriers, across which these organisms could migrate easily from one country to the other. The width of Eria cannot be determined by any evidence now at hand.

CLIMATE OF THE DEVONIAN

The Devonian period, like so much of other geologic time, offers no evidence of well-marked climatic zones, such as those of the present. The same genera and species of compound, reef-building corals are found in the Onondaga limestone from Hudson Bay southward to the Falls of the Ohio. Unless such animals have changed their living habits radically since the Devonian period, this distribution is good proof not only of an equable climate but also of very warm seas.

During that period, certain marine faunas were able to migrate from Eurasia to North America along a route that lay far to the north, within the present polar regions, although such migrations would be impossible today because of the severe climatic conditions. The distribution of similar floras in such widely separated places as New York, east Greenland, Spitzbergen, and the British Isles strongly supports the idea of uniform environmental conditions.

All this evidence does not prove that the entire Devonian enjoyed a mild and uniform type of climate or that these conditions prevailed over the entire world at any time during the period. Highly diversified climates probably existed at times, especially during that portion of the period when mountains were formed in the eastern part of North America; but such diversification may not have affected the entire earth, as it does today.

The red beds in the Catskill formation and those along the eastern coast of Greenland could hardly have been formed in arid regions, because fossils are quite common in the rocks and there is no evidence of any material that might have been transported by the wind. They were probably formed in warm, humid regions, where the rainfall came at certain seasons. The sediments were completely oxidized during severe dry parts of the year and the red color was retained because there was no organic matter present to reduce the iron.

THE ACADIAN DISTURBANCE

A new period of orogenic movements began in the northern part of the Appalachian region early in Middle Devonian times, and by the end of the period the sediments in the geosyncline had been uplifted into the Acadian Mountains. The Devonian and older rocks suffered their most pronounced deformation in the Acadian region of Canada, but the effects of the orogeny were felt southward from New Hampshire along the borderland, east of the Appalachian geosyncline, as far as South Carolina. As a result of both the Taconic and Acadian disturbances, the sediments in the northern part of the Appalachian trough had been folded and faulted into mountain ranges, and this portion of the geosyncline was never again invaded by marine waters.

Volcanic Activity. The extensive earth movements that attended the Acadian disturbance were accompanied by a great

amount of volcanic activity.   Eruptive volcanoes appeared in the
Gaspé Peninsula, where great thicknesses of lava and tuff are still
preserved.   Through New Brunswick, Nova Scotia, Maine, and
the White Mountains of New Hampshire, deep-seated granite

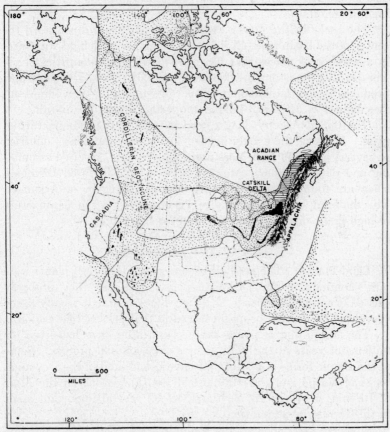

FIG. 104.—North America in the Late Devonian period.   Stippled areas show
the inferred extent of the seas.   Outcrops are black.   White areas are land.   The
southern limit of the Acadian Mountains is uncertain but the intensity of the disturbance indicates that the ranges extended a considerable distance south of the
New England region.   (*Modified from Schuchert and Dunbar.*)

batholiths of Devonian age have been exposed by removal of the
overlying sediments.   Mt. Katahdin, in the north central part of
Maine, is a portion of one of these intrusive masses that rises to a
height of 5,200 feet above sea level.   At the time of the granitic
intrusions, the White Mountains were probably elevated to a
height of at least 12,000 feet.

ECONOMIC PRODUCTS OF DEVONIAN ROCKS

Devonian rocks in many parts of the United States have produced important quantities of petroleum. The historically famous field in western Pennsylvania, discovered in 1859, still produces very high-grade oil.

The rocks in the Lower Peninsula of Michigan dip toward the center of the basin from all sides and there are anticlinal structures in a number of places that have produced large quantities of oil. The Hunton limestone in Oklahoma, of Silurian and Devonian age, produces a moderate amount of oil. Devonian rocks in the Manistee district of Michigan produce important quantities of salt.

The pure Oriskany quartz sand is used in the manufacture of glass. Some of the evenly bedded Devonian sandstones, quarried at several places in New York and Pennsylvania, are used as building and paving stones. Massive beds of even-textured Devonian silica are found in the Ouachita Mountain region of Arkansas. This material, called "novaculite," is employed in the manufacture of high-grade oilstones that are used for sharpening tools.

LIFE OF THE DEVONIAN

Land Plants. The geologic record shows that land plants were quite common in the Devonian period and that they probably existed even in the Silurian, although a lack of tough, woody tissue prevented them from being preserved in the rocks of that period.

The adaptation of plants to the land, after they had lived for millions of years in the water, was a very gradual process. Some of the simple forms of plants that have been found in the Devonian rocks of Gaspé and the Middle Old Red Sandstone on the Muir of Rhynie, in Aberdeen, Scotland, reveal several important steps in this terrestrial adaptation.

Silicified specimens of the Psilophytales (Fig. 105) were discovered in a place that had evidently been an ancient Scottish peat bog and the plants were preserved in their original positions. The preservation is so perfect that minute details of structure are clearly revealed and satisfactory reconstructions have been possible.

Psilophyton was a small, leafless plant with cylindrical, branching stems, from 1 to 7 millimeters in diameter. The spores were formed at the ends of some of the branches and the stomata, or breathing pores, were located on the surface of the stems, since there were no leaves present. The lower parts of the stems were underground and apparently functioned as roots. Such plants as these required a moist environment, as they were not yet completely adapted to the dry lands. *Psilophyton* has been found in the Lower Devonian at Gaspé, Canada, as well as in Norway and Scotland. A closely related species, *Psilophyton wyomingense*, was discovered in Lower Devonian rocks at Bear Tooth Butte, Wyoming.

Hornea lignieri and *Asteroxylon mackiei*, from the Lower Devonian of Rhynie, Scotland, are other examples of primitive plants

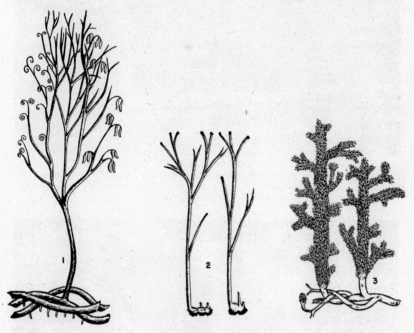

Fig. 105.—Primitive land plants from the Devonian. 1, *Psilophyton princeps* from the Lower Devonian of Gaspé, 2, *Hornea lignieri*, and 3, *Asteroxylon mackiei*, from the Lower Devonian of Rhynie, Scotland. (*After Kidston and Lang.*)

that were beginning the process of adapting themselves to the dry lands.

The primitive fern *Archaeopteris* has been collected from Upper Devonian rocks in many parts of the world. Tall scale-trees, called "Protolepidodendron," were present in this period, clearly foreshadowing their giant descendants of the Pennsylvania. Forests of seed ferns grew in the swampy flood-plain lands that bordered the Upper Devonian sea. The remains of these trees were discovered at three distinct levels in the rocks (Fig. 106) near the village of Gilboa, in Schoharie County, New York. Many of the stumps (Fig. 107) were rooted in black shale, which represents the

FIG. 106.—Devonian rocks in the Riverside Quarry at Gilboa, New York, where the famous seed-fern trees were found in place. The original soil in which the trees grew is now represented by a bed of shale located just below the loaded bucket. (*Courtesy New York State Museum.*)

FIG. 107.—Stump of a Devonian seed-fern tree, *Eospermatopteris textilis*, found at Gilboa, New York, still resting upon the original soil in which it grew. (*Courtesy New York State Museum.*)

original soil, and numerous strap-like roots were still in place. Some of these remarkable seed ferns, which have been called "Eospermatopteris" (Fig. 108), were trees that stood over 40 feet high and were more than 3 feet in diameter. The bases of the stumps are bulbous, like those of modern trees that grow in marshy

FIG. 108.—A Devonian seed fern, *Eospermatopteris*. Restoration by Winifred Goldring. (*Courtesy New York State Museum.*)

places. It seems probable that these forests were killed by temporary advances of the fluctuating sea and that the trees were then buried beneath accumulating Catskill sediments.

The appearance of forests and land plants in the Devonian gave new beauty and interest to the landscape, which before that time had been treeless like our modern prairies.

Marine Invertebrates. Invertebrates were abundant in the Devonian seas, and great numbers of beautifully preserved fossils have been found in the shales and shaly limestones that are common in many parts of the country.

Sponges. In western New York during Chemung time in the Late Devonian, there was an extraordinary development of siliceous sponges (Fig. 109). These sponges, which were similar to the modern Venus's-flower-basket, lived locally on the sandy bottom of the shallow sea in vast numbers, and in real life must have presented a very striking appearance. Great colonies of these organisms were exterminated and buried beneath heavy deposits of

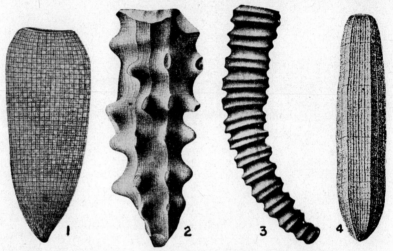

FIG. 109.—Devonian siliceous ("glass") sponges. 1, *Cyathodictya reticulata;* 2, *Hydnoceras bathense;* 3, *Ceratodictya carpenteriana;* 4, *Prismodictya telum.* (*After Hall and Clark.*)

coarse gravel washed down from the rising highlands to the east. *Hydnoceras* and *Prismodictya* are typical of this group of "glass" sponges.

Corals. Cup corals reached their greatest development during this period. Certain genera, such as *Heliophyllum* (Fig. 110), *Cystiphyllum,* and *Zaphrentis,* are found in great numbers in some localities, especially in Michigan and Ontario. Of compound corals, which were very abundant, the genera *Acervularia, Favosites, Prismatophyllum,* and *Phillipsastraea* were conspicuous elements in the fauna. The coral reefs were favorite places for bryozoa and *Stromatopora.*

Crinoids and Others. Crinoids flourished in the clear waters, while blastoids, starfish, and echinoids were becoming more numerous and varied.

Fig. 110.—Devonian corals. 1, *Prismatophyllum percarinatum;* 2, *Cystiphyllum sulcatum;* 3, *Thecia ramosa;* 4, *Heliophyllum halli;* 5, *Zaphrentis davisona;* 6, *Favosites helderbergiae;* 7, *Cladopora robuta;* 8, *Syringopora perelegans;* 9, *Blothrophyllum decorticatum.* 3, 5, 7 to 9 are from the Falls of the Ohio. (*From Rominger, Michigan State Geological Survey.*)

Brachiopods. There is some doubt as to just when the brachiopods (Fig. 112) reached their climax. Over 3,000 species from the Ordovician and Silurian have been described, but the Devonian probably witnessed their zenith, as far as numbers and varieties are concerned. Their fossil shells are incredibly numerous in some of the shaly limestones and calcareous shales of this period. *Strophe-odonta* (Fig. 113), *Chonetes*, and *Spirifer* (Fig. 112) are a few of the commonest genera.

Pelecypods and *Gastropods*. Pelecypods (Fig. 113) flourished in the environmental conditions afforded by the sandy and muddy sea bottoms of the Devonian and became greatly diversified. Winged forms like Pterinea were especially common. Gastropods are not often well preserved in the rocks of this period. Loosely coiled types like *Platyceras* are among the most distinctive forms. The first known air-breathing gastropods lived in the Devonian.

Fig. 111.—The light-colored part of the quarry wall, indicated by the letters *R*, is the center of a bioherm in Devonian rocks at Alpena, Michigan. (*Photographed by G. M. Ehlers.*)

Cephalopods. Goniatites were the most characteristic cephalopods. This group developed sutures that no longer had straight edges, like the Ordovician *Orthoceras*, but were bent into lobes and saddles. These mollusks are very widely distributed through Devonian rocks, but they are common only in certain beds.

Decline of the Trilobites. Trilobites (Fig. 113) showed a marked decline; Devonian formations have yielded only about 200 different species. *Proetus*, *Phacops*, and *Cryphaeus* are among the most characteristic types. *Dalmanites* reached the gigantic length of 29 inches. The decline of the trilobites has been attributed to a number of causes. Powerful cephalopods, which were very common in the Ordovician, and hordes of voracious Devonian fishes must have preyed constantly on these arthropods and probably were important factors in their downfall. Trilobites, which evolved

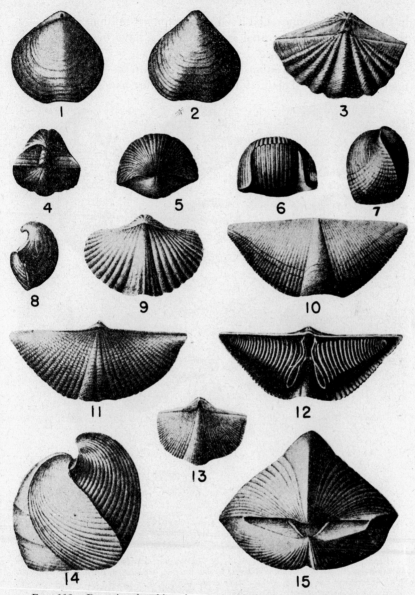

Fig. 112.—Devonian brachiopods. 1, 2, *Meristella arcuta;* 3, *Delthyris perlamellosa;* 4, 8, *Cyrtina alpenensis;* 5–7, *Hypothyridina venustula;* 9, "*Spirifer*" *concinna;* 10, *Adolphia audacula;* 11, 12, *Mucrospirifer mucronata;* 13, *Cyrtospirifer whitneyi;* 14, 15, *Paraspirifer acuminatus.* (*From New York State Reports.*)

in Pre-Cambrian times, had lived through many millions of years by the Devonian, so their final extinction may have been caused, in part, by racial senescence.

Eurypterids. Devonian eurypterids are always found in continental sediment. This may indicate that they had adapted them-

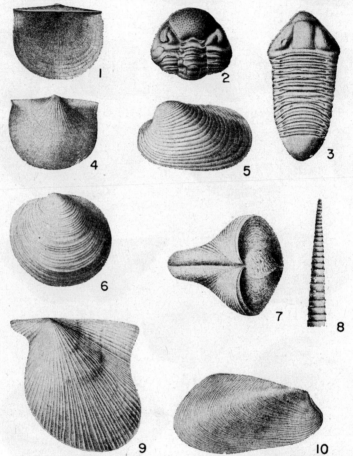

Fig. 113.—Devonian fossils.   1, 4, *Stropheodonta demissa;* 2, *Phacops rana,* an enrolled specimen; 3, *Dipleura dekayi;* 5, *Grammysia arcuata;* 6, *Paracyclas elliptica;* 7, *Conocardium cuneus;* 8, *Tentaculites scalariformis;* 9, *Pterinea chemungensis;* 10, *Modiomorpha concentrica.*   (*From New York State Reports.*)

selves to fresh or brackish water in rivers and estuaries, or that they may have visited such places during the spawning season.

Insects. Several species of spiders, and a very primitive type of insect without wings, have been found associated with land plants in the Old Red series of Rhynie, Scotland.

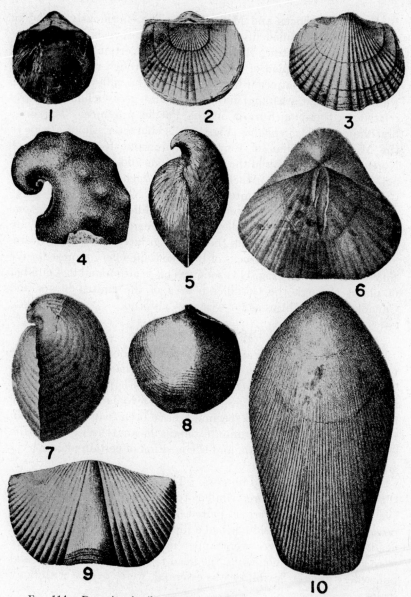

FIG. 114.—Devonian fossils. 1, *Spirifer hungerfordi;* 2, 3, *Tropidoleptus carinatus;* 4, *Platyceras nodosum;* 5, *Stringocephalus burtoni;* 6, 7, *Gypidula romingeri;* 8, *Athyris spiriferoides;* 9, *Spirifer mesistrialis;* 10, *Rensselaeria elongata.*

Faunal Provinces and Migrations. The enormously abundant and greatly diversified life of the Devonian reveals the existence of a number of distinct faunal provinces. Certain species, found in the Lower Devonian of the Appalachian trough region, are very much like those that occur in Bohemia and the valley of the Rhine, while faunas that are found in the Cordilleran geosyncline are clearly related to those of Eurasia in the Pacific province. The large brachiopod *Stringocephalus* (Fig. 114) is characteristic of a zone in the Middle Devonian of Eurasia. This same form migrated to North America by way of the Arctic regions and is found in Devonian limestones of the Mackenzie River region in northwestern Canada, as well as in Manitoba, Utah, and Nevada.

There is a black shale overlying the Middle Devonian limestone in the Mackenzie River Valley, and this contains fossils that are similar to some of those from the Naples group in New York State.

The Upper Devonian rocks of Iowa contain a very representative *Spirifer hungerfordi* (Fig. 114) zone. This is also found in a number of places through the Cordilleran area of the United States and Canada, with localities as far west as California.

THE AGE OF FISHES

Ostracoderms. The appearance of ostracoderms in the Middle Ordovician was an epoch-making event in the evolution of life. These early forms of vertebrates (chordates) left a comparatively meager record of themselves before the Devonian period. Some remarkably well-preserved specimens have been found in Devonian rocks, which reveal even minute details of anatomy, such as the shape of the primitive brain and the position of certain main nerves and blood vessels.

The ostracoderms had no jaws. The mouth was a small hole or slit-like sucking aperture, similar to the mouth of the modern cyclostomes. There were no paired fins, such as most modern fish possess, but some individuals had a flipper on either side behind the head region. The eyes were apparently well developed. There were thick plates of bone over the head region, while the trunk and tail, where greater flexibility was essential, were covered with bony scales.

The position of the ostracoderms with relation to the higher fishes and land vertebrates is not entirely certain. It has been commonly assumed that they are not in the main line of vertebrate descent, but that they represent, rather, a side branch, which became extinct in the Devonian. Some recent work, however,

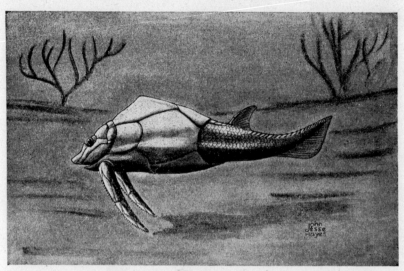

FIG. 115.—*Pterichthyodes milleri*, a placoderm, from the Old Red Sandstone of Scotland. (*Drawn by John Jesse Hayes.*)

FIG. 116.—*Dinichthys*, the giant Devonian arthrodire, was at least 20 feet long, and the greatest carnivore in the seas. *Cladoselache*, a shark, is at the extreme left. (*Drawn by John Jesse Hayes.*)

has tended to indicate that the ostracoderms are a true ancestral group and that some of them lie close to the evolutionary line of the higher fishes.

Arthrodira. The most powerful fish in the Devonian seas belonged to the Arthrodira. *Dinichthys* (Fig. 116) was one member of this group that reached a length of 20 feet and had heavy bony plates over the head and anterior portion of the body. Some of the plates along the sides of the jaws developed sharp processes that served in place of teeth.

Sharks. Primitive sharks, with cartilaginous skeletons like those of today, lived in the seas. The Devonian shales near Cleveland, Ohio, have preserved some wonderful specimens of *Clado-*

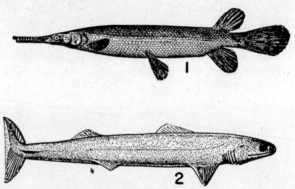

FIG. 117. —1, The living gar-pike, a ganoid fish; 2, *Cladoselache,* a Devonian shark.

selache (Fig. 117), which show the carbonized skin and details of the muscle fibers.

Ganoids. The ganoids had scales with an outer covering of enamel and a thick base of bone. These fish formerly lived both in the sea and in fresh water. The ganoids are represented today by the sturgeons and gar pikes (Fig. 117), which live only in lakes and rivers.

THE EVOLUTION OF LUNGS

Lungs (Fig. 118) developed from a sac-like expansion of the alimentary canal in the chest region of the fish. This structure occupied a ventral position, two lobes developed, and a network of blood vessels formed throughout the inner walls. Air was drawn down the throat and through a tube into this organ, so that the fish was able to obtain oxygen just as the higher vertebrates do.

Many fish apparently did not develop functional lungs, but,

instead, the expansion from the alimentary tract occupied a dorsal position and became merely an air-filled sac with little or no vascular tissue.   The connection to the open air was eventually lost and the function of the organ became entirely hydrostatic.

Fish with Lungs.   *The Dipnoi.*   There are a number of fish (Fig. 119) living today in various parts of the world that breathe by means of lungs, and they give us valuable information about the habits of their ancestors in the Devonian period, when lungfish were abundant.   All the modern Dipnoi are found in places where the rainfall is highly seasonal and the water in which they are living either disappears entirely during the dry season or becomes so foul

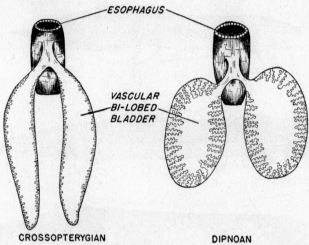

FIG. 118.—These bilobed swim bladders are very much like the lungs of higher vertebrates.   (*After Dean.*)

with decaying organic matter than an ordinary gill-breathing fish could not survive.

Protopterus (Fig. 119) lives in Africa, ranging from the White Nile to Lake Tanganyika and the Zambesi River.   This fish has vestigial gills, which cannot supply the creature with sufficient oxygen to sustain life; so it rises to the surface at intervals and fills its lungs with air.   During the dry season, many of these animals are trapped in marshes along the lakes and rivers, where, as the water gradually disappears, they burrow into the soft sediment at the bottom of the swamp.   While they are buried in the mud, some of the natural slimy secretion that covers the body dries and forms a tough envelope, resembling cellophane, that completely encloses the fish and prevents it from drying.   *Protopterus* may remain in this position for several months, breathing air and nourished by the fat stored up in its body.   When the rainy season returns, the mud is softened and the fish soon resumes its normal existence.   A specimen of *Protopterus* has been known to live for 4 years in this condition of suspended animation, which is called "estivation." These fish sometimes reach a length of 6 feet.

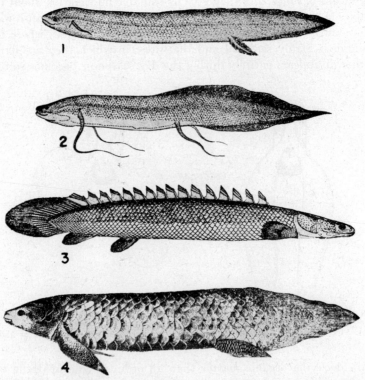

Fig. 119.—Modern air-breathing fishes. 1, *Lepidosiren* from South America. (*After Norman.*) 2, *Protopterus* from Africa. (*After Norman.*) 3, *Polypterus* from Africa. (*After Agassiz.*) 4, *Epiceratodus* (*Neoceratodus*) from Australia.

Lepidosiren (Fig. 119) lives in the Amazon basin and has habits quite similar to those of Protopterus.

Epiceratodus (Fig. 119) is found in the Mary and Burnett Rivers of Queensland, Australia.   This fish possesses gills, but its lungs are used constantly as supplementary breathing organs.   When the water is too foul for the gills to function properly, the lungs became indispensable.   The animal rises to the surface at irregular intervals and, with its snout above the water, it first exhales and then fills its lungs with a supply of fresh air.

The Crossopterygians. The crossopterygians, or lobe-finned fishes, were most abundant in the Devonian. These remarkable animals, besides possessing functional lungs, had developed fleshy fin lobes with skeletal supports of the same basic pattern as that which is found in the legs of land vertebrates.

The coelacanths, a branch of the crossopterygians, migrated into the seas, and their fossil remains have been found in marine deposits of the Mesozoic era (Fig. 120). This group was supposed to be extinct until, in 1939, a living specimen was dredged up by fishermen operating along the coast opposite East London, South Africa. This astounding discovery was a true "living fossil" from the Age of Dinosaurs.

Ray-finned Fishes. The oldest ray-finned fishes are found in the Middle Devonian, but they were greatly outnumbered at that

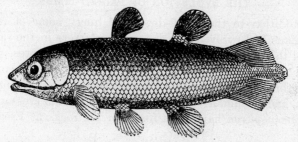

Fig. 120.—A fossil coelacanth, a crossopterygian, from the Mesozoic. (*From Traquair.*)

time by the lungfish and the lobe-finned fishes. The modern African form *Polypterus* (Fig. 119) is a representative of this group. It has thick, bony scales and completely functional lungs with openings on the under side of the throat. This fish lives in parts of tropical Africa where seasonal droughts are very severe and its lungs are absolutely essential for survival. *Polypterus* was formerly classed with the crossopterygians because the pectoral fins have fleshy lobes like those of the true lobe-finned group.

The air bladder of the modern lungfish is clearly an adaptation to recurring conditions that are unfavorable to the gill-breathing habits of ordinary fish. Extremely stagnant water or the seasonal drying up of ponds and swamps make it impossible for fish that live in such places to use their gills; then, only certain individuals whose air bladders can be used for breathing purposes are able to survive such conditions. It is impossible to say just what caused the fish to develop the air-breathing habit. Recurring periods of drought may have exercised a very important influence upon this momentous evolutionary advance, which must be regarded as ranking next in importance to the appearance of the vertebrate line itself.

It is certain that highly seasonal rainfall was characteristic of many places during the Devonian. The Old Red Sandstone series and much of the Catskill sediment were probably deposited under these conditions. Scores of fish might have been trapped in some shrinking Devonian ponds or bayous. If a few fortunate individuals were able to gulp air into swim bladders that were supplied with blood vessels, they might survive until the rainy season brought them relief. The recurrence of such conditions for countless generations, together with continued use of the air bladder for breathing purposes, might have brought about the development of the very efficient lungs that some of the crossopterygian fish possessed.

THE EVOLUTION OF PAIRED LIMBS

In addition to their well-developed lungs, some of the crossopterygians had evolved paired fins, which were in the same positions as the paired limbs of the lower land vertebrates, while the skeletal structure (Fig. 121) of these fins was fundamentally the same as that which is found in the front and hind legs of amphibians, reptiles, and mammals. Remains of the Devonian crossopterygian fish *Eusthenopteron* have been found in the rocks at Escaumenac, Quebec.

The actual forerunner of the Amphibia was probably some undiscovered Devonian fish that was ancestral to both the Dipnoi and the crossopterygians.

With their functional lungs and fin-limbs, there is no reason why some crossopterygian fish of the Devonian should not have been able to crawl out of the water (Fig. 122) and move about, to a limited extent, upon the land. Because it was necessary for the skin of the fish to remain moist, these excursions were probably made during the night or in rainy weather; and such trips, for the most part, were taken across marshy flats and through damp vegetation. When one pool dried up, their land-going ability made it possible for them to seek another pond or stream. The necessity for food and safety is a powerful factor that has profoundly influenced the evolutionary course of many animals.

The skulls of the typical Devonian crossopterygian fish are remarkably like those of certain primitive amphibians. This close correspondence is not a matter of general appearance but of detail. Essentially the same bones are present in the roofs of both types of skulls, and their arrangement and relative positions are very much

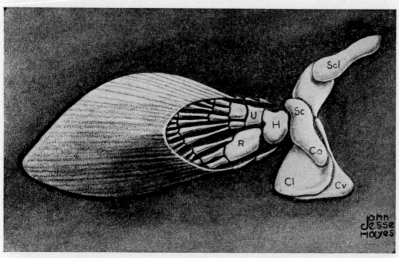

FIG. 121.—Bones in the shoulder girdle and pectoral fin of the Upper Devonian crossopterygian fish, *Sauripterus taylori*.   These are similar to the bones found in the pectoral fins of *Eusthenopteron*.   Key: *Scl*, supracleithrum; *Sc*, scapula; *Co*, coracoid; *Cv*, clavicle; *Cl*, cleithrum; *H*, humerus; *R*, radius; *U*, ulna.   (*Drawn by John Jesse Hayes.*)

FIG. 122.—The Devonian crossopterygian fish, *Eusthenopteron*, coming out of the water and moving about upon its strong fin-limbs.   The individual in the foreground shows some details of the scales.   (*Drawn by John Jesse Hayes.*)

alike. A microscopic study of the teeth in both groups shows, in
cross section, the same complex infolding of the enamel. The
amphibians have lost the series of opercular bones that lie immediately behind the upper jaws of the fish.

The skulls of the small amphibians, which the Lauge Koch
expedition found in Upper Devonian rocks along the eastern coast
of Greenland, have the external nasal openings below the margin
just as they are in the Devonian crossopterygians. In later forms
these openings are on top of the skull, close to the anterior edge.

Modern amphibians reveal their close relationship to the fish
in the manner in which they cling to a watery environment. The
frog lays its eggs in the water; and, when the young tadpoles first
appear, they are essentially fish. Their only method of breathing
is by means of gills, and their appearance is decidedly fish-like.
Within a few weeks, legs and lungs begin to develop, so that eventually the animal is able to breathe air and move about upon the land.
However, the adult frogs spend a great deal of time in the water or
in damp places, because the skin must be kept moist.

DEVONIAN AMPHIBIANS

An impression that may have been made by the foot of an
amphibian was discovered in Upper Devonian rocks near Warren,
Pennsylvania. This much-discussed specimen is named *Thinopus
antiquus*, but it may be merely some inorganic structure instead of
a footprint.

One of the most important discoveries made by a Danish Arctic
expedition, led by Lauge Koch and working in eastern Greenland
during the year 1928, was a number of amphibian skulls and parts
of skeletons. The largest skull was 7 inches long, and the entire
animal probably measured about 4 feet in length. The rocks in
which these stegocephalian remains were discovered have been
correlated with the Upper Devonian. If this is correct, these are
the earliest land vertebrates of which we have any record.

The amphibians never completed the conquest of the land that
was begun by their crossopterygian ancestors. This great step was
reserved for the reptiles. The amphibians have failed because they
retain a conservative process of development that makes it necessary for them to return periodically to the water, where their
eggs are laid. As the amphibians have never been able to get rid
of the gill-breathing larval stage, the race is still chained to its
ancient aquatic environment. Today the amphibians occupy

a comparatively insignificant position among the hosts of four-footed vertebrates.

Reading References

MENCHER, ELY: Catskill Facies of New York State, *Geol. Soc. America Bull.*, vol. 50, pp. 1761–1794, Nov. 1, 1939.

MILLER, HUGH: "The Old Red Sandstone," E. P. Dutton & Company, Inc., New York, 1906.

SMITH, HOMER W.: The Lungfish, *Natural History Magazine*, November, 1939, pp. 224–225.

WALTON, JOHN: "An Introduction to the Study of Fossil Plants," Chap. III, A. & C. Black, Ltd., London, 1940.

CHAPTER XII

THE PALEOZOIC ERA

THE MISSISSIPPIAN PERIOD

The Land of Appalachia was greatly elevated as a result of the Acadian disturbance, and the agents of weathering and erosion renewed their attack upon this ancient region with increased vigor during the Mississippian period. The quantity of material carried into the geosyncline from the bordering highland was so great that, during much of the period, subsidence in the trough area was not able to keep pace with deposition; therefore, continental sediments predominate in the region.

During the times when the rivers running westward from Appalachia were carrying unusually heavy loads of mud and sand, the trough became a wide alluvial plain that stretched from the foot of the mountains westward to the interior sea. At other times, when the Appalachian highlands stood at a lower elevation and the streams were transporting smaller quantities of sediments, the trough subsided faster than the sediments accumulated and the sea was able to enter the geosyncline. At such times marine materials were deposited, but the sea changed its outlines frequently as the shore line shifted toward the east or the west in response to the varying conditions of sedimentation.

THE APPALACHIAN REGION

Mississippian rocks are found in the Appalachian region from Pennsylvania to Alabama. Shales and sandstones of continental origin predominate, indicating vigorous erosion of the mountainous Land of Appalachia. During the early part of the period, thick deposits of black shale were spread widely over Ohio and eastern Kentucky, and southward through the Appalachian region.

The Lower Missippian Pocono group occurs in the Appalachian district from northern Pennsylvania to Virginia. The rocks consist of thick sandstones with important shale and siltstone members, while in the northern part of Pennsylvania there is a considerable thickness of conglomerate, which is very resistant to erosion. This forms some of the present ridges in the folded region of the Appalachian Mountains. In Virginia, the Pocono contains some thin coal beds. The thickness of this group varies from about 100 feet in the south, to a maximum of 2,000 feet in Pennsylvania. Westward into Ohio, the Pocono rocks change gradually into fine-grained marine sandstones and shales belonging to the Waverly group.

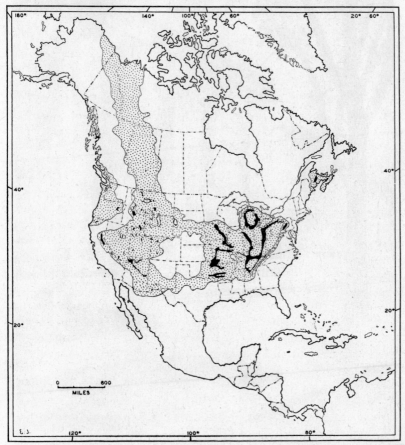

Fig. 123.—North America in the Mississippian period. Stippled areas show the inferred extent of the seas. Outcrops are black. White areas are land. (*Modified from Branson and Tarr, Schuchert and Dunbar.*)

This whole series is a great piedmont and alluvial-plain deposit, which grades toward the west into a delta. The thickest part of the Pocono is in eastern Pennsylvania, close to the Appalachian highland, from which the sediment was derived.

The Mauch Chunk group, in the northern Appalachians, consists of red sandstone, sandy shales, and siltstones, which reach a thick-

Fig. 124.—Detail of the Horace H. Rackham School of Graduate Studies at the University of Michigan. This building is constructed of Indiana Limestone. (*Ivory, Photographer.*)

ness of 3,000 feet in eastern Pennsylvania. This great deposit was formed upon a low alluvial plain, where seasonal rainfall alternated with dry periods and the red color developed as the sediments were oxidized.

In the southern part of the Appalachian region, especially through West Virginia and Virginia, the Mississippian rocks consist chiefly of marine limestones, with some sandstones and shales in the upper part of the section, which were probably of continental origin.

Depositional conditions in the Appalachian trough varied greatly during the Mississippian. Most of the deposits are of fluvial origin, but there were occasional incursions of the sea over portions of the geosyncline, and during these invasions, limestones and dolomites were deposited.

The Lower Mississippian is represented in New Brunswick and Nova Scotia by two important groups of rocks. The lower member, called the "Horton," consists largely of conglomerate, arkose, shaly sandstone, and shale. The materials, which are very poorly assorted, suggest deposits made by streams whose velocity and volume varied greatly according to the amount of rainfall. The thickness of this continental deposit is about 3,000 feet. Certain horizons contain numerous stumps of trees that are still in their original positions. The Horton and the Pocono are of approximately the same age.

The upper member of the two groups, called the "Windsor," is made up of red conglomerate, sandstone, and shale, which are largely of continental origin, with thin beds of dolomite containing an abundance of marine fossils and several local deposits of gypsum. As the Windsor group was deposited under conditions very much like those of the Mauch Chunk, the two are probably of the same age.

THE MISSISSIPPI VALLEY REGION

The Mississippian period gets its name from the fine exposures along the Mississippi River in Missouri, Illinois, and Iowa. The rocks are highly fossiliferous, and the various divisions of the section have been worked out in great detail. Limestones are the rocks most characteristic of this period throughout the Central Interior region of the United States. Some of the limestone formations have a wide distribution.

The Kinderhook series is one of the most variable members in the entire Mississippian sequence, because it is the deposit of a sea that advanced across an old land surface where many different kinds of rock, belonging to several geologic periods, had been weathering for a great length of time. The deposits of this group vary from place to place according to the variety of material that was present on the surface across which the waters advanced and also in accordance with conditions on the bordering land.

When the Kinderhook sea moved from the Gulf of Mexico area across the eastern interior region of the United States, there were extensive lowlands covered with a black soil, which the waves of the advancing sea reworked and deposited as a widespread black shale. In the South this deposit is known as the "Chattanooga" shale. Its thickness is about 100 feet through eastern Tennessee, Kentucky, and Ohio. Eastward, this black shale interfingers with the gray shales found in the basal part of the Pocono group. In the Ohio Valley region, where there are shales of both Devonian and Mississippian age, the scarcity of fossils makes it difficult to find the dividing line between the deposits of the two periods.

As the waters gradually cleared, gray shales, sandstones, and finally limestones were deposited in the Kinderhook sea. A great amount of fine-grained sand was laid down in northern Ohio and southern Michigan, during the Lower Mississippian or Waverly time. This now forms the Berea sandstone, which is quarried in Ohio and used for decorative effects on buildings where carved stonework is desired. The Berea, which is of even texture, is easily worked; and, after a period of weathering, its color changes to a pleasing, uniform buff. In Michigan, this sandstone has yielded some oil.

The Osage series, lying directly above the Kinderhook, includes the thick-bedded, coarse-grained Fern Glen, Burlington, and Keokuk limestones, which were deposited in a clear sea that spread widely over the Mississippi Valley region. Certain layers in the Burlington and Keokuk members are made up almost entirely of crinoidal remains. A great quantity of chert is found in the Osage rocks, where it occurs in bands and lenses or as rounded masses. In places, this siliceous material has replaced much of the original limestone, including the fossils. The Boone chert, which is correlated with the Osage series, contains important deposits of zinc and lead ores in southwestern Missouri, northeastern Oklahoma, and southeastern Kansas. A peculiar feature of the Osage limestone is the great development of stylolites, which form very conspicuous parallel rows on the vertical faces of the rock.

The Meramec series is composed chiefly of limestones and calcareous shales. The Salem member (Fig. 125) of this series is a soft, massive-bedded, oölitic limestone, which is widely used for building purposes. The main quarries are in southern Indiana, around the city of Bedford, and the common name for this rock is the "Bedford" oölite. The Salem limestone is also quarried at Bowling Green, Kentucky.

Fig. 125.—The Salem limestone or Bedford oölite exposed in a quarry near Bedford, Indiana. (*Courtesy of Indiana Limestone Company.*)

The St. Louis member of the Meramec series is a thick-bedded, fine-grained, bluish-gray and white limestone, which is widely distributed from Iowa to Alabama. This rock is especially well exposed along the Mississippi River near St. Louis, where it reaches a thickness of 300 feet.

The final deposit of the Middle Mississippian sea was the Ste. Genevieve limestone. This extensive deposit is well developed in southern Illinois, southeastern Missouri, and western Kentucky, where it is largely oölitic. As the Ste. Genevieve is very soluble, the thousands of caves and sinkholes in Kentucky have been formed in this limestone by the solvent action of ground water.

Mammoth Cave, the most famous of all these caverns, has many miles of passageways, formed at several different levels. Some of the galleries have great dome-shaped rooms, 250 feet high. During the War of 1812, nitrate obtained from bat guano on the floor of this cave was used in making gunpowder.

A local unconformity occurs at the base of the Ste. Genevieve in a few places, while at other localities the line of contact with the underlying St. Louis is difficult to determine.

The Chester series of rocks in the Mississippi Valley consists of alternating sandy and calcareous beds, which have been divided into sixteen formations, with a maximum thickness of 1,500 feet. The numerous vertical changes are contrasted with the persistence of many of the beds when traced horizontally. There is a widespread disconformity between the rocks of Chester age and the different underlying Mississippian formations. In some places the contact is with various horizons in the Ste. Genevieve; in others, with the St. Louis; while on the southwestern flank of the Ozarks the Chester rests upon rocks of Burlington age. The sandstone in this great series, which is widely distributed over the Mississippi Valley region, apparently was derived from the rising land of Llanoria to the south and from uplifted areas in southern Appalachia.

THE CORDILLERAN REGION

In the Cordilleran trough, during the Early Mississippian, extensive deposits of limestone were laid down, and these rocks are now widely exposed throughout the western part of the United States and Canada. This far-spreading deposit, which forms prominent cliffs at most of the outcrops, is known by several different names, such as the Madison limestone in the Northern Rockies and the Redwall limestone in the Grand Canyon. In the walls of the canyon the beds are 500 feet thick. The conspicuous red color is only a surface stain derived from the overlying Supai formation. Limestones of Upper Mississippian age are found in California, Nevada, Utah, Wyoming, and Idaho.

UPLIFT AND OROGENY IN THE MISSISSIPPIAN

The Interior Region. The close of the Mississippian period was marked by considerable crustal unrest in several parts of North America. Over the interior of the continent, there was a broad uplift and some local faulting, without any mountain making. This was followed by a long emergent period, during which the Mississippian rocks were subjected to much erosion. In Kansas,

Colorado, Oklahoma, and Missouri, the soluble limestones were honeycombed by numerous sinks and caverns, which resulted in the development of a typical karst topography with many depressions 100 feet or more in depth. Pennsylvanian sediments were later deposited upon this very uneven surface, filling the caves (Fig. 126) and valleys.

Fig. 126.—A cave in Mississippian limestone filled with red shale of Pennsylvanian age. Near State Bridge, Colorado. (*Photographed by Henry Donner.*)

The Ancestral Rockies. Several areas in Colorado and neighboring states began to rise in the latter part of the Mississippian period, and in the Pennsylvanian period (Fig. 137) they became well-defined uplifts. One of these areas, called the "Colorado" highland, extended, eventually, from southeastern Wyoming to the northeastern part of New Mexico. Another, the Uncompahgre-San Luis highland, lay in southwestern Colorado and northern

New Mexico. Between these two highlands lay the Central Colorado Basin, and here Mississippian rocks are found in a number of places, such as the Leadville district and the Sangre de Cristo Mountains.

Thick beds of limestone were deposited in several parts of Colorado during the early half of the Mississippian, only to be eroded later in the period, following the rise of the Ancestral Rockies. The original distribution of this limestone is revealed at several localities along the Front Range in Colorado, where cherty boulders containing Mississippian fossils are found in a basal conglomerate of Pennsylvanian age. Around Hartville, Wyoming, the Lower Mississippian has been deeply eroded, but not completely removed by erosion.

Deposition in the Ouachita Geosyncline. The old land of Llanoria lay in Louisiana, the southern part of Arkansas, and eastern Texas, including a portion of the present Gulf of Mexico. During Late Mississippian and Early Pennsylvanian times, this land was being rapidly eroded. From 17,000 to 20,000 feet of sediments belonging to these two periods were deposited in the Ouachita geosyncline, which lay to the north of Llanoria. In the Permian, these sediments were folded and thrust-faulted northward to form the Ouachita Mountains.

The Variscan Mountains. Mountain making on a grand scale began in Europe during Late Mississippian time and was renewed in the Pennsylvanian and the Permian. These crustal movements formed several ranges of mountains. One great arc ran southeastward from Ireland through southern England and across France, where it turned to the northeast and extended through southern Germany into Austria. These ranges have been called the Paleozoic Alps, the Hercynian Alps, and the Variscan Mountains. During the course of this long-continued orogeny, both in England and on the continent, volcanoes were active at various times.

CLIMATE OF THE MISSISSIPPIAN

The presence of reef-building types of corals in Mississippian rocks along the northern coast of Alaska indicates a mild climate for that part of the Arctic. The red beds of the Mauch Chunk group may have been deposited under conditions of alternate seasonal rainfall and periods of aridity. The Windsor group in Newfoundland and Nova Scotia includes not only red beds, but a great amount of gypsum and a few local deposits of salt. This may indicate that in a number of places very pronounced aridity existed—at least, temporarily. The arid conditions must have extended at least as far west as Michigan, where red beds and brines are found in Mississippian rocks.

ECONOMIC IMPORTANCE OF MISSISSIPPIAN ROCKS

Brines in the Mississippian rocks of southern Michigan are a very important source of salt and bromine. They also contain large stores of magnesium, which is now being recovered in considerable quantities.

Mississippian limestone in the Leadville, Colorado, district is the main host rock for the great replacement deposits of gold, silver, and lead that made the district famous. The Cherty Boone limestone of Mississippian age has long been an important source of zinc and lead in southwestern Missouri, southeastern Kansas, and northeastern Oklahoma. Most of the petroleum that is now produced in Illinois comes from Mississippian formations, and rocks of the same age in the Mid-Continent field have also yielded some oil.

LIFE DURING THE MISSISSIPPIAN

Marine Invertebrates. Foraminifera were very abundant in the warm, clear seas that covered the Mississippi Valley area. The Salem limestone of Indiana contains vast numbers of these organisms.

Corals. It is difficult to explain the absence of extensive coral reefs in the warm, clear Mississippian seas. The compound coral Lithostrotionella (Fig. 127) was common locally in the St. Louis epoch, but it did not form extensive colonies. *Favosites,* which was abundant during the Silurian and Devonian periods, had completely disappeared by the Mississippian.

Bryozoa. The most representative bryozoa belong to the genus *Archimedes* (Fig. 127). In this form, the tiny openings in which the animals lived were located upon a band that ran spirally around the central axis. This axial portion of the structure is the part that is commonly preserved as a fossil. Other distinctive types of bryozoa, belonging to the Fenestellidae, developed a lattice-like framework as a support for the colony.

Crinoids and Blastoids. Crinoids (Fig. 128) reached their climax in the shallow, clear Mississippian seas. The celebrated localities at Burlington and Keokuk in Iowa, and at Crawfordsville, Indiana, are world famous for the beautifully preserved specimens that they have furnished. These gregarious animals lived in such enormous numbers in certain places that their plates and stems built up extensive deposits of crinoidal limestone. Blastoids (Fig. 127) were at their height during this period, and the genus *Pentremites* contributed largely to the making of pentremital limestones.

Brachiopods. A great variety of brachiopods lived during the Mississippian; the most representative form has a very convex

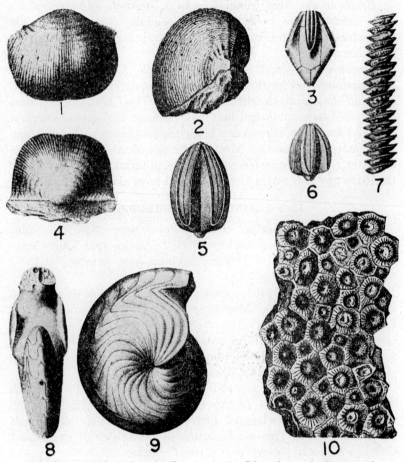

Fig. 127.—Mississippian fossils. 1, 2, 4, *Dictyoclostus burlingtonensis;* 3, *Pentremites pyriformis;* 5, *Pentremites elongatus;* 6, *Pentremites conoideus;* 7, *Archimedes wortheni;* 8, 9, *Aganides rotatorius;* 10, *Lithostrotionella castelnaui.*

pedicle valve and a shallow, concave brachial valve (Fig. 127). The outer surface of both valves was covered with spines of various lengths.

Pelecypods, Gastropods, and Cephalopods. Many varieties of pelecypods and gastropods, which were locally abundant, are

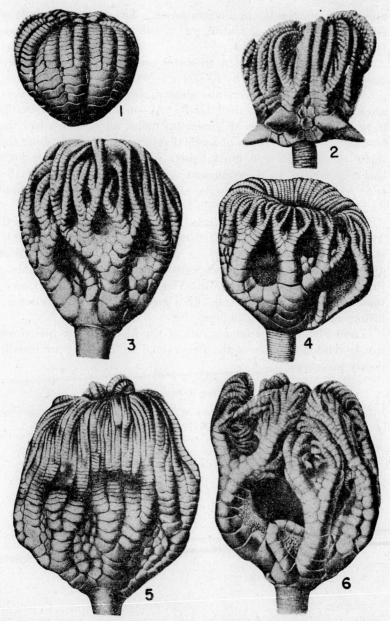

FIG. 128.—Mississippian crinoids. 1, *Metichthyocrinus clarkensis;* 2, *Wachsmuthicrinus spinifer;* 3, *Taxocrinus ungula;* 4, *Taxocrinus intermedius;* 5, *Forbesocrinus wortheni;* 6, *Onychocrinus ulrichi.* (*From "The Crinoidea Flexibilia" by Frank Springer.*)

especially common in the Pocono series. The commonest type of cephalopod was the goniatite, of which the genus *Aganides* is typical.

Trilobites. Mississippian trilobites are quite rare, only a few genera being represented by fossils.

Vertebrates. Fish were abundant during this period, but they are known chiefly from their teeth. About 300 species of sharks have been found in the Mississippian rocks, all of which had the blunt, "pavement" types of teeth that were used for crushing the shells of mollusks and crustaceans. The modern Port Jackson shark is related to these ancient forms. Predatory fish of this type were probably responsible—at least, in part—for the rapid decline of the trilobites after the Devonian.

The existence of amphibians in the Mississippian of North America has been inferred from numerous footprints, but until recently no skeletal material was known. In 1940 a number of disarticulated amphibian bones were found in the Hinton shales of the Mauch Chunk group in West Virginia. This is a very important discovery—one that helps fill a great gap in the evolutionary history of the early amphibians.

Land Plants. The land plants of the Mississippian period are closely related to those of the Pennsylvanian, but they are usually poorly preserved.

Reading References

BUTTS, C.: "The Mississippian Series of Eastern Kentucky," *Kentucky Geol. Survey*, (6), vol. 7, 188 pp., 1922.

CHAPTER XIII

THE PALEOZOIC ERA

THE PENNSYLVANIAN PERIOD

LANDS AND SEAS

During the Pennsylvanian period most of the interior region of North America was a broad, featureless lowland, with mountains on the old marginal land of Appalachia in the east and Llanoria on the south. The Pennsylvanian rocks rest unconformably upon the deposits of several different periods, from Pre-Cambrian to the Mississippian, and the contact is very irregular in many places.

One of the particularly interesting characteristics revealed by the Pennsylvanian deposits in a number of localities is the alternation of marine and continental conditions of sedimentation that prevailed over large areas for considerable stretches of time. Through Kansas and Missouri, at least fifty changes of this sort are recorded in beds that have a total thickness of 2,500 feet. Some of the deposits are thin but remarkably persistent for many miles. This shows that the advances and retreats of the sea were widespread and not just local.

These interesting cycles of marine and nonmarine deposits probably have their explanation in certain recurring conditions of sedimentation. If the land subsided over a considerable area somewhat faster than usual, the region might be depressed below sea level and a marine invasion would occur. After a comparatively short period of time, subsidence might stop or proceed so slowly that sedimentation would build the area above sea level and produce continental conditions again. Some of these beds have been traced for 500 miles along the outcrop without any important change in the character or thickness of the material. Several horizons of marine limestone may be followed from Iowa to northern Oklahoma. The Pittsburgh coal seam in western Pennsylvania and neighboring states covers an area of 6,000 square miles, and coal beds in the Indiana-Illinois field cover 50,000 square miles. Great stretches of the country must have been very flat and almost at sea level during the deposition of these beds, so that when the sea covered the land the water was doubtless extremely shallow.

SEDIMENTS OF THE PENNSYLVANIAN

The Appalachian Region. Pennsylvanian rocks are found in the Appalachian region from southwestern New York to Alabama, and most of the deposits occur west of the folded mountain belt. These

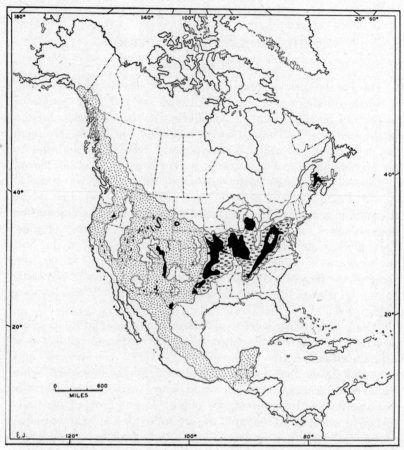

Fig. 129.—Generalized map of North America in the Pennsylvanian period. The stippled areas show the inferred extent of the seas. Outcrops are in black. White areas are land. The fresh water coal swamps are shown over the eastern and central parts of the United States. Very shallow fluctuating seas covered portions of these swampy areas during a part of the period. (*Modified from Branson and Tarr, Schuchert and Dunbar.*)

deposits, which were derived largely from the highlands of Appalachia, consist of cross-bedded sandstones and dark-colored shales, with some conglomerate along the eastern side of the region. These materials were spread by rivers over extensive piedmont

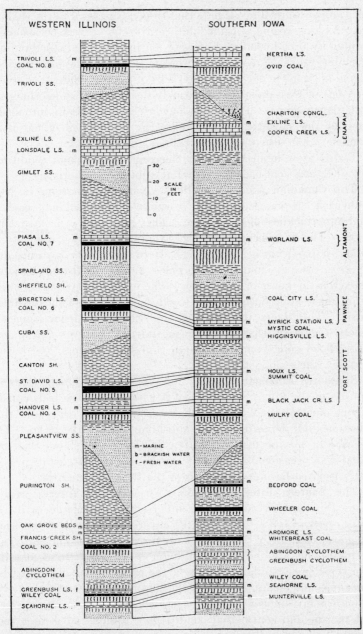

Fig. 130.—Two sections to illustrate the close correlation of Pennsylvanian beds in southern Iowa with those in western Illinois. Correlation is by means of lithologic similarity, similarity of index fossils, and similarity of sequence. (*From "Interbasin Pennsylvanian Correlations, Illinois and Iowa," by J. M. Weller, H. R. Wanless, L. M. Cline, and D. G. Stookey, Bulletin of the American Association of Petroleum Geologists, Vol. 26, No. 10, October, 1942.*)

areas and swampy alluvial flats that sloped westward to the shallow sea. As this region subsided intermittently, it was occasionally invaded by broad, shallow bodies of marine water in which impure limestones and calcareous shales were deposited. There are thirteen marine horizons in the Pottsville rocks of eastern Ohio.

A few of the sandstones are widely distributed, while others are lenticular in shape. They pinch out or change laterally into shale. Some of the sandstone lenses represent the fillings of old river channels, while others are offshore bars and barriers.

Plants grew luxuriantly over this region when land conditions prevailed, and coal beds are found at a number of horizons.

The Canadian Area. The Pennsylvanian formations in New Brunswick, Nova Scotia, and western Newfoundland reach a maximum thickness of 13,000 feet. They are entirely of continental origin. The Joggins section (Fig. 131), at the head of the Bay of Fundy, is particularly interesting. Here the petrified stumps and trunks of trees are found, still in place, at twenty distinct horizons through a thickness of 2,500 feet. The low, swampy parts of this region must have been heavily wooded during the Pennsylvanian period. The rivers that carried the sediments down from the eastern highlands changed their meandering courses occasionally during flood times, spread through timbered districts, and buried the trees where they stood.

Southern Michigan. There are 700 feet of Pennsylvanian deposits in the Lower Peninsula of Michigan. These beds consist of conglomerates, sandstones, shales, several coal beds, and thin limestones, all deposited in the subsiding, saucer-like basin. The presence of marine fossils in a few of the layers shows that the region was occasionally invaded by the sea, but the state was a partly isolated basin during most of the Pennsylvanian period.

The Eastern Interior Region. The Eastern Interior region covers Illinois, western Indiana, and Kentucky, together with the eastern part of Iowa. Glacial drift covers a large part of this area, and good exposures of the bed rock are not common. The sediments in this region are thinner, containing much less coarse material than the Pennsylvanian deposits of the east. Some of the marine limestones and shales, as well as the coal beds, are continuous over wide areas in Illinois and Indiana, which is clear evidence of alternate marine and continental conditions. A thin bed of limestone is often found directly above a layer of coal, and this may be followed by shale containing marine fossils, with final deposits of continental shale and sandstone that were laid down as the sea was gradually filled and land conditions returned. Similar cycles of sedimentation were repeated several times in the Eastern Interior coal region.

The Mid-Continent Region. The Pennsylvanian section in the Mid-Continent region is unusually complete, with excellent exposures of the various formations in many places from Iowa to Texas.

FIG. 131.—A fossil tree trunk still standing where it grew in the Joggins section, Nova Scotia. (*Photographed by E. C. Case.*)

These rocks also underlie nearly all of the Great Plains area east of the Rocky Mountains. The Pennsylvanian beds are from 2,000 to 3,000 feet thick through central and southern Iowa, southeastern Nebraska, northwestern Missouri, and eastern Kansas. The same alternations of marine limestones and continental shales that are characteristic of other Pennsylvanian regions are found here, as well, and there are occasional beds of sandstone with some siltstone.

The rocks of the Pennsylvanian system gradually thicken southward to a maximum of more than 23,000 feet in Oklahoma and Arkansas. This great deposit was formed in the Ouachita geosyncline, and the source of most of the material was the rugged land of Llanoria on the south. Sandstones and siltstones are the predominant rocks in this important section.

The Cordilleran Region. Rocks of Pennsylvanian age are widely distributed over the Cordilleran region (Fig. 132) of the United States, varying greatly in character and thickness from place

FIG. 132.—Pennsylvanian sandstones, shales, and limestones, about 1300 feet thick, exposed in the canyon of the San Juan River, southeastern Utah. (*Photograph courtesy of Utah Guide and of Utah Historical Society.*)

to place. The deposits, which are largely marine, consist of limestones and sandstones, with smaller amounts of shale.

The red Fountain formation, extending along the eastern side of the Front Range in Colorado, varies in thickness from 100 to about 2,000 feet. The Pennsylvanian rocks in many parts of Colorado are characterized by an abundance of clastic mica and debris that has been derived from Pre-Cambrian rocks. Beds of salt and gypsum occur in the upper part of the section, through central and southwestern Colorado, and in east central Utah. There are very extensive deposits of Pennsylvanian sediments through the Great Basin region of Utah and Nevada. The materials here are limestone, sandstone, and shale, largely of marine origin, that reach a thickness of several thousand feet in the Oquirrh range of Utah.

The large amount of coarse detrital material that characterizes the sediments of this period in the Cordilleran region is evidence that the uplifts that had started in the Late Mississippian were still in progress during the Pennsylvanian.

ECONOMIC PRODUCTS OF THE PENNSYLVANIAN DEPOSITS

Coal. *The Process of Formation.* The formation of coal was made possible when land plants first appeared upon earth in great abundance. The Pennsylvanian period, with its widespread fresh-

Fig. 133.—Reconstruction of a coal-forming swamp in the Pennsylvanian period. (*Courtesy of Geological Survey of Great Britain.*)

water swamps (Fig. 133), mild climate, and luxuriant growths of vegetation, furnished just the proper conditions for making coal on a great scale; therefore, the coal fields of this period cover more than 250,000 square miles in the United States alone.

During the Pennsylvanian period, great areas of the earth's surface were so flat and poorly drained that fresh-water swamps of tremendous size existed, especially upon the broad coastal plains that bordered the interior seas. The vegetation that fell into these swamps decayed so slowly under water that, year after year, there was a gradual accumulation of coal-forming plant material. Under the action of bacteria, the plant tissues were broken down, oxygen and hydrogen were released, and peat or muck was eventually produced. The process might have stopped there, but in those areas where the coal swamps were later covered with thick deposits of sedimentary rock the heat and great pressure generated by this heavy load of sediments eventually converted the muck into lignite and finally into bituminous coal.

The change from bituminous to anthracite coal requires a continuation of the heat and pressure and, especially, a further escape of the gaseous constituents. For this purpose a moderate amount of crustal movement (diastrophism) may be necessary. This, together with a great weight of overlying sediments, is sufficient to convert bituminous, or soft, coal into anthracite, or hard, coal.

Fig. 134.—A coal seam 10 feet thick in a mine near Pittsburgh, Pennsylvania. (*Courtesy of U.S. Bureau of Mines.*)

Spores and pollen, blown by the wind into certain open places in the swamps, where the water was stagnant, formed beds of cannel coal. This material has a high hydrogen content, and the small volume of production lessens its value as a fuel. Cannel coal is burned extensively in fireplaces.

The rate at which the coal-forming material accumulated is largely a matter of speculation. The Pittsburgh coal bed (Fig. 134) is over 6 feet thick. It has been estimated that the organic material that eventually formed this coal could have been deposited in 2,100 years.

The number of coal beds that are present in the different fields varies greatly. At least 20 are known in the Pennsylvania area and 55 in Alabama. The thickness of a coal seam is seldom uniform over large areas, and it may be highly variable within short distances. The mammoth seam in the anthracite region of northeastern Pennsylvania varies from 50 to 60 feet in thickness, but coal beds are rarely thicker than 8 or 10 feet.

The anthracite field (Fig. 136) in the northeastern part of Pennsylvania covers about 484 square miles. The coal beds were strongly folded during the Appalachian revolution, and only those that were in the synclines are preserved today, while the many seams that were in the anticlines have been removed by erosion.

Fig. 135.—Outcrop of Pennsylvanian rocks showing coal seam seven feet thick. Near Pittsburgh, Pennsylvania. (*Photograph courtesy of U.S. Bureau of Mines.*)

Of this anthracite coal, 4,400,000,000 tons have already been mined and about 9,000,000,000 tons are still available.

The Appalachian Field. This coal field, which is the greatest producer in the United States, extends for approximately 850 miles from the northeastern part of Pennsylvania to Alabama. The width of the field varies from 30 miles in Tennessee to about 180 miles farther north. The coal seams are accessible and are thick enough to make them workable over 75 per cent of the area.

The Eastern Interior Field. This coal field is located in an oval-shaped basin with the long axis running northwest and southeast across Illinois, southwestern Indiana, and western Kentucky. The coal is mined chiefly around the margin of this area, where it is close to the surface, while toward the center of the basin it cannot be profitably recovered because of the thick sedimentary covering.

The Mid-Continent Field. Extending for a distance of over 800 miles, this coal field reaches from northern Iowa southward through parts of Missouri, Kansas, and Oklahoma, to central Texas. The coal seams, which are horizontal over a large part of this area, are so close to the surface in many places that mining is done by means of power shovels.

The closest approach today to the coal-forming conditions of the Pennsylvanian period is found in the great Dismal Swamp of

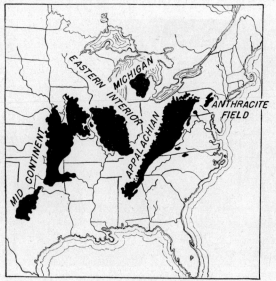

Fig. 136.—Map showing coal fields of Pennsylvanian age in the United States.

Virginia and North Carolina, which covers an area of over 500 square miles. Muck has already accumulated to a depth of 12 feet in parts of this swamp. The entire region is only a few feet above sea level.

Fossil charcoal is sometimes found in coal beds, but its origin is uncertain. In some of the brown coal, or lignite, beds the charcoal was probably caused by forest fires, but its presence in the bituminous coal was probably the result of some special decomposition processes.

Other Economic Products. Tremendous quantities of oil and gas have been produced by Pennsylvanian rocks in the Mid-Continent region of Kansas, Texas, and Oklahoma. Oil is obtained from rocks of the same period in Wyoming, Utah, and New Mexico.

Pennsylvanian limestones and shales are used extensively in the manufacture of Portland cement. Some of the plastic clays that lie beneath the coal beds have great fire-resisting properties and make good grades of pottery.

MOUNTAIN-MAKING DISTURBANCES

History of the Wichita Geosyncline. Two distinct Paleozoic geosynclines developed in the Mid-Continent region of the United States. The deformation of the sediments that accumulated in these troughs produced two distinct mountain systems, which differed in structure and in the time of their formation.

The trend of the Wichita geosyncline was in a west-northwestward direction across southern Oklahoma and northern Texas. Along the site of the present Wichita and Arbuckle Mountains this trough received 9,000 feet of marine sediments, mostly limestone, during the Cambrian, Ordovician, Silurian, and Lower Devonian periods. Shallow shelf seas lay to the north and south of the geosyncline, and in these areas only about 1,000 feet of sediments were deposited.

The sediments in the Wichita geosyncline were compressed, in early Pennsylvanian time, into west-northwest-trending fault blocks and folds that make up the modern Wichita Mountains, the Criner Hills, and the echelon folds of the Electra (Red River) and Muenster arches. A narrow, subsiding trough that developed along the northern margin of these growing ranges received many thousands of feet of Pennsylvanian sedimentary materials. These sediments, together with the older Paleozoic rocks, were again subjected to great compressional stresses in the Pennsylvanian period as a second phase of the Wichita orogeny, and the Arbuckle Mountains were formed. This complex of related ranges, with their west-northwest trend, is known as the "Wichita system." The mountains were formed from sediments that were deposited in the Wichita geosyncline.

The Ancestral Rockies. The highland areas (Fig. 137) that began to rise in parts of Colorado and neighboring states in the latter part of the Mississippian period were uplifted intermittently during the Pennsylvanian. They furnished considerable thicknesses of coarse detrital material for the immediately surrounding regions. Farther out from the highlands the sediments were finer and some calcareous deposits were formed.

The Variscan Mountains. There were further strong uplifts of the Variscan Mountains during the middle of the Pennsylvanian

period.   The effects of this long-continued and widespread orogeny
may still be seen in truncated folds through the southern part of

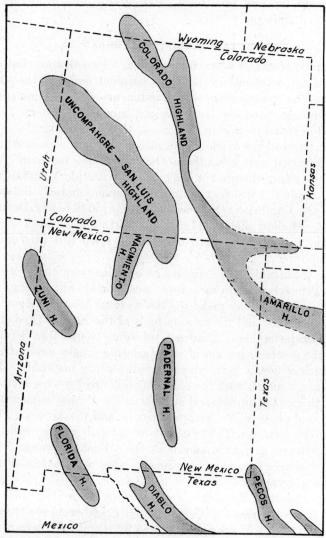

Fig. 137.—The Ancestral Rockies at the close of the Pennsylvanian period.   (*From
a map by Armand J. Eardley.*)

England and Wales and central France, as well as in the Black
Forest and Hartz regions of Germany.

    In other parts of the world at this time great mountain-making
disturbances began, reaching their greatest intensity during the

Permian. There were uplifts in the Himalayan region, the Ural Mountains area, and along the western side of South America.

CLIMATE OF THE PENNSYLVANIAN

Mild climatic conditions prevailed over far greater areas of the earth's surface during the Pennsylvanian period than they do at present, and rainfall was very abundant in the coal-forming regions. Many of the tree trunks found in the deposits of this period are of great size. The absence of growth rings in them shows that there

Fig. 138.—Red arkose of the Fountain formation exposed at the gateway to the Garden of the Gods, Colorado Springs, Colorado. Pikes Peak is in the distance. The Fountain is of Permo-Carboniferous age. (*Photographed by H. L. Standley.*)

was no freezing weather over the extensive lowlands. The mildness of the climate is further indicated by the luxuriant growth of vegetation; the great size of the leaves and cells; the smooth, thick bark; and the development of aerial roots. The rainfall was not highly seasonal but was rather evenly distributed throughout the year.

The animal life of the Pennsylvanian gives some indication of the tropical or subtropical climate. Many types of insects attained gigantic size during the period, and today the larger representatives of the insect group are found within the tropics. Great numbers of Foraminifera, belonging to the Fusulinidae—forms that are characteristic of warm oceans—existed in many places throughout the northern hemisphere. The presence of coral reefs on islands of the Spitzbergen group, in latitude 78° N., is another convincing proof that the climate was mild. Most of the Pennsylvanian amphibians were small, but there were some large forms that would not have been able to find protected places in which to pass the cold winter seasons.

There is no evidence that the climate was mild and moist over the entire earth during the Pennsylvanian period. Cold conditions doubtless prevailed in the higher mountains, and there is evidence of aridity in the salt deposits of eastern Utah and western Colorado, as well as in the red beds of the Fountain formation (Fig. 138) through central Colorado. The unusually mild climate of Spitzbergen might have been quite local—possibly, the result of some warm ocean current from the south, similar to the modern Gulf Stream. The polar regions were certainly cooler, in general, than the lower latitudes.

Climatic fluctuations of considerable magnitude are likely to occur many times during the course of a geologic period that is several millions of years in length. The warm, humid conditions that were necessary for the accumulation of coal-making vegetation existed during only a portion of the Pennsylvanian; and the abundant rainfall that made the swampy conditions of the eastern interior region possible was brought by westerly winds whose moisture content was precipitated as they rose to cross the high Land of Appalachia.

Some geologists believe that the great continental glaciers that covered vast areas in Australia, India, South Africa, and South America were formed chiefly in the Late Pennsylvanian instead of in the Permian.

LIFE OF THE PENNSYLVANIAN PERIOD

Plants of the Coal Swamps. Dense, jungle-like masses of vegetation grew widely over the warm, humid lowlands where the coal was forming. The prevailing color of the plants was doubtless green; and the small, primitive flowers that were characteristic of this period probably lent very little color to the monotonous landscape. Although many of the plants reproduced by means of seeds, the spore-bearing types were far more common. As cannel coal is composed largely of spore cases, at certain seasons of the year vast clouds of spores must have been blown about by the wind.

There were many different kinds of ferns, some of which reached the enormous height of 50 feet, while single fronds have been found that were more than 5 feet long. Seed ferns were especially common. Plants of this type, which bore small seeds instead of spores, looked very much like the true ferns.

Scouring rushes reached the size of trees. Some individuals of the genus *Calamites* (Fig. 139) were 3 feet in diameter and 100 feet high. These ancient forms were very similar to their modern relative, *Equisetum*. The jointed stems were characterized by vertical ribs, and a whorl of leaves was developed at each joint. The whorls, which are called Annularia, are not commonly preserved in place. The trunks of the scouring rushes were not solid, but con-

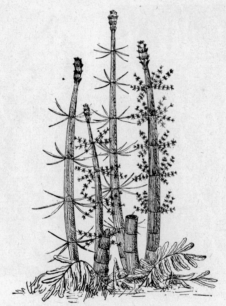

Fig. 139.—Restoration of *Calamites*, a scouring rush.

tained much pith and a thick outer covering of bark. Reproduction was by means of spores. The Pennsylvanian rushes probably grew in dense, jungle-like fashion, similar to the present canebrakes of the Southern states, and the fossil forms are usually preserved as molds of the hollow stems.

The scale trees were real giants among the other plants of the coal swamps. Among those that have been found are many stumps that had a diameter of 6 feet and tapering trunks that reached a height of 100 feet. The leaves of these trees were set close together; when they fell off, permanent scars (Fig. 140) were left upon trunk and branches, to mark the bases of the leaves.

The leaves of *Lepidodendron*, which resembled great pine needles, were arranged in very regular, parallel, spiral rows around the trunk and limbs. The branches were carried near the top. The roots (Fig. 141) of these great trees are often found, and they show scars where the rootlets were attached. The spores of *Lepidodendron* were formed in cones, which grew at the ends of the branches. The bark of *Sigillaria* (Fig. 142) is vertically ribbed, and the leaf scars are arranged in vertical rows. *Cordaites* was another very conspicuous Pennsylvanian tree. This form had a slender trunk,

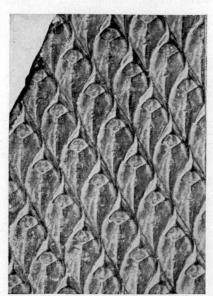

FIG. 140.—Leaf scars of *Lepidodendron*.   FIG. 141.—*Stigmaria*. The underground stems of *Lepidodendron* and *Sigillaria*.

seldom more than 2 feet in diameter, but the height varied from 30 to 100 feet, and the branches were found only near the top. The blade-like leaves often grew to be 6 feet long and 15 inches wide. The cordaites were seed-bearing forms.

The great majority of Pennsylvanian plants that have been preserved as fossils lived in the coal swamps. Very little is known of the upland vegetation, which grew in drier places and in regions where important seasonal changes of climate occurred.

The Pennsylvanian floras were very much alike in widely separated parts of the world. This probably indicates that the plants migrated from one continent to another across old land bridges, which have long since disappeared. It is evidence also of the uniform climatic conditions that prevailed over large areas of the earth's surface.

Marine Invertebrates. *Fusulinids.* The fusulinids are spindle-shaped Foraminifera that lived on the sea bottoms in many parts of the world. Their skeletons are so extremely abundant in places that they make up extensive beds of limestone.

Corals. Corals were abundant only in certain localities. Most of the types belong to solitary forms, but in western Spitzbergen compound corals formed reefs during the early part of the period.

Fig. 142.—Leaf scars of *Sigillaria*.

Crinoids and Blastoids. Crinoids were common, but well-preserved fossil specimens are rare. Blastoids disappeared from the North American seas after the Early Pennsylvanian, but they lived in the East Indies region until the Permian.

Other Forms. Brachiopods of the *Productus* type (Fig. 143) were far more numerous than any other kind. Bryozoa lived in great numbers. The environmental conditions were favorable for pelecypods and gastropods, and these mollusks were extremely common.

Land Snails. A particularly interesting occurrence of land snails has been reported from the great Joggins section in Nova

Scotia. Some of these gastropods had crawled into the hollow stumps of Pennsylvanian trees, where they died and were preserved when the stumps were buried beneath accumulations of mud and sand.

Shells of Pelecypods. The great majority of pelecypods that have been found in rocks earlier than the Pennsylvanian period

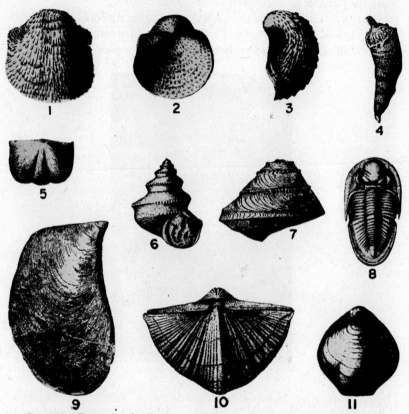

Fig. 143.—Pennsylvanian fossils. 1–3, *Juresania nebrascensis;* 4, *Lophophyllum profundum;* 5, *Mesolobus mesolobus;* 6, *Worthenia tabulata;* 7, *Trepospira sphaerulata;* 8, *Phillipsia major;* 9, *Myalina subquadrata;* 10, *Neospirifer triplicatus;* 11, *Composita subtilita.*

show none of the original shells, but are preserved merely as molds and fillings. Beginning with this period, the shells themselves are often discovered. Possibly, the valves of the older Paleozoic pelecypods were built largely of aragonite, which is unstable and easily destroyed, while those of later generations were made of calcite, which is a more resistant material, not so difficult to preserve either entirely or in part.   Fresh-water pelecypods are quite common in certain Pennsylvanian shales of Europe and Nova Scotia.

Goniatites, the most distinctive form of cephalopods, had evolved into a great many varieties.

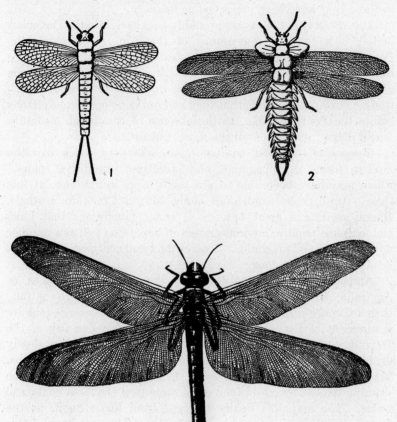

Fig. 144.—Pennsylvanian insects. 1, *Eubleptus danielsi;* 2, *Stenodictya lobata;* 3, *Meganeura monyi.* (*After Handlirsch and Brongniart.*)

Insects.   An amazing variety of insects (Fig. 144) lived in the Pennsylvanian forests and swamps, where they found environmental conditions ideal for their development.   Many of them resembled modern forms, but for the most part they belong to archaic stocks.   Insects of giant size were quite common.   The Coal Measures of Belgium have yielded the remains of a dragonfly type (Fig. 144) with a wingspread of 29 inches. Cockroaches, very much like those of today, were especially numerous, and some of the individuals reached a length of 4 inches. Doubtless, many other types of insects existed during the Pennsylvanian, in addition to those that have been preserved as fossils.

The ancestry of the insects probably goes back into the Devonian period. The sudden appearance of these invertebrates in the Pennsylvanian rocks is another illustration of the numerous gaps that exist in the evolutionary story of life. Insects are very fragile creatures, difficult to preserve except under most unusual conditions. It is quite possible that they had not developed exoskeletons before the Pennsylvanian, as the absence of this tough structure would make fossilization all the more difficult.

Eoscorpius, the first true scorpion, was very much like the modern forms in appearance and structure. Primitive spiders, which may have been able to spin webs, were in existence at this time. Argillaceous sandstones along Mazon Creek in northern Illinois contain a great number of small concretions that have yielded some remarkably well-preserved insects, as well as a number of myriapods and arachnids. One of the fossil centipedes from this locality is 12 inches long.

Amphibia. The difficulties that the modern lungfishes of Australia, Africa, and South America encounter in order to continue their existence during the dry season or when the water is foul are reminiscent of the problems that the crossopterygian fish of the Devonian must have met and solved while their lungs were slowly evolving and as their paired fins were changing into paired limbs. Many years passed while these fish were floundering over the swampy flats in search of food or of some pool that still contained water. The amphibia finally emerged from this struggle as the first land-living, air-breathing vertebrates. The members of this group must have been quite abundant during the Mississippian period, but their remains are not common.

The Pennsylvanian rocks of North America have given us 88 species of amphibia, distributed through 46 genera, 19 families, and 7 orders. This indicates that the group was highly diversified during the coal-forming period and that their numbers must have been very great in the rivers, lakes, and swamps throughout the world. Fifty species of amphibia have been found in the Pennsylvanian shales at Linton, Ohio.

Some of the Pennsylvanian forms were small creatures, only a few inches long, but there were also larger individuals that reached a length of about 10 feet. The footprints of *Wakarusopus gigas*, from the Middle Pennsylvanian of Kansas, are 5 inches long, and the impressions of the right feet are widely separated from those of the left, indicating a heavy-bodied animal that weighed several hundred pounds.

Most of the Paleozoic amphibia had broad, flat skulls, roofed with heavy bones. They belong to an extinct subclass called "Stegocephalia." There were three eyes on top of the head, all directed upward. The small pineal eye was in the midline of the skull, behind the other two. The crossopterygian fish, from which the amphibia were probably derived, possessed this third eye; and it still exists as a vestigial structure in the higher vertebrates, including man. The legs were placed at the sides of the body—a position that forced the animals to move with a sprawling or waddling gait. The larger forms must have been slow, ponderous creatures, with the same sluggish habits possessed by their modern descendants.

Some of these animals had long, laterally flattened tails, which were useful in swimming. Undoubtedly, they all spent more time in the water or in wet places than on the land. Modern amphibia have moist skins and cannot endure long exposure to the hot sun or to dry air. Stegocephalians lived in the fresh water, and their teeth indicate carnivorous habits. Insects, fish, and other amphibians furnished them with food, which they swallowed without any mastication.

The First Reptiles. A few reptiles have been found in Pennsylvanian rocks, but their fossil remains are exceedingly rare. They were, apparently, all small animals, looking very much like the amphibians, with weak limbs and sprawling bodies. The reptiles did not become prominent until the Permian period, but they were destined to rule the world for many millions of years.

Reading References

CAMPBELL, M. R.: The Coal Fields of the United States, *U.S. Geol. Survey Prof. Paper* 100-A, 33 pp. 1917.

MOODIE, ROY L.: "The Coal Measures Amphibia of North America," *Carnegie Inst. Washington, Pub.* 238, 222 pp., 1916.

WELLER, J. M.: Cyclical Sedimentation of the Pennsylvanian Period and Its Significance, *Jour. Geology*, vol. 38, pp. 97–135, 1930.

WHITE, D., and R. THIESSEN: "The Origin of Coal," *U.S. Bur. Mines Bull.* 38, 390 pp., 1913.

CHAPTER XIV

THE PALEOZOIC ERA

THE PERMIAN PERIOD

The Early Permian deposits in the eastern part of North America rest upon Pennsylvanian beds with no apparent break; therefore, it is difficult to draw any precise boundary between the rocks of the two periods. There was a slight elevation of the land over the eastern and most of the central interior regions of the continent in the Late Pennsylvanian that drained the swamps and gradually brought the period of coal formation to an end, as the climate became drier.

Transition. The Pennsylvanian sea that covered the central and southwestern parts of the country may have continued into the Permian without withdrawing, because sedimentation was apparently continuous from one period into the next and it is impossible to determine the exact boundary between the Pennsylvanian and Permian periods in this part of the United States.

Appalachia was mountainous at the beginning of the Permian. Streams flowing down the western slopes of this old land deposited sediments over the Appalachian trough area, which was then a broad, gently sloping alluvial plain. The eastern part of the United States continued to rise, and by the middle of the period sands and silts from Appalachia were accumulating over the very flat, interior continental basin.

SEDIMENTATION IN THE PERMIAN

The Dunkard Series. The Dunkard series occupies about 8,000 square miles in the northwestern part of West Virginia, as well as adjoining portions of Ohio and Pennsylvania. The strata, which are nearly horizontal, consist of sandstones, sandy shales, a few beds of impure limestone, and a little coal. The deposits are largely reddish in color. They may originally have extended as far west as Kansas.

The Dunkard series (Fig. 145) is mostly of continental origin; but the presence of brachiopod shells belonging to the genus *Lingula* in certain layers, together with shark spines, shows that

216

marine or brackish water reached into this area for a short time. *Lingula* is a very adaptable brachiopod. The modern representatives can live for at least a short time in water that is quite fresh. The shark spines are not very numerous, and that portion of the

FIG. 145.—Generalized map of North America in the Permian period. Stippled areas show the inferred extent of the seas. Outcrops are in black. The small area in Ohio, West Virginia, and Pennsylvania represents the Dunkard series, a portion of which is marine. The volcanoes were active in the Middle Permian. (*Modified from Branson and Tarr, Schuchert and Dunbar.*)

sea in which the marine beds of the Dunkard were deposited may have been brackish.

The sediments of the Dunkard series rest upon Pennsylvanian rocks without any evidence of a break, indicating that deposition was continuous from one period into the next. The boundary between the deposits of the two periods is based entirely upon fossils.

The Mid-Continent Region.   In the early part of the Permian period, a shallow sea extended across New Mexico and western Texas northward through Oklahoma and Kansas into southeastern Nebraska.   The borders of this inland sea, like those of the preceding Pennsylvanian, fluctuated over considerable areas.   It was a temporary extension of this sea eastward into Ohio and West Virginia that was responsible for the marine portions of the Dunkard series.

The earliest sediments that were deposited over the Mid-Continent region consist of alternating beds of light-colored marine

Fig. 146.—Permian gypsum in a mine at Sun City in Barber County, Kansas.
(Photographed by Oren Bingham, Kansas Geological Survey.)

limestones and shales, which are continuous with the Pennsylvanian rocks below.   The earliest beds are very fossiliferous.   Farther up in the section, however, there is a gradual but very obvious decrease in the numbers and varieties of the organisms, until they disappear entirely.   Above the unfossiliferous zone lie the thick Wellington shales, which contain the extensive salt beds of Kansas. The rest of the sequence consists of several hundred feet of barren red beds that represent continental deposits.

The cause of this remarkable series of changes is not difficult to determine.   The sea that lay over Kansas and Oklahoma was at first in open communication with the ocean by way of a channel reaching across Mexico and the Gulf region.   This seaway was gradually restricted by deposits that were built out from the highlands in southeastern Colorado and southern Oklahoma. In the meanwhile, the climate was growing more arid; and, when water from the ocean could no longer flow freely into the Kansas and Oklahoma sea, evaporation exceeded the inflow and salt was eventually precipitated. This increasing salinity was responsible also for the gradual extinction of the marine life. A periodic flow of ocean water across the partial barrier, renewing the supply of salt, was responsible for the great thickness of this material that finally accumulated.

When the water in this great arid basin finally disappeared by evaporation, over a thousand feet of red sands and siltstones were

Fig. 147.—Coconino sandstone below and Kaibab limestone above at Lee's Ferry on the Colorado River.

washed into the region from the surrounding land. This material is mostly of continental origin, but there are beds of gypsum (Fig. 146) at certain horizons that suggest temporary returns of the sea. Deep wells in western Kansas and Oklahoma have revealed places where the red beds change laterally into dolomite and anhydrite.

The Texas and New Mexico Region. The Permian rocks in the western part of Texas and southeastern New Mexico, which are nearly 14,000 feet thick, present some particularly interesting stratigraphic and faunal problems. This area was covered by a sea long after the marine water had disappeared from the rest of the Mid-Continent region, and the Permian record here is unusually complete.

An examination of the Permian rocks in the Trans-Pecos region of Texas reveals a number of complex relationships. In one place the rocks are almost entirely limestones, while in a near-by area there are successive beds of limestone, shale, and sandstone, and in certain places, the interfingering of various deposits is common. When a bed is traced laterally, it is frequently replaced within a short distance by another type of deposit. It is obvious that conditions of deposition were highly variable over the region and that this gave rise to different faunal assemblages in adjacent areas, with each fauna adapted to its own peculiar environment.

The floor of the Permian sea in western Texas was uneven because of the existence of several irregular subsiding basins (Fig. 148), where the water was comparatively deep, separated by platforms covered with shallow water. These irregularities may

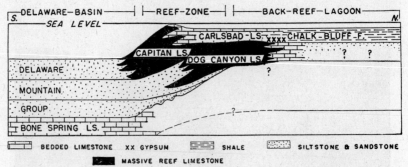

FIG. 148.—A generalized section showing the conditions of deposition near the northern edge of the Delaware Basin with the Capitan reef and the shallow lagoon back of the reef. (*Modified from W. B. Lang, U.S. Geological Survey.*)

have been determined by structural features in the older rocks that had been folded and subjected to deep erosion before the Permian.

The Delaware Basin is the best defined of these structures. Here the chief exposures of Permian beds are found around the margins. The deposits exhibit three facies, each one characteristic of special depositional conditions. The materials in the basin itself are ordinary dark-colored limestones, with shales, sandstones, and siltstones that were probably derived from some uplifted land to the southwest near the entrance into this subsiding area.

Along the sides of the basin, especially northward to the Guadalupe Mountains (Fig. 149), there are massive limestones that rise as prominent cliffs over a thousand feet high. Back of this great reef-like mass, in what must have been the shallow waters of extensive coastal lagoons, the deposits are thin-bedded limestones,

Fig. 149.—The Point of the Guadalupes showing the Guadalupe Escarpment, facing westward, and a portion of the eastern reef front. The Bone Spring limestone (*BS*) occurs in the rounded hills in the foreground. The Delaware Mountain formation (*D*) consists of sandstone which grades upward into siltstone. The bold cliff is formed of Capitan limestone. At (*C*) the reef beds of the Capitan may be seen dipping down to meet the relatively horizontal Delaware Mountain formation (*D*) with which they interfinger. (*Photographed by W. B. Lang, U.S. Geological Survey. Reproduced by courtesy of W. B. Lang and the Am. Assoc. of Petroleum Geol. Bull.*)

Fig. 150.—Deposits formed in the Back Reef or Lagoon Zone. Carlsbad limestone (Ca), Capitan limestone (C), Dog Canyon limestone (DC), middle portion of the Delaware Mountain formation (mD), gray limestones (gl). (Photographed by W. B. Lang, U.S. Geological Survey. Reproduced by courtesy of W. B. Lang and the Am. Assoc. of Petroleum Geol. Bull.)

gypsum, salt, and red beds.   The strata of these three zones grade locally into one another through very short transition phases, and there is considerable interfingering of the beds.

The massive limestones that were deposited so extensively around the margin of the Delaware Basin during the Permian contain many varieties of marine organisms, such as algae, sponges, bryozoans, corals, and specialized brachiopods with thick shells and high, irregular, cardinal areas.   The fauna varies somewhat from place to place, and the limestone may be largely of organic origin.   These reefs originally rose sharply from the basin floor to heights of from 300 to 500 feet.

Fig. 151.—The entrance to Carlsbad Caverns in the Capitan limestone of Permian age.   (*Courtesy of U.S. Department of the Interior.*)

Immediately behind the reefs, in the shallow waters of the coastal lagoon (Fig. 150), the thin-bedded limestones continue shoreward for a distance of several miles.   Fusulinids in vast numbers lived throughout this area.   Closer to the shore, where the deposits are variable, are found the red shales, gypsum, and salt.

Late in the Permian, the connection to the southwest between the Delaware Basin and the open sea was greatly restricted, so that the inflow of sea water was impeded until it finally ceased.   The climate was extremely arid, and, as the water slowly evaporated, great thicknesses of salt and anhydrite were eventually precipitated. Near the center of this area, deep wells have penetrated about 3,500 feet of these materials.   The water occasionally disappeared completely or almost entirely from certain portions of the basin, and

Fɪɢ. 152.—"Frozen Niagara" in the Big Room of Carlsbad Cavern, New Mexico.
(Courtesy of U.S. Department of the Interior.)

then layers and lenses of potash-bearing salts were formed.   These
are found interbedded with the anhydrite and salt.

Carlsbad Caverns. The Carlsbad Caverns (Fig. 151) are
located upon the eastern slope of the Guadalupe Mountains, in the

southeastern part of New Mexico. These vast underground passages have been formed largely by the solution of Permian limestone (Capitan), which is here about 900 feet thick. Where some of the deeper parts of the caves penetrate the underlying gypsum formation, great vaulted rooms (Fig. 152) have been formed, as much as 4,000 feet long, 600 feet wide, and 350 feet high.

Red Beds of the Cordilleran Region. The deposition of red beds continued on a great scale during the Permian (Fig. 153). This type of deposit may be associated with arid conditions, for

FIG. 153.—Red beds exposed near Espanola, New Mexico. The hard and soft layers are very characteristic. (*Photographed by E. C. Case.*)

at this time deserts were widespread over the central and western parts of the United States. The aridity was more intense than that of the Great Basin region today, and red beds accumulated over many of the Permian areas, the thickness of the deposits amounting to several thousand feet. The agents of deposition were largely torrential streams, with slope wash an important factor. The finer materials were spread over broad flood plains during times of high water. The bedding is very irregular (Fig. 153)—in many places, entirely absent. There is a general lack of fossils except locally where water holes or temporary lakes existed. The source of a great part of the red-bed material lay in the different uplifted areas that formed the Ancestral Rockies.

The coarse conglomerate that is so important a feature of the red beds is distributed over considerable areas. This material must have been carried down steep slopes by swiftly flowing streams, especially during flood stages, and deposited over the lower and flatter slopes, as well as over the piedmont regions. The pebbles and boulders would soon fill the bed of a stream, forcing the water to flow in new channels, which, in turn, were rapidly filled. This process, repeated on a great scale, may help to explain the wide distribution of the conglomerates in the Mesozoic red beds.

Fig. 154.—Red beds west of Cañon City, Colorado.

Not all red sediments have been produced under the same climatic conditions. Red color may develop within the tropics in a very moist climate. The salt and gypsum that are associated with the Permian formations, however, are indicative of a hot, dry climate, where complete oxidation of the sediments could take place.

Monument Valley. This great national monument (Fig. 155) is located in northeastern Arizona. Its scenic marvels have been eroded out of red sandstone that is, at least in part, of Permian age. Slender spires and larger masses of rock rise hundreds of feet above the desert valley floor, producing effects that are extremely spectacular.

The Grand Canyon Region. Marine waters occupied the southern end of the Cordilleran trough during most of the Permian period, and thick deposits of sediments were left in Arizona, Utah, Nevada, Idaho, and Wyoming. A very good section of Permian rocks is exposed in the walls of the Grand Canyon and the surrounding region.

The Kaibab formation (Fig. 147) is found along the rim of the Grand Canyon, where it stands in sheer cliffs about 600 feet high. This very interesting formation varies greatly when traced either vertically or horizontally. It consists of limestones, sandstones, shales, and bedded chert, all indicating highly variable conditions of deposition. In the early part of Kaibab time, when the sea was beginning its advance over the region, the deposits indicate deposition in localized basins and probably under brackish-water conditions. The fauna of this facies consists almost exclusively of mollusks. As the water continued its advance, normal marine conditions prevailed and deposits were formed in the open sea. Brachiopods, simple or cup corals, pelecypods, bryozoans, and crinoids are common in the rocks that were deposited at this time. In late Kaibab time, when the sea was retreating, shallow-water and continental conditions existed. The deposits of that stage consist of thin-bedded magnesian limestones, red beds, gypsum, and cross-bedded sandstones. The fauna of this facies consists largely of mollusks and a few types of brachiopods.

The Toroweap (Fig. 29) formation lies unconformably below the Kaibab. The upper and lower members consist almost entirely of soft red beds, which weather easily and form slopes. The central member consists of resistant limestone, which forms a prominent cliff. Toward the east, the Toroweap grades first into red beds and then into the cliff-forming Coconino sandstone.

When the Toroweap and Kaibab formations were deposited, the region of northern Arizona and southern Utah was close to sea level and the bordering lands were low. The clastic or land-derived sediments are extremely fine and the highly uniform character of the thick limestones shows that the sea bottom was covered with calcareous ooze over thousands of square miles.

The Coconino sandstone, which lies immediately below the Toroweap in the Grand Canyon section (Fig. 37), is widely distributed over the plateau region of northern Arizona (Fig. 156). This very distinctive rock is made up largely of fine-grained quartz sandstone, commonly white or buff colored, with very prominent cross-bedding in many places. This great cliff-forming sandstone

FIG. 155.—Permo-Triassic rocks are exposed in Monument Valley. (Courtesy of Spence Air Photos.)

is 375 feet thick in the Grand Canyon walls, but it thins toward the north and disappears near the Arizona-Utah boundary line.   Many footprints of crawling amphibians and reptiles have been found on the slanting foreset beds of this sandstone.   Apparently, the animals were climbing up the front slopes of extensive sand dunes, where their tracks were preserved in the moist sand.

The red Hermit shale (Fig. 29) lies below the Coconino, and the contrast between the two formations is very striking.   Below the Hermit is the Supai formation, which consists of red shale, sandstone, and siltstone.   In the Grand Canyon region the Supai

Fig. 156.—Coconino sandstone (Permian) exposed in the walls of Canyon de Chelly, Arizona.   (*Courtesy of Spence Air Photos.*)

rests upon the old eroded surface of the Redwall limestone of Mississippian age.

Canada and Alaska.   Permian rocks are found in the western part of Canada and over large areas in the Arctic regions of North America, particularly along the Yukon River and the west coast of Alaska.

PERMIAN VOLCANOES IN THE WEST

The first evidence of Paleozoic volcanic activity in the western part of North America is found in the Permian (Fig. 145).   The Nosoni formation of California includes a great amount of lava and tuff. Several thousand feet of volcanic materials are found in the western part of Nevada, and in eastern Oregon and western Idaho there is a vast accumulation of lava, tuff, and breccia, called the "Castro formation," which includes a few beds containing Permian marine fossils. During this period, volcanoes were active in Alaska and Mexico, also.

ECONOMIC PRODUCTS OF THE PERMIAN

Oil and gas are found in the Permian rocks of southern Oklahoma, the Texas Panhandle, Kansas, and Wyoming. Very important potash deposits occur in Permian marine rocks of southeastern New Mexico and western Texas. Great salt deposits of this period are found in Kansas, Oklahoma, New Mexico, and Texas; Permian gypsum beds, in Iowa, Oklahoma, Kansas, New Mexico, Texas, South Dakota, and Colorado. Valuable deposits of calcium phosphate, which is important as a fertilizer, occur in a number of western states, especially Idaho, Wyoming, and Utah.

CLIMATE OF THE PERMIAN

When continents are elevated and epeiric seas have withdrawn into the ocean basins, climatic conditions are always more diversified than during those times when the lands are widely covered by marine waters. When North America emerged from the sea in the latter part of the Permian, those warm oceanic currents that had formerly flowed across the continent into the polar regions must have disappeared.

The old land bridge, Gondwana, which spanned the Atlantic between South America and Africa during the Permian, must have exercised a great effect upon ocean currents in the southern hemisphere.

The upheaval of many great mountain ranges in this period doubtless had a profound effect upon the wind circulation and distribution of moisture over certain portions of the continents. All these conditions produced many climatic differences upon the earth's surface. The variations ranged from extreme aridity to an abundance of rainfall and from tropical heat to the cold of continental glaciation.

CONTINENTAL GLACIATION

One of the outstanding events of the Permian was the development of continental glaciers (Fig. 157) on a grand scale, especially in the southern hemisphere. South Africa was extensively glaciated, and the tillite reaches the enormous thickness of 2,000 feet in the southern Karroo. Here the glacial material apparently accumulated in water. Layers of quartzite, interbedded with the tillite, may represent sands that were deposited during the interglacial epochs. There are five distinct zones of tillite at Laingsburg. The principal center from which the African glaciers spread was an elevated region just inside the Transvaal, and from this area the ice moved to the southwest for a distance of 700 miles.

Tillite is found at five horizons in the Permian of Australia, and glaciers formed in Brazil and Argentina.

The glaciation was very heavy in India, where one of the chief centers of ice radiation was within 20 degrees of the equator.

The Squantum tillite, near Boston, Massachusetts, was probably deposited by glaciers from the Permian Appalachian Mountains.

According to some geologists, the main part of this great glaciation occurred, not in the Permian, but in the Pennsylvanian (Carboniferous) period. It is quite possible that the ice sheets did not develop at the same time on all the continents.

GONDWANA LAND BRIDGES

The *Glossopteris* flora (Fig. 162) had a wide distribution in the southern hemisphere during the Permian period, and its presence in Antarctica, South America, Africa, and India is strong evidence that these countries were joined by land masses, across which the plants were able to migrate quite readily. These continental connections were not necessarily of great width; they may have been comparable to the modern Isthmus of Panama. In certain Paleozoic and Mesozoic rocks there is faunal evidence, also, that these land bridges existed and that the connections remained until about the middle of the Mesozoic era.

CHANGES IN THE EARTH'S SURFACE IN THE PERMIAN

History of the Ouachita-Marathon Geosyncline. The trend of the Ouachita geosyncline was toward the west through southern Arkansas and southeastern Oklahoma, then southward across central Texas, finally curving westward around the central mineral region, where it connected with the Marathon geosyncline of western Texas and northern Mexico. The Ouachita geosyncline was also continuous with the great Appalachian geosyncline; so, together, the Marathon, Ouachita, and Appalachian troughs formed

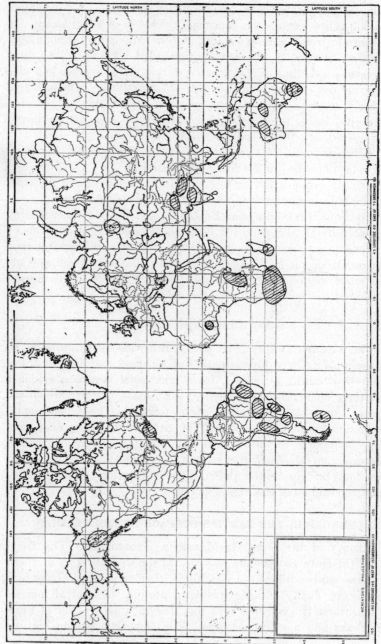

Fig. 157.—Map showing distribution of continental glaciers in the Permian.

a very long geosyncline bordering the southeastern and eastern margins of the North American continent. The Wichita trough, an arm from this great geosynclinal belt, penetrated toward the interior of the continent.

While the Wichita geosyncline was subsiding 9,000 feet and receiving sediments during the early Paleozoic, the Ouachita, or Llanorian, trough subsided only about 3,000 feet. The sediments, which are quite distinct from those in the Wichita area, consist of

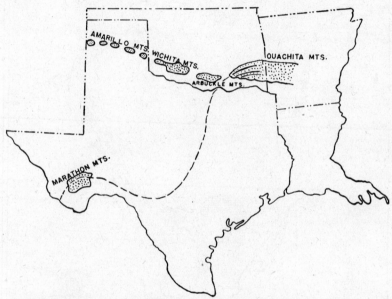

Fig. 158.—Sketch map showing the approximate positions of mountains that were formed in the south-central part of the United States in the Late Paleozoic era. The broken line running from the Ouachita Mountains to the Marathon Mountains indicates the front of the buried Ouachita System. The Amarillo Mountains are now buried beneath a cover of sediments. (*After van der Gracht.*)

cherts, siliceous shales with graptolites, and fine-grained quartzitic sandstones. During Mississippian and Lower Pennsylvanian times the Ouachita trough received over 17,000 feet of sandstones and shales. These clastic sediments are not found in the Wichita system of mountains.

The great thickness of sedimentary material in the Ouachita-Marathon geosyncline was subjected to compression in the Permian period, and tremendous thrust sheets were moved northward and northwestward. The front of the most northerly of these thrust sheets is now only 12 miles east of the outcropping sediments in the

Wichita sequence. Great masses of rock that were moved northward considerable distances during these overthrusts are now resting upon the sediments and structures of a province that was
originally remote from that of the Ouachita-Marathon geosyncline.

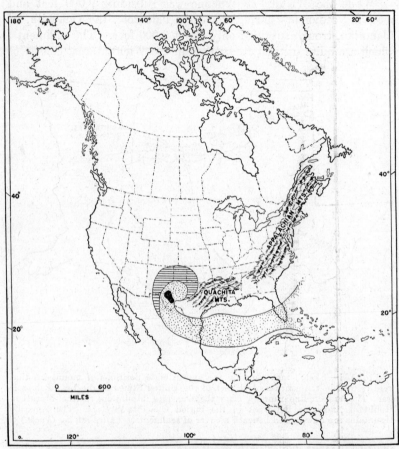

Fig. 159.—North America in the Late Permian period. The stippled area
shows the inferred extent of the sea. The lined area indicates deposits that are
largely nonmarine. The black area in western Texas and southeastern New Mexico
shows the approximate location of the Delaware basin. (*Modified from Schuchert
and Dunbar.*)

The structural evidence of the Marathon phase of this great disturbance may be clearly noted today in the Trans-Pecos region of
Texas. There are places where Permian strata may be seen resting upon the truncated Marathon folds with a strong angular
unconformity.

Mountains in Eurasia. The Ural Mountains, between the Russian and Siberian areas, were formed in the Permian from sediments that were deposited in a great geosyncline. The culminating uplifts in the Variscan mountains of southern England, northern France, and Germany also took place during this period.

The Appalachian Revolution. The old borderland of Appalachia was a prominent feature along the eastern side of North America during most of the Paleozoic era. It extended eastward

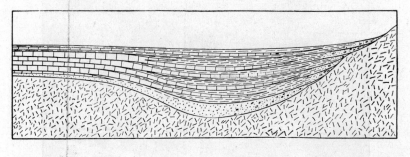

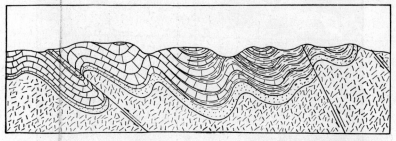

Fig. 160.—Generalized drawings to show how the Permian Appalachian Mountains were formed. The upper drawing shows the western side of Appalachia and the Appalachian geosyncline. The lower drawing shows how the sediments in the geosyncline were folded and faulted during the Appalachian revolution. (*Drawings by John Horeth.*)

into the Atlantic at least as far as the outer edge of the continental shelf, while its western side was bordered by the Appalachian geosyncline (Fig. 160). At the time of its maximum extent, this trough stretched from Labrador and Newfoundland southwestward to the Gulf of Mexico.

Appalachia was uplifted to considerable heights several times during the Paleozoic, and rivers running down the western slopes of this old land carried vast quantities of sediment into the subsiding trough. The thickness of the deposits, which was not the same throughout the entire geosyncline, was more than 40,000 feet in some places. The entire trough was not covered by marine waters in all of the Paleozoic periods. Several times the area remained dry land for considerable stretches of time.

About the middle of the Permian, when tremendous horizontal compressive stresses were applied to the eastern side of Appalachia,

FIG. 161.—Owachomo Natural Bridge, San Juan County, Utah. The rock is Permian (Cedar Mesa) sandstone. The span of the bridge is 180 feet. (*Courtesy of U.S. Department of the Interior.*)

it was thrust westward against the belt of weak sediments in the Appalachian geosyncline, and these rocks were folded and faulted into a great chain of mountains that stretched from Newfoundland to Alabama. A number of thrust faults developed along the eastern side of the folded belt. Cambrian as well as younger Paleozoic rocks were pushed so far westward that in some places they are now resting upon Pennsylvanian formations. The Blue Ridge thrust extends for more than 700 miles from Pennsylvania to Alabama. The rocks have suffered their greatest deformation along the eastern side of the disturbed area and the folds gradually die out westward in gentle undulations. The original width of the Appalachian trough was shortened as much as 100 miles in some places, while that of the entire geosyncline was greatly reduced. Intense igneous activity took place in the zone of crustal movements during the revolution. After the thrusting had ceased, there were great intrusions of granite, which erosion has uncovered in a number of places.

The effects of this widespread orogeny are difficult to separate from those of the older Taconic and Acadian disturbances, which folded the rocks in the trough through New England and the Maritime Provinces of Canada. The mountain structures south of the New England region are largely the result of the Appalachian revolution.

LIFE OF THE PERMIAN

Plants. The luxuriant growth of plants in the Pennsylvanian period was possible largely because of the mild climate and an abundant supply of moisture. The Permian witnessed a far more diversified climate, with widespread aridity on many continents and extensive glaciation in the southern hemisphere. Under these climatic conditions, the old Pennsylvanian plant stocks began to decline, so that by the end of the period the giant sigillarias and lepidodendrons, together with the calamites, cordaites, and seed ferns had almost disappeared from the earth. In their places appeared plants that were adapted to more severe climates, and conifers slowly came into prominence.

The Glossopteris Flora. A group of very hardy plants belonging to the *Glossopteris* and *Gangamopteris* floras (Fig. 162) evolved in the southern hemisphere during the Upper Pennsylvanian (Carboniferous) and Lower Permian periods. Their remains are found in a number of places through India, Australia, South Africa, South America, and Antarctica. These were small, seed-bearing plants with thick, tongue-shaped leaves and reticulate venation. In South Africa these plants are found interbedded with glacial material and the floras were apparently adapted to a cold climate. By the Middle Permian, representatives of these floras had reached northern Russia, but they have never been found in the western part of Europe or in North America.

Marine Invertebrates. The marine faunas of the Early Permian were not greatly different from those of the Pennsylvanian; the close relationships are entirely obvious.

The fusulinids were still abundant and important as rock-building protozoa. As conditions generally were not very favorable during this period for the growth of reef-building corals, certain

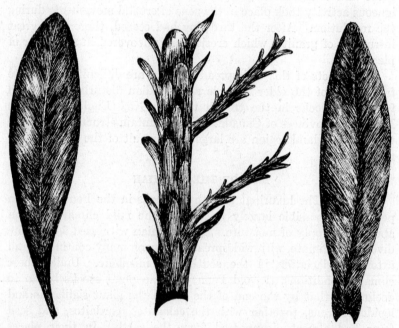

Fig. 162.—Representatives of the *Glossopteris-Gangamopteris* flora; left, *Glossopteris communis;* center, *Voltzia heterophylla;* right, *Gangamopteris cyclopteroides.*

groups, such as the tetracorals and the honeycomb types, became extinct.

Echinoderms were rare. All the blastoids and many of the crinoid groups disappeared. The characteristic *Productus* group of brachiopods, which had been exceedingly abundant during the Pennsylvanian, was still common, but in the course of the Permian, along with many other forms, it became extinct. Certain highly specialized types of brachiopods evolved at this time. One kind grew in so distorted a shape that it resembles a cup coral. Many varieties of bryozoa were present and built reefs in a number of places.

Pelecypods and gastropods were much like those of the Pennsylvanian. The cephalopods made great evolutionary progress, and the ammonoids became the dominant forms. The many genera that were present in the Permian clearly foreshadowed the remarkable development of this group during the Mesozoic era.

The trilobites had begun to decline in numbers and varieties during the Silurian, and this great subclass became extinct in the Permian.

The climatic conditions that caused a great restriction of land life during this period did not greatly limit the development of marine faunas except in a few areas.

Fig. 163.—*Diplocaulus*, a grotesque water-dwelling amphibian from the Permian. (*Drawn by John Jesse Hayes.*)

Insects. Insect life was greatly diversified during the Permian, but fossils are not common except locally. Over 10,000 specimens of insects have been found in Lower Permian rocks near Elmo, Kansas, and the Dunkard series of Ohio has yielded a few forms. This group of invertebrates shows many important changes that had taken place since the Pennsylvanian. Although a few large forms still existed, most of the individuals were small. Several new orders appeared—among them, some of the modern types, such as true dragonflies, many varieties of flies, and beetles. Cockroaches, which had played so important a part in the insect world during the Pennsylvanian, were now reduced to a minor position.

Vertebrates. *Fish.* The Permian seas doubtless contained many kinds of fish, but most of the fossils have been found in sediments that were deposited on the land by streams. A remarkable black-shale horizon in the Zechstein (Upper Permian), of Germany, has furnished the remains of many beautifully preserved fish.

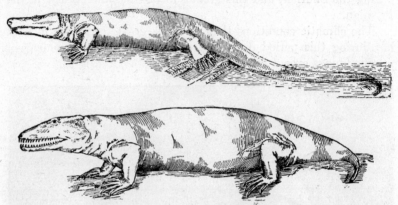

FIG. 164.—Permian vertebrates. Limnoscelis above and Seymouria below. (*Restorations by E. C. Case. Carnegie Institution of Washington. Publication 207.*)

Amphibians. Many stegocephalians (Fig. 163) continued to live in permanent rivers, even in regions that were quite arid, and in other places where there was an abundance of moisture. The remains of amphibians are very common at certain restricted local-

FIG. 165.—Cacops, an amphibian. (*Restoration by E. C. Case, Carnegie Institution of Washington Publication 207.*)

ities in the red beds of Oklahoma and Texas. Such places often represent water holes, where great numbers of the animals perished during the driest season of the year. The stegocephalians had heavy bodies; broad, flat skulls; and short, comparatively weak legs.

They were all sprawling, sluggish creatures, and had a maximum length of about 10 feet.

Reptiles.   An amazing variety of reptiles lived during the Permian, when they were the unquestioned rulers of the lands. Many of them showed a high degree of specialization and some were beginning to adapt themselves to an aquatic life in the rivers and the seas.

Fig. 166.—*Dimetrodon*, a carnivorous reptile of the Permian period.   (*Drawn by John Jesse Hayes.*)

The cotylosaurs—the most primitive members of this group— were slow-moving, crawling reptiles, probably representing the central stock from which a number of terrestrial types evolved. *Limnoscelis* (Fig. 164), from the Permian of New Mexico, was like several of the large modern lizards.   The short, stubby legs were ineffective for walking purposes, and the animal may have been semiaquatic in habits and a good swimmer.   *Seymouria*, which was formerly classed with the *cotylosaurs*, is now an amphibian, but it is close to the reptiles and so may be called a reptile-like amphibian.

Some of the Permian reptiles had sharp teeth, fitted only for holding and tearing their prey.   Such forms were carnivorous. Others had blunt teeth, well suited for crushing the shells of mollusks and crustaceans, while several—like *Endothiodon* from South Africa—were toothless and probably fed largely upon plants.

The group of pelycosaurs includes a number of specialized land reptiles, among which *Dimetrodon* (Fig. 166) and *Edaphosaurus* were outstanding because of their strange appearance. These animals had long, bony spines (neural spines) growing up from their backs—enormously elongated, slender bones, connected by skin, which gave the structure a sail-like appearance. The function of this remarkable growth is unknown. *Dimetrodon* was the commonest and fiercest carnivore of the Permian, while *Edaphosaurus* was a harmless herbivore.

Ancestors of the Mammals. The rocks of the Karroo formation of South Africa, which belong to the Late Permian and the Triassic, have yielded a group of reptiles (Fig. 184) that represent a particularly significant evolutionary advance. These are the *theriodonts*, which were probably the ancestors of the mammals. There is a differentiation of their teeth into incisors, canines, and molars. The limbs had shifted into the typical mammalian position, and their bodies could be carried off the ground. Some of the bones that are absent in the mammal skull were already being reduced in size, while others had entirely disappeared. All the bones that are found in the jaw of the reptile were present, but the dentary (tooth-bearing) bone was much larger than any of the others. A secondary palate had formed in the roof of the mouth. This is a mammalian characteristic.

Reading References

CASE, E. C.: "The Permo-Carboniferous Red Beds of North America and Their Vertebrate Fauna," *Carnegie Inst. Washington Pub.*, 207, 176 pp., 1915.

————: "Environment of Vertebrate Life in the Late Paleozoic in North America," *Carnegie Inst. Washington Pub.* 283, 273 pp., 1919.

COLEMAN, A. P.: "Ice Ages Recent and Ancient," 296 pp., The Macmillan Company, New York, 1926.

DARTON, N. H.: Permian Salt Deposits in the South Central United States, *U. S. Geol. Survey Bull.* 715, pp. 205–223, 1921.

————: The Permian of Arizona and New Mexico, *Am. Assoc. Petroleum Geol. Bull.*, vol. 10, pp. 819–952, 1926.

KEITH, A.: Outlines of Appalachian Structure, *Geol. Soc. America Bull.*, vol. 34, pp. 309–380, 1923.

KING, PHILIP B.: Permian Stratigraphy of Trans-Pecos, Texas, *Geol. Soc. America Bull.*, vol. 45, pp. 697–798, Aug. 31, 1934.

McKEE, EDWIN D.: "Environment and History of the Toroweap and Kaibab Formations of Northern Arizona and Southern Utah," *Carnegie Inst. Washington Pub.* 492, 268 pp., 1938.

Romer, Alfred S.: The First Land Animals, *Natural History*, November, 1941, pp. 236–243.

Schuchert, Charles: Gondwana Land Bridges, *Geol. Soc. America Bull.*, vol. 43, pp. 875–915, 1932.

Van Waterschoot Van der Gracht, W. A. J. M.: Permo-Carboniferous Orogeny in South-Central United States, *Am. Assoc. Petroleum Geol. Bull.*, vol. 15, no. 9, pp. 991–1057, September, 1931.

CHAPTER XV

THE MESOZOIC ERA

THE TRIASSIC PERIOD

The broad continental uplift that accompanied the great Appalachian revolution lifted North America well above the ocean level, and it was not until late in the next period that another epeiric sea was able to invade the land.

During the early part of the Triassic, the rugged Appalachian Mountains were undergoing vigorous erosion, so that by the latter part of the period they had been greatly reduced in height. As there is no record of deposition in the eastern part of the country during the Early and Middle Triassic, it is probable that sediments derived from the Appalachian highlands were carried eastward and now lie buried beneath the waters of the Atlantic.

TRIASSIC OF THE EAST IN NORTH AMERICA

The Newark Group. A series of fault troughs or grabens (Fig. 167) began to develop, in the Upper Triassic, along the Atlantic border region from Nova Scotia to North Carolina. These subsiding, down-faulted areas were receiving basins for great quantities of clastic sediments, derived from bordering highlands, and this material, together with some igneous rocks, is called the "Newark group" (Fig. 168).

The Connecticut trough extended for 100 miles in a north and south direction through western Massachusetts and central Connecticut, with a maximum width of about 25 miles. A great fault runs along the eastern side of this area, where the rocks dip to the east at angles that vary from 15 to 30 degrees. The total displacement along this fault line is about 15,000 feet.

Newark sediments in the Connecticut fault trough consist chiefly of sandstones, shales, and siltstones, with some conglomerate along the eastern side of the area, which was nearest the bordering highland. The poor sorting and irregular bedding of the sediments in many places indicate deposition by torrential streams running

244

swiftly down from the rugged land that bordered the eastern side of the graben. Some of the beds are more regular in their stratification and sorting. These apparently represent deposits that were made on flatter portions of the graben floor, where the rivers spread widely over their flood plains.

Feldspar is a common constituent of the Newark group, and most of this material is extremely fresh, indicating that mechanical

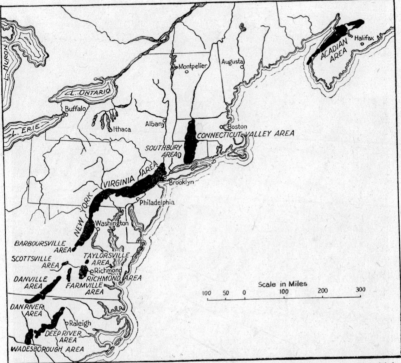

Fig. 167.—The black areas show the locations of the fault troughs in which the Newark continental sediments and igneous rocks accumulated. (*After I. C. Russell, U.S. Geological Survey.*)

weathering was especially active in the regions from which the sediments were derived. The beds are dominantly red in the lower part of the section, gray through the middle portion, and red again toward the top. Ripple marks and mud cracks are common and impressions of raindrops are found on many of the layers. The red beds may have been deposited under conditions of seasonal dryness, although it is impossible to demonstrate the real nature of the climate. The gray sediments were probably formed under fairly humid conditions when plants were abundant. As the vegetation decayed, the iron oxide was reduced and dark-colored deposits were formed.

Lava flowed quietly out over the floor of the Connecticut fault trough at least three times, forming extensive, flat-lying sheets, one of which is nearly 500 feet thick. An upturned edge of this

Fig. 168.—A diabase sill overlying Brunswick shale of the Newark group, near Pottstown, Pennsylvania. (*Photographed by Dean B. McLaughlin.*)

great flow forms the Hanging Hills of Meriden, Connecticut. Some volcanic ash and bombs found near the Holyoke Range in Massachusetts indicate local volcanic eruptions of considerable violence. Great numbers of dikes cut through the Newark strata, some of them extending for several miles beyond the Triassic area into regions of older rocks. Three extensive flows and a great sill are associated with the Newark group in the New Jersey–New York area.   The exposed edge of the sill forms the Palisades of the Hudson River.

Many different kinds of dinosaurs walked over the mud flats in Newark time, leaving great numbers of their footprints.   No marine fossils have been found in the Newark group, but considerable numbers of fresh-water fishes and land plants, which occur at certain localities, probably mark the positions of permanent lakes.

The Triassic deposits are from 10,000 to 13,000 feet thick in the Connecticut Valley and about 20,000 feet thick in New Jersey.

Fig. 169.—Gray sandstone and red shale of the Newark group exposed in Brogan's Cut 3½ miles west of Wadesboro, North Carolina.   (*Photographed by I. C. Russell, U.S. Geological Survey.*)

The thickness is not more than 2,000 to 3,000 feet in the basins through Virginia and North Carolina (Fig. 169).

The Newark group rests, in several places, upon the truncated folds of old Paleozoic rocks.   In these areas the Triassic deposits were laid down upon portions of the Appalachian Mountain region that had been peneplaned by Newark time.

TRIASSIC OF THE WEST IN NORTH AMERICA

The most extensive and typical continental deposits of Triassic age in North America occur throughout the Rocky Mountain region from western Texas, New Mexico, and Arizona to Wyoming and Idaho.   Brilliantly colored muds and sands of this period, found in

a number of places, have been given the name "Painted Deserts."
A great amount of Triassic sediment was derived from the Ancestral
Rockies. Wherever the deposits can be traced toward their source,
they grow much coarser. Several beds of rhyolitic volcanic ash,
now altered to purple, gray, and reddish bentonitic shales, are
found in Arizona and Utah. Deposits of gypsum are very prominent in a number of places.

The Colorado Plateau. The Triassic over the Colorado Plateau
area has three divisions: the Moenkopi, the Shinarump, and the
Chinle.

The Moenkopi. The Moenkopi, (Fig. 171), in the eastern part of
the region, consists of red and brown sandy shales and siltstones, with

Fig. 170.—The Chinle formation in the Petrified Forest near Holbrook, Arizona.
(*Photographed by Minnie S. Hussey.*)

sandstones and interbedded layers of salt and gypsum, which are
local in their occurrence. The bedding of the Moenkopi is generally
quite even. Most of this formation was deposited in a large body
of water. When the rocks are traced westward, they gradually
thicken to about 2,000 feet in southern Nevada, where limestones of
marine origin occur. The deposits of gypsum are also much
thicker toward the west. The beds containing this material may
have been deposited in lagoons or as part of a delta. The average
thickness of the Moenkopi, which belongs to the Lower Triassic,
is about 500 feet in Arizona.

The Shinarump. A period of erosion followed the deposition of
the Moenkopi, and the succeeding Shinarump grits and gravels
rest unconformably upon an irregular surface. In places the coarse

materials fill ancient valleys that had been eroded out of the underlying sandy shales. The Shinarump was originally spread over about 75,000 square miles along the western side of the Colorado Plateau, with an average thickness of only about 50 feet. This extensive veneer was deposited upon long piedmont slopes by torrential streams, which varied greatly in volume and velocity according to the highly seasonal rainfall. This variation is shown particularly by the numerous lenses of fine and coarse sand, covered by lenses of conglomerate. Petrified logs are common in a number

Fig. 171.—Triassic and Jurassic rocks near Lee's Ferry on the Colorado River. Lower slope of Moenkopi shale followed by the Shinarump conglomerate and Chinle shale. The Wingate sandstone, forming the vertical cliff at the top, is Jurassic.

of places, and the Shinarump caps many of the mesas in Nevada, Utah, Arizona, and New Mexico.

The Chinle. This vividly colored formation (Fig. 170) consists of shales, sandy silt, soft sandstone, impure limestone, and conglomerate. Most of these materials were deposited in stream channels and over broad flats by rivers whose volume and velocity varied with the rainfall. Beds of gypsum and bentonite are found in the lower part of the Chinle in a few localities, and the formation as a whole is so soft that it has given rise to the badland type of topography. The Moenkopi, Shinarump, and Chinle are exposed in the walls of Zion Canyon in southern Utah.

The Petrified Forest. The Chinle formation of Arizona is characterized by a great number of petrified logs (Fig. 172), some of them 10 feet in diameter and a few 120 feet long. The trees are mostly conifers, with araucarians very prominent. There has been a great deal of discussion about the climatic conditions under which these trees grew during the Triassic and how they reached their present positions in the sediments.

The logs themselves are not in their original places of growth, but a number of stumps have been found that are apparently in place, with roots 10 feet long, still enclosed by the old soil, which contains fragments of cone scales and leaves. Some stumps show evidence of having been carried short distances, probably down near-by slopes.

FIG. 172.—Petrified log showing the expanded base.

Judging from the habits of araucarians that are living today in South America and Australia, the trees of Chinle time must have grown along rivers or on higher ground where moisture was abundant during the growing season. The size of the logs and the thickness of the growth layers show that the dry or cold season was very short. Specimens of *Schilderia adamanica* have been found with swollen and fluted bases (Fig. 172) similar to those of the modern cypress, which suggests that they grew in swamps. Evidence of wood-boring beetles has been found on many of the logs and stumps. Similar boring animals that live today in dead trees never work on logs that are under water or buried in mud. This seems to prove that many of the logs in the petrified forest were not buried immediately after they fell to the ground. Several of the logs are encrusted with charcoal, which apparently formed after the trees had fallen,

but there is no evidence of healed-over fire scars.   This indicates
that there were occasional dry seasons when fires occurred, but
that the trees were not growing under conditions like those in the
modern tropical rain forests, where thunderstorms are of daily
occurrence.

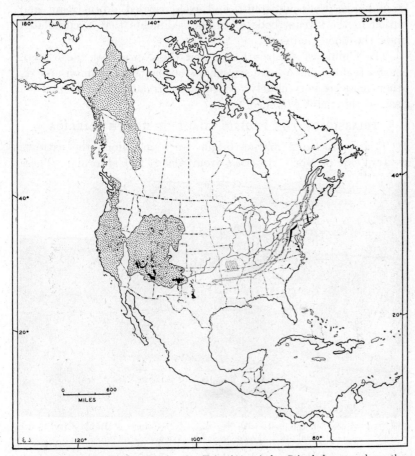

Fig. 173.—North America in the Triassic period. Stippled areas show the
inferred extent of the seas.   Outcrops are in black.   Areas of Newark sedimentation
are shown along the Atlantic coast.   (*Modified from Branson and Tarr.*)

With this information, we are able to reconstruct the environmental conditions in Arizona during the time when the trees of the
petrified forest were living.   Certain types of ferns show that the
climate was tropical or subtropical and that there were severe dry
seasons, but that the rainfall was sufficient to maintain several
permanent streams and swamps over the lowlands.   Dense forests

grew along the rivers, and more open stands of timber lived upon the near-by slopes and distant uplands. The dry periods were short but intense, and the Chinle sediments were oxidized during the periods of aridity, when the red colors developed. Those trees that grew close to the streams fell into the water, wherever the river banks were undercut, and were carried downstream and buried in the stream beds or in the sediments that accumulated upon the flood plains.

The Chinle of the southwest and the Newark of the eastern coastal region, which have six species of plants in common and six others that are very closely related, are correlated largely upon the basis of this plant evidence.

TRIASSIC OF THE PACIFIC COAST OF NORTH AMERICA

Triassic rocks of marine origin are found along the extreme western side of North America, from Alaska to California. These

Fig. 174.—Spearfish red beds with gypsum exposed west of Rapid City, South Dakota. (*Photographed by Armand J. Eardley.*)

sediments were deposited largely in the Pacific Coast geosyncline, which continued to be an important basin of deposition during the Jurassic and part of the Cretaceous. Triassic deposits, which are over 4,000 feet thick in California, reach the amazing thickness of about 25,000 feet in the south central part of Nevada.

The Upper Triassic in the area of Vancouver Island and the Queen Charlotte Islands is 13,000 feet thick and consists mostly of submarine lava flows, tuffs, and breccias, with some interbedded shales and quartzites that contain marine fossils.

During the Early Triassic, a sea spread from the Pacific Coast trough across Nevada to southeastern Idaho and then northward between British Columbia and Alberta. Lenses of gypsum, which vary in thickness from less than an inch to 30 feet, are found in the Spearfish red beds as far east as the Black Hills of South Dakota (Fig. 174). This material was probably deposited in temporary

FIG. 175.—Triassic sandstone and clay in the Bad Lands east of Tucumcari, New Mexico. (*Photograph by E. C. Case.*)

arms of the sea stretching in shallow embayments across Wyoming. No marine fossils have been found in the Triassic sediments that were deposited in the eastern parts of these embayments, probably because the water was unfit for life.

CLIMATE OF THE TRIASSIC

During the Triassic, which was a time of widespread aridity in many parts of the world, extensive desert areas developed in North and South America, western Europe, and South Africa. Great deposits of salt and gypsum, associated with the red beds in many different localities, are further evidence of the arid climate. The Triassic rocks of France and Germany are important sources of salt.

The widespread distribution of large amphibians and reptiles in this period is a strong indication that the climate was mild over far greater areas of the earth's surface than it is today. The

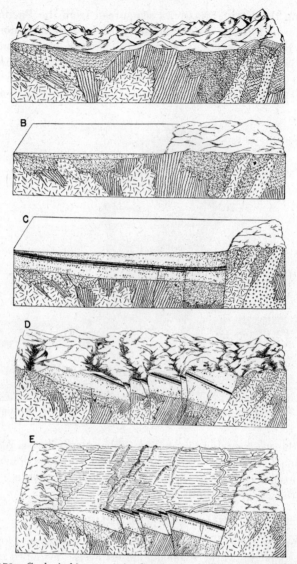

FIG. 176.—Geologic history of the Connecticut Valley and the Palisade Mountains. Modified from sections by Joseph Barrell. *A*. Generalized section across a portion of the Appalachian Mountain chain during Early Triassic time. *B*. The region has been peneplaned and Triassic sedimentation has begun. *C*. Newark sediments and trap sheets have accumulated in a downfaulted trough. Heavy black lines represent sills and lava flows. *D*. During the Late Triassic the Newark group was broken by block faulting and the Palisade Mountains of Early Jurassic time were formed. *E*. The region was peneplaned and resistant traprocks now rise as ridges from the floor of the Connecticut Valley.

environmental conditions under which these Triassic reptiles and amphibians lived were probably similar to those that are necessary for the existence of modern crocodiles, alligators, and giant snakes.

The ferns that flourished in the Upper Triassic of Arizona are related to types that live today in tropical or subtropical regions. Many of the plants that have been found in the Petrified Forest of Arizona lived also in the Triassic of Virginia and North Carolina. This is evidence of relatively uniform climatic conditions throughout the southern part of the United States.

THE PALISADE DISTURBANCE

Several thousand feet of Newark continental sediments and igneous rocks had accumulated in a series of downfaulted troughs

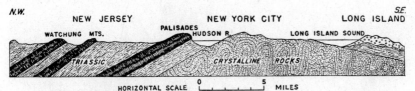

FIG. 177.—Geologic section showing sills (shaded dark) of Triassic traprock. The edge of one sill forms the Palisades of the Hudson. All the Triassic rocks were tilted during the Palisade disturbance. (*After D. W. Johnson, U.S. Geological Survey.*)

that extended along the Atlantic coastal region from North Carolina to Nova Scotia. Late in the Triassic period, these rocks were broken by normal faulting into a number of great earth blocks, which were tilted at various angles to produce block mountains. This orogeny has been called the Palisade disturbance.

Weathering and erosion have since exposed the edges of the sills and flows, and their superior hardness has resulted in the formation of such prominent features as the Palisades of the Hudson (Fig. 177), the Hanging Hills of Meriden, Connecticut, and the Holyoke Range in Massachusetts.

LIFE OF THE TRIASSIC

Land Plants. Scouring rushes and ferns have been found in the Newark shales of Virginia and the Carolinas. These plants grew in swampy places that existed locally within the areas. Forests of conifers, many of giant size, grew in Arizona, where their trunks are preserved in the famous Petrified Forest, near Holbrook.

Algae. Lime-secreting algae were extremely abundant in the Triassic sea that covered southern Europe and the Mediterranean

basin.   These marine plants lived in such vast numbers that they
built up great thicknesses of dolomites in the southern Tyrol.

Marine Invertebrates.   Reef-building types of corals lived
along the western coast of North America, where their remains are
found as far north as Alaska.   The thick deposits of dolomite and
limestone in the Himalayas and the Alps contain great numbers of
corals.   Starfishes and echinoids belonging to modern types had
evolved by this time, but they were not yet common.   Brachiopods
were greatly restricted in genera and species.   Pelecypods and
gastropods were becoming increasingly common.   The first lobsters
appeared in the Triassic; they were all small forms.

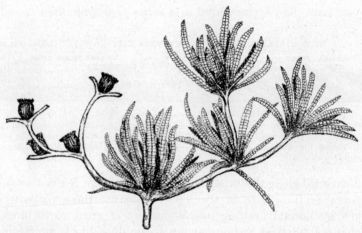

Fig. 178.—*Wielandiella angustifolia.*   A primitive type of flowering plant from the
Triassic of Sweden.   (*After Nathorst.*)

In the seas lived vast numbers of ammonites (Fig. 179)—the
most important and distinctive invertebrates of the time.   Many
of them built beautifully ornamented shells, some of which reached
great size.   This group evolved rapidly during the Triassic, but
declined in a very dramatic manner toward the close of the period,
becoming almost extinct.   Several species of the genus *Phylloceras*
that survived the near-extinction phase repopulated the seas with
ammonites during the Jurassic.   The decline is difficult to explain,
but it may have been caused by the rise of predatory marine
reptiles during the Triassic or by some climatic change that brought
about lower temperatures in the seas.   Certain cephalopods, somewhat like the later Jurassic belemnites (Fig. 193), appeared at this
time.

Vertebrates. Sharks and several types of ganoid fish were quite common, while the ancient crossopterygians had almost

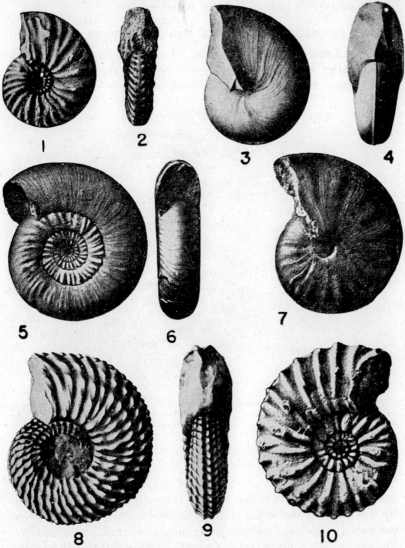

FIG. 179.—Triassic cephalopods. 1, 2, *Ceratites trinodosus;* 3, 4, *Paratropites americanus;* 5, 6, *Columbites spencei;* 7, *Beryichites rottelliformis;* 8, 9, *Trachyceras meeki;* 10, *Nevadites merriami.* (*Courtesy of U.S. Geological Survey.*)

disappeared. The Dipnoi, or true lungfish, lived in the Triassic, and a few teleosts, or bony fish, were present.

The stegocephalians were the largest and most important

amphibians of the time. These large-skulled, heavy-bodied creatures were no match for the more active reptiles, which were increasing rapidly in numbers and varieties.

BEGINNING OF THE AGE OF REPTILES

True Land-living Vertebrates.   The amphibian method of reproduction is very conservative.   Because the eggs are laid in the water, the group has never been able to free itself from the

FIG. 180.—*Desmatosuchus spurensis*, a reptile from the Triassic of Texas.   (*Restoration made under the direction of Dr. E. C. Case from a specimen in the University of Michigan Museum.   Carnegie Institution of Washington, Publication No. 321.*)

gill-breathing larval stage and become completely adapted to the land.

The reptile evolved a new type of egg, which is laid upon the land, and there is no aquatic stage in the early life of the individual. By this method, the reptiles have completely freed themselves from the water.   The animals breathe by means of lungs throughout life. The egg, which is quite large, is covered with a thick shell, and the yolk furnishes food for the embryo until it grows to be essentially a small adult.   The individual is thus able to take care of itself as soon as it is hatched.

The reptiles also lost the special glands that keep the amphibian's skin moist; and there were changes in the limbs, muscles, heart, blood vessels, and other structures, which enabled the group to adapt itself completely to life on the land.

The phytosaurs (Fig. 181) lived in considerable numbers along permanent streams during Triassic times. In appearance and habits these animals were similar to the crocodiles, but they belong to a distinct group. Their jaws were narrow and greatly elongated, and the sharp teeth were fitted for a carnivorous diet. The dorsal surface was covered with large, overlapping bony plates, while the sides and ventral portion of the body were protected by small,

Fig. 181.—The Triassic phytosaur, *Rutiodon.* (*Drawn by John Jesse Hayes.*)

irregular scutes of bone. As the race of phytosaurs was short-lived, they are unknown outside the Triassic. The largest known specimen reached a length of 25 feet. Their fossil remains have been found in Europe, Asia, Africa, and North America.

Triassic Dinosaurs. Well-preserved footprints (Fig. 182) have long been known from the Triassic shales of the Connecticut Valley. Some of these, showing the impressions of three toes, were described by early writers as bird tracks. When a few incomplete skeletons of reptiles were found in the same rocks, the footprints proved to be those of dinosaurs (Gr. *deinos*, terrible + *sauros*, reptile). These animals walked or ran on their hind legs in search of food; then, when they occasionally sat down, impressions of their small front feet and sometimes of their bodies were recorded, and in several cases marks made by the dragging tail are shown. Some of the footprints are so well preserved that they reveal the character of the skin on the bottom of the feet.

Most of the Triassic dinosaurs were comparatively small, although some of them may have reached a length of 15 feet. The largest footprint measures 18 inches long and about 9 inches wide. This was made by a large dinosaur of the genus *Otozoum*. *Anchi-*

Fig. 182.—Dinosaur footprints from the Triassic of the Connecticut Valley. The animal was sitting down, and impressions of the small front feet are shown. The imprints of raindrops are also seen.

saurus (Fig. 183), one of the commonest genera of the Triassic dinosaurs, varied in length from 5 to 8 feet, leaving tracks from 3 to 6 inches long. Triassic dinosaurs have also been found in Europe and in South Africa.

Marine Reptiles. The earliest known marine reptiles are found in the Lower Permian rocks of South Africa and South America. These animals, which had evolved from land forms, are examples of secondary adaptation to aquatic life.

The ichthyosaurs (Gr. *ichthys*, fish + *sauros*, reptile), which looked like some of the sharks or like the modern porpoise, were powerful swimmers. Their teeth indicate a carnivorous diet, which probably consisted largely of fish and cephalopods. Remains of these ichthyosaurs are quite common in the Late Triassic rocks of Oregon and California. The largest specimen from this period was about 25 feet long.

Plesiosaurs (Gr. *plesios*, almost + *sauros*, reptile) have been found in the Triassic of Europe, but later in the Mesozoic they were

Fig. 183.—*Anchisaurus* and *Anomoepus*, Triassic dinosaurs.

widely distributed over the world. The body of the plesiosaur was broad and flattened, the tail short, and the neck long and snake-like.

These two groups of reptiles are more fully discussed in the chapter on the Jurassic period.

Mammal-like Reptiles. The theriodont reptiles, from the Upper Permian and Triassic of South Africa, have great evolutionary significance because they were the probable ancestors of the mammals. *Cynognathus* (Fig. 184) was a very advanced type of reptile, with a skull that was intermediate in type between that of the reptile and that of the mammal. The third eye on top of the head was very small; the dentary was the largest and most important bone in the jaw; there were two occipital condyles; and the teeth were differentiated into incisors, canines, and cheek teeth. Very little is known about the soft anatomy of *Cynognathus,* but it may have been warm-blooded and covered with hair instead of scales. Although this animal is arbitrarily classed as a reptile, it was really a transition form between the reptiles and the mammals.

The causes of this evolutionary advance from reptiles to mammals are unknown, but some of the controlling or contributing factors may have been the diversified and stimulating climate of South Africa during the Permian and the aridity that continued through-

Fig. 184.—A scene in the Karroo region of South Africa in the Triassic period. The animals are mammal-like reptiles. The carnivorous type, shown at the left and right, is *Cynognathus.* These are about to attack the herbivorus form, *Kennemeyeria.* (*Drawn by John Jesse Hayes.*)

out the Triassic. Such environmental conditions must have stimulated the theriodonts to increased bodily activity in order that they might maintain themselves in a rigorous environment where food was scarce.

The vital processes are maintained at a much higher level in the mammals than in the reptiles. The four-chambered heart and the powerful circulatory system maintain an even body temperature. The change from scales to hair gave greater flexibility to the body and helped insulate the animal against temperature changes, while the more complex nervous system made the mammals more responsive to their surroundings and far more adaptable to a wide variety of environmental conditions than was possible in the case of any of the reptiles.

Triassic Reptilian Mammals. The question of whether true mammals existed in the Triassic has been discussed for many years, the meager fossil material consists largely of jaws and teeth. These Triassic animals were probably reptiles, although some of them may have been related to the ancestral stock from which the mammals evolved. The teeth are somewhat mammalian in character and consist of incisors, canines, and molars instead of the more unspecialized teeth that are commonly characteristic of reptiles.

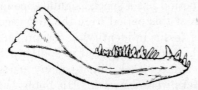

Fig. 185.—Lower jaw of *Dromatherium*, a mammal-like reptile from the Upper Triassic of North Carolina. About twice natural size.

Triassic mammals may have existed somewhere, but they have not been identified with certainty and they could hardly have been common. However, a recent publication of Simpson mentions three Triassic mammals.

Throughout almost the entire Mesozoic era, the mammals were held in check by the vast hordes of reptiles, especially the dinosaurs, but they continued to develop and were somehow able to hold their own against almost overwhelming odds. The superior intelligence of the mammals has always been an important factor in their dramatic history.

Reading References

Daugherty, Lyman, and Howard R. Stanger: The Upper Triassic Flora of Arizona, with a Discussion of its Geological Significance, *Carnegie Inst. Washington Pub.* 526, 107 pp., 1941.

Vokes, H. E.: The Story of a Tree, *Natural History*, Vol. 49, pp. 104–107, February, 1942.

CHAPTER XVI

THE MESOZOIC ERA

THE JURASSIC PERIOD

The Jurassic period has a special significance in geologic history because the rocks of this period were the first used to demonstrate the importance of fossils in identifying certain geologic horizons.

William Smith (1769–1839) lived in southern England, and his work as a civil engineer took him to many parts of the country where Jurassic rocks were exposed. His hobby was fossil hunting. As he collected and classified all sorts of marine invertebrates from different localities, he discovered that certain recognizable layers of rock always produced the same kinds of fossils, even though the outcrops were several miles apart. He also observed that the rocks contained a succession of distinct faunas, instead of just one assemblage. These discoveries by Smith mark the beginning of stratigraphic geology.

The term "Oölite series" was first applied to the Jurassic rocks of England, because many of the limestones are oölitic, but when formations of the same age were found later by von Humboldt and Brongniart in the Jura Mountains, the name "Jurassic" was given to them and has been used ever since.

THE EASTERN REGION OF NORTH AMERICA

As no Jurassic rocks have been recognized anywhere in the eastern part of North America, it is probable that this portion of the continent was undergoing vigorous erosion and that the sediments were carried eastward into the Atlantic. The long history of Appalachia as a prominent land mass came to an end in the Jurassic, when this ancient portion of North America began slowly to subside beneath the waters of the ocean.

The block-fault mountains that were upheaved during the Palisade disturbance and the Appalachian ranges of the Permian period had all been greatly reduced in height by the close of the Jurassic, and large areas of these ancient hills were peneplaned.

THE COLORADO PLATEAU REGION

Jurassic sandstones are responsible for much interesting geology and provide some of the most beautiful scenery in the south-western part of the United States. Northward from the Grand

Fig. 186.—Generalized map of North America in the Jurassic period. Stippled areas show the inferred extent of the seas. Outcrops are in black. White areas are land. (*Modified from Branson and Tarr, Schuchert and Dunbar.*)

Canyon, in southern Utah, there are vast deposits of sandstone that form high, vertical cliffs many miles in extent. The lower forma-tion, called the Wingate (Fig. 171), which is reddish brown in color, forms the Vermilion Cliffs. Above this, the light-gray or white Navajo sandstone is exposed in the White Cliffs. The Navajo is over 1,000 feet thick in southern Utah, increasing to about 3,500 feet in southern Nevada—an indication that the source of the sand was somewhere to the west. These two spectacular formations, which were originally vast dunes of fine-grained quartz sand, are beauti-

Fig. 187.—Jurassic sandstone exposed in Zion National Park, Utah. (*Courtesy of Union Pacific Railroad Company.*)

fully exposed along the walls of Zion Canyon (Fig. 187) in the southeastern part of Utah. The vertical cliffs that form this magnificent canyon rise more than a half mile above the valley floor, along which runs the Virgin River. Cross-bedding is developed on a vast scale in the Navajo sandstone and presents a very striking appearance.

Rainbow Natural Bridge (Fig. 188) in southern Utah has been formed from these Jurassic sandstones. The arch of the bridge, rising 309 feet above the creek bed, has a span of 278 feet.

The thick sandstones of the Vermilion and the White cliffs compose the Glen Canyon group. The absence of fossils in the rocks makes it difficult to determine their exact age.

Fig. 188.—Rainbow Natural Bridge, in southern Utah, is composed of red Jurassic sandstone. (*Photographed by Elzada U. Clover.*)

The San Rafael group in southern Utah is composed of dark-red shales, siltstones, and sandstones, with siliceous limestone and gypsum that reach a thickness of 1,500 feet. Marine fossils are found in at least two horizons within this group, and these represent an interfingering from the northwest of the gray marine shales and sandstones of the Sundance with the rocks of the San Rafael. Some of the red-bed sediments in these two groups came from the Uncompahgre highland of western Colorado, but a great part of the sandstone must have been derived from the high Mesocordilleran geanticline, which lay just west of the Rocky Mountain trough.

The sandstones thicken toward this long, narrow land mass, which became a very prominent feature in the Cretaceous.

THE SUNDANCE SEA AND THE ROCKY MOUNTAIN GEOSYNCLINE

Late in the Jurassic period, a sea spread from the Arctic region of northwestern Canada southward across British Columbia into central Utah and southern Wyoming and eastward to the Black Hills of South Dakota. This was the Sundance sea (Fig. 186), and its deposits are spread widely over the northern part of the Great Plains region, where they make up the Sundance formation. These sediments, which are seldom more than 200 or 300 feet thick, consist largely of shales and sandstones, with a few horizons of calcareous material that contains great numbers of pelecypods, especially oysters, and of cephalopod shells. The water in the Sundance sea was very shallow over large areas, and the conditions of sedimentation were so variable that the deposits change frequently within short distances from shale to pure sandstone.

The present Colorado Plateau region was an arid basin long before the invasion of the Sundance sea; enormous accumulations of wind-blown sand had formed extensive dunes over Utah and Arizona; while meandering rivers from highlands on the west were depositing muds over portions of the basin, especially after heavy rains.

The lagoons at the southern end of the sea were occasionally shut off from the main body of water. During the extremely arid conditions that prevailed, excessive evaporation soon reduced the water in these lagoons to a highly saline condition, and gypsum was precipitated. This material is interbedded with continental sediments. The fluctuating southern shore line of the Sundance sea is shown by occasional interfingering of marine and land-laid deposits.

Jurassic marine sediments are about 6,000 feet thick in the southeastern part of Idaho, largely because this area of deposition was close to the Mesocordilleran geanticline, from which much of the clastic material was derived.

There are numerous outcrops of late Jurassic limestone along a belt extending northwestward through Mexico, in the Malone Mountains of southwestern Texas, and in the southeastern part of New Mexico. The ammonites found in these rocks, closely related to species that occur in the Jurassic of southern and southwestern Europe, indicate a direct water connection between the two continents. The marine water in the southern part of the Rocky

Mountain geosyncline, which is called the "Mexican trough," was never connected with the Sundance sea.

Deep wells drilled in southern Arkansas and neighboring states have penetrated a considerable thickness of Jurassic sediments consisting of dark shales, impure limestones, sandstones, red beds, and about 1,000 feet of salt. This great salt series grades laterally into red beds; below this deposit, beginning at depths of more than 9,000 feet, there are shales and siltstones, which are probably of Jurassic age.

THE MORRISON FORMATION

The arid conditions that had gripped a large part of the southern Cordilleran region during most of the Jurassic were gradually modi-

Fig. 189.—Site of the Marsh Dinosaur Quarry in the Morrison formation, Garden Park, north of Cañon City, Colorado.

fied, following the retreat of the Sundance sea, and a large part of the area became a well-watered lowland, sloping gently north and eastward from some highland area not far to the west and southwest. This is the region over which the Morrison continental formation (Fig. 189) was deposited. The sediments consist of shales, siltstones, sandstones that become arkosic in places, some moderately coarse conglomerate, and a few thin beds of limestone. The character of the material varies rapidly within short distances, and the bedding is often very irregular. The Morrison sediments present a variegated appearance, with shades of red, chocolate, brown, greenish gray, purple, black, and white.

At the time the sediments were being deposited, the area was a swampy plain across which rivers meandered widely, spreading mud and silt over their flood plains during times of high water, while the channels (Fig. 190) were filled with cross-bedded sands

Fig. 190.— A sand-filled erosion channel in the Morrison formation, Garden Park, north of Cañon City, Colorado.

and conglomerate, such as are typical of braided streams. A few lakes, scattered over the region, received the fine, banded clays that are found in several places. The rainfall was sufficient to support a luxuriant vegetation, upon which the huge sauropod dinosaurs subsisted. The climate was probably tropical or sub-tropical, because the great dinosaurs that lived widely over the Morrison area in the rivers and swamps were cold-blooded animals, sensitive to temperatures that approached the freezing point. They must have lived out of doors in a temperature that was mild the year round, because their giant size would have made it impossible for them to find sheltered places in which to pass a cold winter season.

The Morrison originally covered about 100,000 square miles of the Cordilleran region, from Montana southward through Utah and Colorado to the northern part of New Mexico. The thickness of the beds varies from 100 to about 900 feet, but in most places it is less than 400 feet. The fauna includes 69 species of dinosaurs— among them, the spectacular sauropods. In addition, there are a number of primitive mammals, a few species of crocodiles, and a variety of fresh-water clams and gastropods. Twenty-three species of plants have been found in the Morrison sediments, but others were doubtless present, especially the soft varieties upon which the dinosaurs fed.

The age of the Morrison is still in doubt. Some writers place it in the Late Jurassic and others in the Early Cretaceous, but it cannot be strictly correlated with any formation whose exact age is known, because its fauna is not sufficiently like that of any other horizon in the world. The Tendaguru formation in East Africa contains three horizons of continental shale deposits that have yielded the remains of dinosaurs similar to those in the Morrison, and these shales are interbedded with sandstones and conglomerates that have an abundant marine fauna of unquestioned Jurassic age. The Morrison lies directly above the Sundance in a number of places; in several localities it is found below the Washita, which is correlated with the Early Cretaceous.

JURASSIC OF THE PACIFIC BORDER REGION

There are extensive areas of Jurassic rocks exposed in many places along the Pacific Coast of North America, but they present many unsolved problems, which will have to await the results of further research. The Jurassic record in California is quite complete, especially the Mt. Jura section in the northern part of the Sierra Nevada, but even here the geologic history is very difficult to read.

Volcanic Activity. There are great thicknesses of volcanic material in most of the Jurassic sections of California and southwestern Oregon. These igneous rocks are, for the most part, found interbedded with marine sediments. Several volcanic centers have been found where the igneous materials are especially thick and the breccias unusually coarse. One particularly impressive center is located in the Horseshoe Bend Mountains of Mariposa County, California. At this locality there are at least 12,000 feet of flows, tuffs, and extremely coarse breccias, which have been traced for 30 miles to the southwest.

A number of actual volcanic necks and conduits are known, and there is a locality on the Merced River where pillow basalts are piled up to a thickness of 1,400 feet. The volcanic rocks, as well as the sediments, have been folded and metamorphosed. The Mariposa slates in eastern California are interbedded with volcanics. The whole series is about 10,000 feet thick.

The Franciscan Series. The Franciscan is extensively exposed in the Coast Ranges of California, especially in the region of San Francisco, which is the type locality. This series is composed of clastic, chemical, and organic sediments, together with volcanics, all deposited in the shallow water of a subsiding geosyncline that extended along the region of the present Coast Ranges in California and for some distance into Oregon. The rejuvenated land of Cascadia lay to the west of the trough and the ancestral Sierra Nevada on the east. The high land to the west was composed chiefly of igneous and metamorphic rocks, and these furnished most of the Franciscan sediments. The lower part of the section contains coarse, arkosic materials. As the borderland was slowly worn down, the clastics become finer; and toward the upper part of the Franciscan the shales show that Cascadia had been greatly reduced in height.

The Knoxville Series. The Franciscan grades into the overlying Knoxville, which is composed chiefly of shales, with lenses of limestone and sandstone. The two series are at least 25,000 feet thick. Some of the Knoxville was probably deposited in broad, shallow, coastal lagoons and swamps, where the water was brackish or where continental conditions prevailed.

The enormous thickness of the Franciscan and Knoxville clastics shows that the great Nevadian orogeny was in progress and that this disturbance was probably responsible for the geosyncline in which the Upper Jurassic and Cretaceous sediments of California and southwestern Oregon were deposited.

Jurassic rocks of sedimentary and igneous origin are especially well exposed in the southern coastal region of Alaska, but the formations have not been thoroughly studied.

MOUNTAIN BUILDING ON THE PACIFIC COAST

The Nevadian Disturbance. The Jurassic and older rocks of the Pacific region were folded and thrust-faulted during an important orogeny that occurred in the late Jurassic, but there are uncertainties as to the areas involved in the orogeny and the exact time of the disturbance. Although some authors believe that a great part of the Cordilleran region, from Mexico to Alaska, was involved in mountain building, the evidence for this is not conclusive. The orogeny certainly affected California, western Nevada, Oregon, Washington, and a part of British Columbia. Great overturned folds were formed in the Sierra Nevada area, together with extensive thrusts, and the rocks were metamorphosed over an extensive region. There were widespread uplifts in the Cordilleran area.

Fig. 191.—The granitic rocks of the Sierra Nevada Mountains were intruded during the Nevadian disturbance. Split Mountain on the right and Mt. Cardinal on the left. (*Courtesy of Spence Air Photos.*)

After this disturbance, the sea never again invaded eastern California and Oregon or the Nevada area. The belt of deformed rocks cannot be traced by continuous exposures into Oregon, because the rocks are covered in many places by Tertiary sediments and volcanic materials.

The youngest beds involved in the Nevadian disturbance belong to the Upper Jurassic. The unmetamorphosed Franciscan rocks lie close to those of the highly metamorphosed Mariposa group in northern California, and in Oregon neither the Franciscan nor the Knoxville rocks have been altered. Along the eastern side of the Sacramento Valley there is a strong angular unconformity between the gently dipping Upper Cretaceous beds and the folded Mariposa.

The Coast Ranges in Oregon and California exhibit Mariposa sediments that were folded and metamorphosed before the Franciscan and the Knoxville were deposited.

Great Batholiths. Intense volcanic activity occurred at times during the Nevadian orogeny, and after the folding and thrusting had largely ceased there were extensive intrusions of granodiorite batholiths (Fig. 191) into the overlying rocks. These enormous masses of igneous rocks do not represent a single uprising of the granitic magma but rather a series and, in places, one batholith may be seen intruding another. Some of the intrusions may have continued into the Lower Cretaceous.

The great gold-bearing quartz veins in the famous Mother Lode region of California, which break through some of the folded Jurassic rocks, must have been formed late in the Nevadian disturbance.

The Diablan Orogeny. The Jurassic period was ended by a comparatively short but intense period of mountain building that affected the entire region of the present Coast Ranges. The effects of this Diablan orogeny were particularly severe in the Diablo Range of California. The evidence for this disturbance is found in many small but widely scattered localities. Much of the original evidence has either been removed by erosion or is now buried beneath the rocks of later periods.

ECONOMIC PRODUCTS OF JURASSIC ROCKS

Coal. Important coal deposits occur in the Jurassic rocks of Siberia, China, India, Hungary, Tasmania, Australia, and Spitzbergen. There are also extensive coal beds of this age along the Arctic coast of Alaska, but these fields are not readily accessible at the present time. Coal of this period is mined on the eastern coast of Greenland, and there is coal in the Jurassic rocks of Antarctica.

Gold. An extensive system of gold-bearing quartz veins was formed in steeply dipping black Jurassic slates along the western side of the Sierra Nevada Mountains. These veins begin in Mariposa County, California, and extend for 112 miles northward, forming the celebrated Mother Lode belt. The gold occurs in the slates and at their contact with dikes of diabase. The gold-bearing quartz was exposed to weathering and erosion during the Tertiary period, and the loosened particles of gold were concentrated in river gravels, where they were finally discovered by the old forty-niners. The total value of gold produced by California up to 1937, from both the veins and the placers, was $1,850,000,000.

CLIMATE OF THE JURASSIC

Arid conditions were widespread in the southern Cordilleran region during much of the Jurassic. The rocks of this age contain great thicknesses of salt in the Gulf Coastal region, indicating severe aridity. Such conditions, however, were not so widespread in this period as they were in the Triassic. Humid climates existed over many parts of the world during the Jurassic, causing abundant growths of vegetation and the formation of extensive coal beds in numerous places. The presence of coal in Greenland, Alaska, Spitzbergen, Siberia, and Antarctica is especially significant, demonstrating the existence of a far milder climate in the polar regions during the Jurassic than is found there at present. However, it must be remembered that coal-forming conditions did not last throughout the entire period.

The near-extinction of the ammonites toward the end of the Triassic period may have been caused by a cooling of the marine waters, which lasted into the Early Jurassic, when we find the geographic range of reef-building corals greatly restricted.

The Jurassic trees that lived within the limits of the present temperate zones show well-developed rings of growth. The insects are commonly dwarfed, as though they were living under adverse conditions of some sort.

Very convincing proof of mild climates in the Late Jurassic is afforded by the distribution of plants and animals. Reef-building corals flourished in high latitudes, and some bioherms have been found 2,000 miles farther north than the present distribution of similar forms. Sponges and bryozoans were very abundant, while great numbers of ammonites ranged from high to low latitudes.

During the Late Jurassic, the great sauropod dinosaurs were widely distributed over the western part of the United States as far north as Montana. They have been found in Mongolia, also. These gigantic reptiles must have lived in a climate that was tropical or subtropical.

LIFE OF THE JURASSIC

Plant Life. Floras of the Middle Jurassic presented a true cosmopolitan aspect. The same species of plants have been found in various parts of North America, including the Arctic regions of Alaska, and in Siberia, Scandinavia, England, Spitzbergen, Japan, and Manchuria.

The scouring rushes were represented by several types, and ferns grew in great abundance. The cycadophytes rose to a dominant position at this time. Some species of these trees had short, bulbous trunks, while others had trunks that were 50 feet high. Long, palm-like leaves grew at the top of the tree. These entirely representative Jurassic cycads were found in many parts of the world, such as Antarctica, Australia, the United States, Greenland, Alaska, and England. Today, similar trees (Fig. 192) grow only in tropical and subtropical climates. The ginkgo, or maidenhair, tree was very common and widely distributed over the world

Fig. 192.—A living cycad in the New York Botanical Garden.

during the Jurassic, although today it is represented by only one species, which is native to Japan and China. These trees sometimes reach a height of 80 feet, with a diameter of 3 feet. While they will grow in Europe and the United States, they must be kept from close competition with the common varieties of trees.

Forests of conifers were numerous at this time in places where moisture was abundant. The angiosperms, or modern types of flowering plants, have not been identified with certainty from Jurassic rocks, although they probably lived in this period, since their remains are so abundant in the Cretaceous.

Marine Invertebrates. Sponges were locally important as reef builders in the Jurassic seas, and several modern types of corals had appeared. Considerable numbers of crinoids have been found at several localities; among these, *Pentacrinus* is especially representative. The small, floating crinoid *Saccocoma* occurs in large

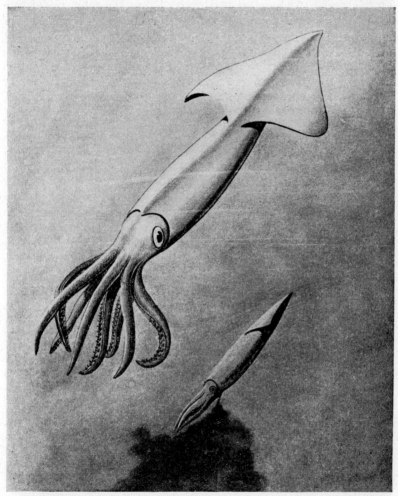

FIG. 193.—Reconstructions of *Belemnites*. One individual is darting backward and ejecting into the water a dark brown ink which serves as a smoke screen. (*Drawn by John Jesse Hayes.*)

numbers in the lithographic limestone near Solenhofen, Bavaria. Sea urchins were common, and the first heart urchins had evolved.

Brachiopods were not conspicuous in the Jurassic seas. Forms with curved hinge lines, like *Goniothyris*, were the most characteristic types. Pelecypods were more abundant than in any previous period.   The irregular, curved shells of *Gryphaea* and *Exogyra* are very conspicuous in places, and true oysters were present.   Gastropods had become numerous, several modern types being in existence at this time.   Ammonites had evolved into the most distinctive invertebrates of the Jurassic.   An astonishing number of genera and species from the rocks of this period have been described, and the group was undoubtedly at its climax.   These marine animals must have presented a very beautiful appearance as they crawled in vast numbers over the sea bottoms and swam in the clear waters. Some of their shells were smooth, while others possessed strong ribs; all had intricate septa.   Some of the ammonite shells reached a diameter of several feet and must have been rather cumbersome structures.   The belemnites (Fig. 193) reached the height of their evolution during the Jurassic.   Some of these squid-like cephalopods (Fig. 194) were over 5 feet long.   A few remarkable fossil specimens from Germany and England have preserved the shape of the body and arms as a film of carbon.   Each of these animals had an ink sac, similar to that of the modern squid, and the fossil pigment has been discovered.

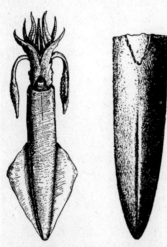

FIG. 194.—Left, *Loligo pealii,* a modern squid (cephalopod), greatly reduced.   The shell is internal.   Right, *Belemnites densus.* A portion of the internal shell of a Jurassic cephalopod related to the squid.   (*Courtesy of The Chicago Apparatus Company.*)

The crustacean group was represented in the Jurassic by many different forms, with lobsters and crab-like animals predominating. Most of the modern orders are represented among the hundreds of insects that have been found in Jurassic rocks.   Such forms as dragonflies, caddis flies, grasshoppers, cockroaches, beetles, and termites were very common.   Highly specialized types, such as the ants, flies, and moths (Fig. 195), were also present.

Vertebrates.   *Fishes and Amphibians.*   Ganoids, sharks, and true bony fishes, or teleosts, were numerous in the Jurassic, while the amphibian group gave rise to the first frogs and toads.

Dinosaurs.   The Mesozoic is called the Age of Reptiles; the dinosaurs ruled the entire world during this era.   The original home of this remarkable group is unknown, but during the Jurassic and Cretaceous periods it was distributed all over the world. Dinosaur remains have been found in the United States, Canada, Brazil, Patagonia, England, Belgium, France, Portugal, Germany, Africa, India, Australia, and Mongolia. No other group of land animals has ever developed more strange and bizarre forms, and no other has evolved so many creatures of such gigantic size and strength. Among the dinosaurs were many weak and inoffensive forms, living in the same region with others that must have been the most terrible animals that ever walked the earth. The dinosaurs as a whole were highly successful, maintaining themselves against all opposition for millions of years; yet, in the end, they failed, for not a single form survived the Mesozoic era. The story of their rise and fall is one of the most dramatic episodes in the history of the earth.

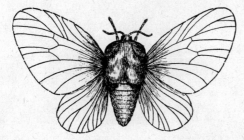

Fig. 195.—The Jurassic moth, *Limacodites mesozoicus*. (*After a restoration by A. Handlirsch.*)

Some of the dinosaurs walked on all fours, while others were bipedal, like the earliest known forms from the Triassic. In a few species the front limbs were so greatly reduced in size that they had become useless. Several varieties were semiaquatic in habit, and others spent most of their lives wading and swimming in the lagoons, swamps, and rivers. There were carnivores and herbivores, while others must have been omnivorous. Dinosaurs varied in length from about 1 foot to over 80 feet and in weight from a few pounds to more than 40 tons.

Stegosaurus (Fig. 196), which was bulkier than an elephant, weighed about 10 tons. His high, arched back supported a double row of great, bony plates that stood on edge and ran from the neck to the tail. Horny nodules embedded in the skin furnished further protection for the animal. These creatures might have defended themselves by lashing out with their powerful tails, which were equipped with long, bony spikes; but they actually lacked adequate protection against the fierce carnivores.

The hind legs of *Stegosaurus* were much longer than the front legs, which suggests that the animal evolved from some bipedal form. The head was small, and the teeth were fitted for eating rather soft vegetation. The brain weighed about 3 ounces; but

Fig. 196.—*Stegosaurus,* a Jurassic dinosaur. (*Courtesy the Sinclair Refining Company.*)

there was a great expansion of the spinal cord over the pelvis, and many of the essential activities of the animal were controlled from this center.

The Giant Dinosaurs. The sauropod dinosaurs, which were the giants of the Mesozoic world, were the largest four-footed animals that ever lived.   These huge reptiles had relatively short bodies, but their necks and tails were extremely long and slender.   The heads were small, containing brains no larger than a man's fist. Although the massive, pillar-like legs were of great size, the articular ends of the bones were weak and cartilaginous.   Some individuals weighed 30 or 40 tons.   They doubtless spent most of their lives in the water, which would sustain at least part of their immense weight.   The position of the nostrils on top of the skull is one indication of aquatic habits.   Most of these animals probably lived in the quiet waters of marshes and bayous along the coasts, where the land was low and the dense, tropical vegetation afforded them plenty of food, as well as considerable protection against their hereditary enemies, the fierce, carnivorous dinosaurs.   Some of them, doubtless, found the great rivers and inland swamps suitable places in which to live.   The coastal plain region of the lower Amazon today would afford an ideal environment for these creatures.

The wide distribution of sauropods over the world raises the question of how they migrated from place to place.   Some might have followed a river system for many miles.   Coastal lagoons sometimes extend for considerable distances and afford easy migration paths.   Others may have waded down to the mouth of a river and then followed the shallow coastal waters until they came to another stream.   This may account for the presence of sauropod remains in certain marine or brackish-water sediments found in East Africa and Madagascar.

As these enormous dinosaurs were plant eaters, the nourishment of such gigantic bodies must have required considerable quantities of nutritious vegetable food.   However, they probably ate much less than we might expect, since their metabolism was low, and their expenditure of energy was not equal to that of more active creatures.   Aquatic plants were loosened by their teeth or claws and swallowed without much chewing.   Some of these swamp-living reptiles had gizzard-like stomachs, which contained stomach stones, or gastroliths, that must have been used to grind up the plant food.   This same digestive habit is observed in certain types of modern birds.   Gastroliths, which received a high polish while inside the alimentary canal, have been found preserved within the body cavities of several dinosaurs.

Some remarkable sauropod remains found in 1934 at the Howe Quarry, not far from Cody, Wyoming, show that the skin was covered with small tubercles, placed close together.   In this same locality a fragment of the actual skin was discovered, revealing a

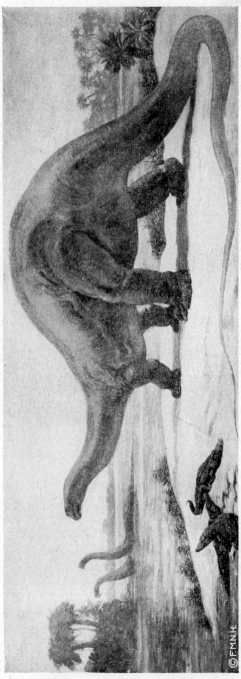

Fig. 197.—*Brontosaurus, a gigantic Jurassic dinosaur. The small animals are crocodiles. (From a painting by Charles R. Knight, courtesy of the Chicago Natural History Museum.)*

structure somewhat like that of a lizard's or a snake's skin after it has been shed.

Some dinosaurs are known to have laid eggs, but the great sauropods may have brought forth their young alive. A few of the skeletons that have been found apparently represent young individuals. It is probable that multiple births occurred. Modern lizards are able to regenerate a tail that has been lost, and the

FIG. 198.—A nocturnal scene in the Jurassic period. The setting is in a Morrison swamp where many different kinds of dinosaurs lived. The great sauropods came into the shallow water and onto the land to feed during the night and they were often caught by predatory carnivores. The *Brontosaurus* (upper right) has slipped and fallen in its haste to get back into the water while in the foreground another *Brontosaurus* has fallen prey to an *Allosaurus*. (*Drawn by John Jesse Hayes.*)

sauropods possessed the same ability. One individual from the Howe Quarry had regenerated not only the soft parts of the tail but 21 vertebrae at the end.

Brontosaurus (Fig. 197), the "thunder lizard," is the best known of the sauropod race. An individual sometimes reached a length of 75 feet. *Diplodocus* was more slender than *Brontosaurus*. The *Diplodocus* skeleton in the Carnegie Museum, at Pittsburgh, is 87 feet long. Of this length, 65 feet are accounted for in the neck and tail alone.

Brachiosaurus was an extremely bulky dinosaur with a comparatively short tail. The front legs were longer than the hind legs, and the neck was so extremely long that the animal could feed on vegetation hanging 40 feet above the ground.

The Flesh Eaters. *Allosaurus* (Fig. 198) was one of the great Jurassic carnivorous dinosaurs. The skeleton mounted in the American Museum of Natural History, in New York City, is 34 feet long. The animal walked on its hind legs, the long tail serving to counterbalance the forward part of the body when the creature was running or bending forward. The jaws, which were loosely

Fig. 199.—*Ichthyosaurus*, a marine reptile. (*Drawn by John Jesse Hayes.*)

fastened, could be opened wide to receive a large chunk of flesh, or even an entire animal, that was to be swallowed. The long, sharp, recurved teeth are an indication of carnivorous habits. The hands and feet were equipped with strong, curved claws.

A new genus of flesh-eating dinosaur, called *Saurophagus*, was recently discovered in the Morrison formation near the town of Kenton, in the northwestern part of Oklahoma. This animal, which stood about 16 feet high, was 42 feet in length. The arms were comparatively long, and the 11-inch claws on the fingers, together with the 6-inch teeth in the jaws, must have been frightful weapons for seizing and tearing. This creature was larger than the

FIG. 200.—Marine reptiles. *Plesiosaurus* on the left and *Ichthyosaurus* on the right. *(From a painting by Charles R. Knight courtesy of the Chicago Natural History Museum.)*

known specimens of *Allosaurus* and only a little smaller than the great *Tyrannosaurus rex* of the Cretaceous.

Reptiles in the Sea. The ichthyosaurs (Fig. 199) reached the peak of their evolution during the Jurassic. These remarkable, shark-like reptiles, which had limbs that had been modified into paddle-like structures, probably never came out of the water. The dorsal fin had no skeletal support, and the lower of the two flukes in the tail was strengthened by the downward-bent backbone.

The young were born alive, and skeletons of embryonic ichthyosaurs have been found within the body of the mother. The margins of the large eyeballs were covered by bony plates, which protected the eyes against water pressure when the animals were diving. The sharp teeth were fitted for seizing prey, which probably consisted largely of fish and the Jurassic forms of squids that are called "belemnites." Two hundred undigested skeletons of these cephalopods were found within the body of an ichthyosaurus.

Some remarkable specimens of these marine reptiles have been found at Solenhofen, Bavaria, with the carbonized skin completely outlining the body. Certain localities have yielded ichthyosaur remains in such abundance that it is believed they were gregarious in habit, like the modern porpoise, and frequented certain places where food was abundant. The Jurassic forms are somewhat smaller than those of the Triassic. These individuals seldom reached a length of 25 feet.

The plesiosaurs (Fig. 200) of the Jurassic and especially those of the Cretaceous were very much like true sea serpents. These animals swam like turtles using their four powerful limbs, which had been modified into paddles that were 5 feet long in some individuals. Gastroliths, found with some plesiosaur skeletons, show that the plesiosaur had a gizzard-like digestive apparatus in which the stones were used to grind or smash up the food. The Jurassic forms were usually not more than 20 feet long but some individuals in the Cretaceous reached a length of over 40 feet.

Great numbers of crocodiles lived in the seas and streams, while marine turtles were numerous.

Flying Reptiles. Great numbers of invertebrates, especially the insects, have learned to fly, but the vertebrates have always been handicapped by their heavy bodies. Within this group, only the birds, the bats, and the flying reptiles, or pterosaurs, have attained true powers of flight (Fig. 201). Very little is known about the ancestry of these extraordinary and highly specialized reptiles, which appeared suddenly in the Upper Triassic rocks of Europe.

The group flourished amazingly for millions of years in many parts of the world and disappeared toward the close of the Cretaceous period.

The pterosaurs (Frontispiece) ranged in size from small forms about as large as sparrows to huge individuals with a wing spread of 22 feet.   The wing membrane, made of thin skin, was stretched from the greatly elongated joints of the fourth finger and attached to the body as far back as the hind legs.   The first three fingers were of ordinary length, each being furnished with a claw, which must have been useful for climbing purposes or for clinging to trees

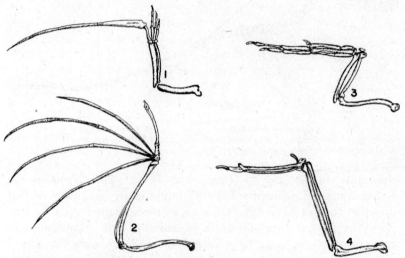

Fig. 201.—Wing structures of flying vertebrates. 1, a flying reptile; 2, the bat, a flying mammal; 3, *Archaeopteryx*, the Jurassic bird; 4, a modern bird.

and the sides of cliffs.   The earliest flying reptiles had teeth, but the later ones were toothless.

The chief long bones in the skeleton were hollow cylinders with walls about as thick as blotting paper.   The bony tissue in the humerus of an undescribed form from the Upper Cretaceous of Texas is about one-fiftieth of an inch thick.   Air circulated through the hollow bones very much as it does in the skeletons of birds, and the pterosaurs were probably warm-blooded.   Birds and bats beat the air vigorously with their wings while flying, but the wing movement in the skeletons of these strange reptiles was so greatly restricted that they probably flew chiefly by gliding.

Rhamphorhynchus (Fig. 202) had a long, slender bony tail, with a vertical, rudder-like expansion on the end, which was useful in

balancing and guiding the animal during flight. Other varieties
had short tails and some of the later forms were tailless.

Although the pterosaurs were constructed chiefly for flight, they
were able to move about to some extent upon the land, but it is

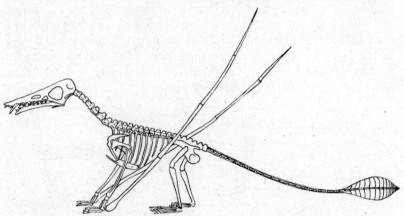

Fig. 202.—Skeleton of the Jurassic flying reptile, *Rhamphorhynchus phyllurus*,
showing the extraordinary length of the fourth finger and the rudder-like expansion
at the end of the tail. (*After Seeley.*)

doubtful whether any of them could swim. Their remains are
found in marine sediments, but they might easily have been carried
down to the sea by rivers and some of them undoubtedly died as
they flew far out over the water in search of fish. Thousands of
broken pterosaur bones have been found in the Cambridge greensand (Cretaceous) of England,
which suggests that the animals
were highly gregarious and lived
in great rookeries.

Fig. 203.—Head of the Jurassic bird,
Archaeopteryx, showing teeth. (*After
Heilmann.*)

The First Birds. While the
pterosaurs were proving highly
successful with their own particular methods of flight, another
group of reptiles was evolving an
equally amazing type of flyer—
the bird. Except for their ability to fly and the peculiar body
covering, called "feathers," the birds are structurally very similar
to certain reptiles. Two good skeletons of Jurassic reptilian birds
have been found in the famous limestone quarries near Solenhofen,
Bavaria. Both specimens show good impressions of feathers on
the wings and tails.

Archaeopteryx (Gr. *archaios*, ancient +*pteron*, wing) (Fig. 203) was about the size of a full-grown crow. The small head was flattened and the eyes were very large. There was no toothless beak, such as modern birds possess, but instead both jaws were set with small, sharp teeth, which indicate carnivorous habits. The long, narrow body was either naked or covered with small, downy feathers that have not been preserved. The short, rounded wings were hardly capable of sustained flight, and the animal was probably more of a glider than a flyer. On each wing there were three functional fingers, each one armed with a claw. The tail was the long, bony, reptilian type, with a row of feathers along each side. The small breastbone is proof that the flying muscles were rather weak. The bones were not hollow. The typical perching feet tend to show that *Archaeopteryx* had evolved from some reptile that

FIG. 204.—*Ctenacodon*, a primitive mammal from the Morrison formation of Wyoming.

lived in the trees. There are reasons for believing that feathers evolved from the scales of reptiles, although no fossils have been found that reveal the steps in this remarkable transformation.

If impressions of the feathers had not been preserved with the skeletons of *Archaeopteryx* and *Archaeornis*, it would be difficult to distinguish these animals from some of the very small dinosaurs. In fact, it is only because of their feathers that these creatures are classed as birds.

Mammals. During the Jurassic period, mammals played a role entirely subordinate to that of reptiles. However, they were slowly evolving and, although their fossil remains are rare, these animals were probably quite abundant in many parts of the world. A few specimens have been found in the Stonesfield slates and the Purbeck beds of England, while the American forms have been found in the Morrison deposits (Fig. 204), especially the famous locality at Como Bluffs, Wyoming. The remains consist mostly of jaws and teeth, with a few skull fragments and some particularly interesting thighbones and bones of the upper arm. The femur from the English Jurassic, which is very primitive, must have had a nearly horizontal position in the skeleton. This would indicate a somewhat sprawling gait like that of the cynodont reptiles. The Stonesfield humerus is also very much like those of the mammal-like reptiles.

The teeth of the Jurassic mammals show considerable evidence of specialization and adaptation to a varied diet. Some of the forms had sharp, pointed teeth, like those of the modern insectivores, while others were equipped with cutting incisors and grinding teeth, suggesting that they were plant eaters. The largest of the Jurassic mammals was about the size of a fox terrier, but most of them were no bigger than rats.

Of the four orders of these primitive mammals that have been found, one, the Pantotheria, has certain characteristics indicating that it may have been ancestral to all the later Eutheria, which includes the marsupials and placentals. Pantotheres have been found in the Jurassic rocks of England, East Africa, and the United States; but they probably were at one time widely distributed over the world.

Nothing is known about the geologic history of the Monotremata, or egg-laying mammals, which are found today only in Australia, New Guinea, and Tasmania. The duck-billed mole (*Ornithorhynchus*) and the spiny anteater (*Tachyglossus*) are the only surviving members of this strange order. These animals reproduce by means of eggs. They still retain a number of reptilian characteristics that have long since disappeared in the higher types of mammals. The Jurassic mammals, which were very primitive forms, are so imperfectly known that it is difficult to compare them with living groups.

THE JURASSIC LAGOONS AT SOLENHOFEN

In the central Bavarian region of southern Germany, along the valley of the Altmühl River, there are a number of quarries that produce a remarkably fine-grained rock called "lithographic limestone." This rock occurs as lenticular masses in the Franconia dolomite and reaches a thickness of about 75 feet. The dolomite contains corals and other reef-building organisms, and the deposits may represent atolls or fringing reefs formed along the shore of the Upper Jurassic sea (Fig. 205). The fine-grained ooze, which later formed the lithographic stone, was probably precipitated by the action of denitrifying bacteria very much as the calcareous muds of the Bahama Islands and the Florida Keys are being formed at present.

A very remarkable fauna of about 450 species of animals has been assembled from the famous quarries near Solenhofen. These include great numbers of floating crinoids, ammonites, jellyfish, horseshoe crabs, 100 kinds of insects, fish, one dinosaur, 29 species

of flying reptiles, crocodiles, turtles, marine reptiles, and the celebrated birds *Archaeopteryx* and *Archaeornis.*

The lithographic stone must have been deposited in shallow
water under very quiet conditions, since the organisms preserved in
the rock are in perfect condition and their remains were not torn
apart before burial.   Apparently, there were no scavengers present,

Fig. 205.—Scene along the shore of a Jurassic lagoon at Solenhofen, Bavaria.
The animals are flying reptiles, birds, and small dinosaurs.   The trees are cycads.
(*From a painting by Charles R. Knight in the Chicago Natural History Museum.*)

and the animals must have been entombed very promptly after they
died.   Otherwise, it is difficult to account for the impressions and
the carbonized films, which show that the soft parts endured for a
considerable period after death.   The numerous trails and tracks
of different animals found in the fine-grained rock were made at
low tide while the mud flats were exposed.

Reading References

Berry, E. W.: The Jurassic Lagoons of Solenhofen, *Sci. Monthly,* vol. 8,
pp. 361–378, October, 1918.

BROWN, BARNUM: Flying Reptiles, *Natural History*, vol. 52, No. 3, pp. 104–111, October, 1943.

CRICKMAY, C. H.: The Jurassic History of North America, *Am. Philos. Soc. Proc.*, vol. 70, pp. 15–102, 1931.

HEILMANN, G.: "The Origin of Birds," 210 pp., D. Appleton-Century, Company, Inc., New York, 1927.

MATTHEW, W. D.: "Dinosaurs," Am. Mus. Nat. Hist., Handbook Series No. 5, 162 pp., 1915.

SEELEY, H. G.: "Dragons of the Air," 239 pp., D. Appleton-Century Company, Inc., New York, 1901.

SIMPSON, G. G.: The Age of the Morrison Formation, *Am. Jour. Sci.*, 5th ser., vol. 12, pp. 198–216, 1926.

CHAPTER XVII

THE MESOZOIC ERA

THE CRETACEOUS PERIOD

The white chalk deposits that appear in such conspicuous cliffs along both sides of the English Channel were originally described as a separate unit, to which the name "Cretaceous" (Lat. *creta*, chalk) was given, and this term is now applied to a great geologic system including many different kinds of rocks that have a wide distribution over the earth's surface. During the entire course of geologic time, the continents have probably never been invaded more widely by epeiric seas than they were in the Cretaceous.

EPEIRIC SEAS IN NORTH AMERICA

The rocks of this period in North America can be separated into a lower and an upper division, which some geologists believe should be considered as separate periods—the lower one called the "Comanchean" and the upper one, the "Cretaceous." Such a division into two systems has not been commonly accepted, largely because it is difficult to find a line of separation between the two that can be recognized everywhere. The retreat of the marine water at the end of Lower Cretaceous time was widespread, but it was apparently only a great oscillation, such as might characterize any large epeiric sea. The most extensive marine invasion came in the upper part of the period, when about half of North America was submerged.

The Lower Cretaceous Seas. At the beginning of the period, marine waters spread slowly northward across eastern Mexico and Texas, where they remained until near the close of the Lower Cretaceous, or Washita time, when there was a temporary advance of the sea that reached across eastern Colorado and Kansas into Iowa, Nebraska, and Montana. The waters over the northern part of this area were very shallow, and the deposits are largely nonmarine.

While the sea lay over the Texas region, another marine invasion spread southward from the Arctic along the Rocky Mountain geosyncline. These northern and southern embayments did not meet in Early Cretaceous time, and the invasions were followed by a general retreat of the seas. It is this break in sedimentation between the lower and upper parts of the period that is regarded by some geologists as sufficient reason for dividing the Cretaceous into two systems.

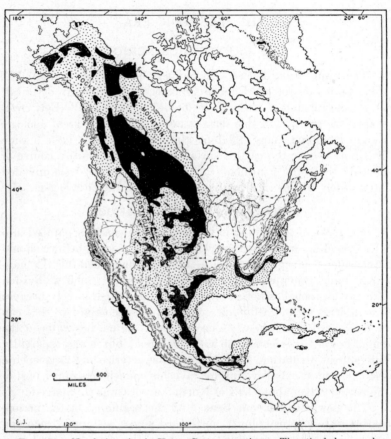

FIG. 206.—North America in Upper Cretaceous time. The stippled areas show the inferred maximum extent of the seas. Outcrops are in black. White areas are land. (*Modified from Branson and Tarr, Schuchert and Dunbar.*)

The Great Upper Cretaceous Sea. Early in the upper part of the period, the seas once more invaded the trough from the northern and southern ends, finally joining to form a great body of marine water that stretched from the Arctic to the Gulf of Mexico and was almost 1,000 miles wide over the northern and central parts of the United States. This great sea had disappeared from the northern end of the trough by the middle of the Upper Cretaceous, and the final retreat was toward the south.

Seas of the Atlantic and Gulf Coastal Regions. The submergence of the Coastal Plain region from New Jersey southward to the Gulf during Upper Cretaceous times is a particularly significant event, because it marks the first time that marine waters were able to invade the continent of North America broadly from the east. This invasion was made possible because the old Land of Appalachia, which had long stood as a barrier against such advances, finally disappeared beneath the waters of the Atlantic. The submergence of the southern borderland of Llanoria, in Upper Cretaceous times, marks the disappearance of this once prominent land and the beginning of the Gulf of Mexico.

DEPOSITS OF THE ATLANTIC COASTAL REGION OF NORTH AMERICA

Lower Cretaceous rocks that form the Potomac group are exposed in a narrow belt along the Atlantic Coastal Plain from New Jersey to Georgia.

The Patuxent Formation. The sediments are entirely non-marine and the basal deposit, called the "Patuxent" formation, consists largely of sands and gravels, which are extensively cross-bedded and largely arkosic, with the rock particles angular or sub-angular. Interbedded lenses and layers of clay are commonly white in color, but may be variegated with shades of red, maroon, brown, yellow, and lavender. In a few places the clays are black or drab colored and contain beds of lignite. Plant remains are locally abundant, and stumps have been found still standing in their original positions. This lignitic material probably marks the former positions of local swamps. The variable nature of the Patuxent sediment and the cross-bedding indicate that this formation was deposited by streams that followed meandering courses across the low coastal plain. Some of the finer sediments probably accumulated in estuaries where the water was very quiet.

The Arundel Formation. Resting unconformably upon the Patuxent, the Arundel formation consists largely of drab-colored clays with some lignite, indicating old swamps, and small accumulations of iron ore, which has been mined on a small scale since colonial times. The clays have been used extensively in the manufacture of brick and pottery. The Arundel fauna includes turtles, crocodiles, and a variety of dinosaurs.

The Patapsco Formation. The deposits of the Patapsco formation consist of sands and variegated clays, which are colored various shades of red and chocolate brown. The sands occur as lenses and beds, and the lithologic character of the deposits varies greatly from place to place. There is always an unconformity at the base of the Patapsco. The Lower Cretaceous formations of the Atlantic Coastal Plain area reach their maximum thickness of about 700 feet in Maryland. Lower Cretaceous rocks (Fredericksburg) have been reached by deep drilling in southern Florida.

Upper Cretaceous formations are found along the western side of the Coastal Plain from New Jersey to Georgia. The two lower divisions, Raritan and Magothy, are chiefly fluviatile and estuarine deposits consisting mostly of unconsolidated sands, gravels, and clays, which grade into each other rapidly both vertically and horizontally.

The Matawan and Monmouth Formations. The overlying Matawan and Monmouth formations are the earliest known marine deposits that were made by a sea that invaded the North American continent from the east across the former site of old Appalachia Land. The two formations, which are very sandy throughout, are separated by a disconformity. Both the Matawan and the Monmouth contain a great deal of glauconite, which is the hydrous silicate of iron and potash. This material, commonly called "greensand," is a valuable commercial fertilizer. The most important deposits are found in New Jersey and Virginia.

The entire Cretaceous section along the Atlantic and Gulf coastal regions is comparatively thin, partly because the eastern portion of North America was a lowland at this time and could not furnish any great quantity of material for either continental or marine beds. The deposits are known to thicken greatly in a seaward direction. Deep wells have penetrated several thousand feet of Lower and Upper Cretaceous strata in the state of Florida, which was almost completely submerged during this period.

DEPOSITS OF THE EASTERN GULF REGION OF NORTH AMERICA

Upper Cretaceous formations are widely exposed around the Gulf coastal region and in the Gulf embayment, which extended up the Mississippi Valley to southern Illinois.

The Tuscaloosa Formation. The basal deposit over the eastern part of this region is the nonmarine Tuscaloosa formation, which consists of mottled clays and interstratified micaceous sands, irregularly bedded and colored purple, white, and yellowish. There are local beds of lignite, which show where swamps formerly stood.

The Eutaw Beds. Resting conformably upon the Tuscaloosa, the Eutaw beds are composed mostly of sands, with some lenses of clay. This shallow-water deposit, chiefly of marine origin, shows the progressive advance of the sea across the area.

The Selma, Ripley, and McNary Formations. Argillaceous limestones, commonly called the "Selma chalk," were deposited above the Eutaw in western Alabama and the eastern part of Mississippi. The Selma changes into sandy, marine shale and calcareous sand, called the "Ripley," when traced into western Tennessee and through the eastern part of Alabama into Georgia. The Ripley, which becomes increasingly sandy toward the west and north, finally grades into the McNary sandstone, which extends through western Tennessee and Kentucky to the northern end of the Gulf embayment in southern Illinois.

The McNary, Ripley, and Selma formations are contemporaneous deposits that were laid down in shallow water during Upper Cretaceous times. While chalk was accumulating to a maximum depth of 1,000 feet over portions of Alabama and Mississippi, where the water was clear, clays and sands were being deposited in other places.

DEPOSITS OF THE WESTERN INTERIOR REGION OF NORTH AMERICA

Lower Cretaceous Rocks. *The Comanche Series.* Early Cretaceous rocks were deposited during the pulsating advance of the sea northward across Mexico and Texas into the Rocky Mountain geosyncline. An unusually complete marine record of this epoch is shown in the 4,000 feet of very fossiliferous limestones that are exposed in Mexico and the 1,500 feet that occur in southern Texas. Toward the shore in eastern Texas and Arkansas these calcareous sediments are replaced by thin-bedded limestones, shales, and sandstones.

There were lowlands around the northern end of the early Cretaceous sea as it advanced across Kansas into Iowa, and the deposits over this area (Fig. 207) gradually thin out by overlap upon the old land surface. The sediments are largely sandstones and shales that were laid down in part by rivers upon a low coastal plain.

In the southeastern part of Arizona, near the famous mining town of Bisbee, Lower Cretaceous rocks are nearly 5,000 feet thick. They consist of limestones, shales, sandstones, and conglomerates. A great part of this material was derived from highlands of the Mesocordilleran region that lay to the west.

In Canada. Important deposits of Lower Cretaceous sediments were made in the Rocky Mountain geosyncline of Canada by a sea that advanced southward from the Arctic. The Kootenai and Blairmore deposits of Lower Cretaceous age, in southern Alberta, which are chiefly of fresh-water origin, contain important coal beds.

Upper Cretaceous Rocks. Vast areas over the western interior region of North America from the Gulf of Mexico to the Arctic Ocean are covered by Upper Cretaceous rocks. The widest part of this great belt is in the United States, extending from Iowa and Minnesota to Utah and Idaho. At the time of its greatest extent

Fig. 207.—Cretaceous shale and sandstone exposed near Florence, Colorado.

this epeiric sea, which is comparable to the great Richmond sea of Upper Ordovician times, probably covered more than 50 per cent of North America.

Conditions of sedimentation were highly variable at times during the Upper Cretaceous, especially along the western side of the Rocky Mountain trough, which lay east of the Mesocordilleran geanticline. This old land was subjected to occasional periods of uplift followed by greatly accelerated weathering and erosion in the highlands. This resulted in the building of extensive piedmont and alluvial-plain deposits, while the great rivers built their deltas eastward into the sea. During this time, the western shore line of the sea that covered the trough moved slowly and intermittently eastward and wider areas of newly formed swampy coastal plain became the site of continental sedimentation, including fine and coarse sediments, while shales and limestones continued to form in the marine waters. At other times, when the Mesocordilleran region stood at a lower level and less sediment was accumulating over the alluvial plain and in the sea, or when there was a comparatively rapid subsidence of the coastal region, the shore line might shift westward. This produced an interfingering of marine beds with continental sediments from the west and has greatly complicated the stratigraphy of Upper Cretaceous rocks in the Western Interior region of North America, which has led to the use

Fig. 208.—Clay and sandstone of the Dakota group in Ellsworth County, Kansas. (*Photographed by Oren Bingham, Kansas Geological Survey.*)

of many local names for the formations. Totally different types of deposits in near-by areas may be contemporaneous, but it is often difficult or impossible to prove their exact relationships.

Four major groups of rocks are recognized in the Upper Cretaceous deposits of the Western Interior region.

The Dakota Group. The earliest sediments of Upper Cretaceous age that were spread widely over the Western Interior region make up the Dakota group (Fig. 208). The hard, dark-brown, resistant Dakota sandstone outcrops in several places along the eastern front of the Rocky Mountains in Colorado and Wyoming, where the inclined beds form a chain of very prominent hogbacks (Fig. 209). This sandstone is an important water-bearing material in parts of the Great Plains, but this condition is not general throughout the region because the aquifer is interrupted by impervious rocks in so

many places.   The presence of salt in a number of localities makes
it impossible to use the water for drinking purposes.   In the Great
Plains region the Dakota group consists mostly of shale or clay and
silt.

Marine and brackish water fossils, found in certain portions of
the Dakota group, show that the beds are of marine origin, while
great numbers of land plants and well-developed cross-bedding
indicate that other parts were deposited under continental condi-

Fig. 209.—The Dakota hogback west of Cañon City, Colorado, looking south.
(Photographed by Mitchell and Egbers.)

tions.   Some of the sediments in the Dakota group (Fig. 210) were
deposited by rivers that ran across the floor of the Rocky Mountain
geosyncline before the Late Cretaceous sea advanced over the
region and the nonmarine materials that had accumulated upon the
floor of the trough were partly reworked by the waves and currents
of the invading marine waters.   Stream-channel fillings are found
in several places, and the finer sands and silts were deposited in the
back waters upon flood plains.   Some of the sand was doubtless
drifted by the wind; in places it represents old bars and beach
deposits.   The Dakota, which is a rather poorly defined group of
sediments, is not of the same age everywhere.

The Colorado Group.   The lower member of the Colorado group (Fig. 211) is a dark-gray marine shale, very uniform in character, called the "Benton," that is widespread throughout the Western

Fig. 210.—Concretions that have weathered out of the Dakota sandstone. Rock City, Ottawa County, Kansas. (*Photographed by Oren Bingham, Kansas Geological Survey.*)

Fig. 211.—Benton and Niobrara rocks of the Colorado Group at Wolcott, Colorado. (*Photographed by T. S. Lovering, U.S. Geological Survey.*)

Interior region.   Toward the middle of the section, in the Great Plains area, there is the thin-bedded Greenhorn limestone, which contains large numbers of the pelecypod *Inoceramus.*

The upper part of the Colorado group consists of soft, argillaceous limestone and chalky shale, called the "Niobrara chalk" (Fig. 212).   Along the eastern side of the Front Range in Colorado and of the Laramie Range in Wyoming, there is a particular horizon in the Niobrara that is characterized by enormous numbers of

Fɪɢ. 212.—Castle Rock, Gove County, Kansas.   Composed of Niobrara chalk.
(Photographed by Oren Bingham, Kansas Geological Survey.)

Ostrea congesta.   The chalk in western Kansas is famous because it has yielded the remains of the giant diving bird *Hesperornis*, huge marine fishes and reptiles, and the great flying reptile *Pteranodon.*

The Montana Group.   The Pierre is the lower member of the Montana group in the Great Plains region.   This rock is very fine-grained, dark-colored marine shale, which is commonly about

2,000 feet thick but in places reaches the great thickness of nearly 10,000 feet.   The Persistent Fox Hills marine sandstone rests upon the Pierre, forming the upper member of the Montana group.   Certain continental deposits of Montana age accumulated upon the swampy coastal plain to the west.   These sediments contain beds of coal and the remains of dinosaurs.

The Laramie Group.   As the sea gradually retreated from the Rocky Mountain geosyncline in Upper Cretaceous times, river systems were once more established over the trough area, and these streams deposited several thousand feet of nonmarine sediments that are included in the Laramie group.

These deposits are very thick in the Laramie and Big Horn basins of Wyoming and in the Denver basin of Colorado, but they thin out eastward toward the Dakotas.   There is a great accumulation of Laramie sediments over the Great Plains region of Alberta. The exact age of the group has long been a matter of controversy. The beds contain an abundance of land plants and many dinosaur bones but no marine fossils.   All the dinosaurs are Cretaceous types, and a recent careful study shows clearly that 90 per cent of the plant species are Upper Cretaceous forms.   The evidence, therefore, indicates that the Laramie belongs to the latest Mesozoic and not the early Cenozoic.

DEPOSITS OF THE PACIFIC BORDER REGION OF NORTH AMERICA

Lofty mountains had been formed along the Pacific Coast of North America, as a result of the Nevadian disturbance in the Late Jurassic, and thick deposits of marine Cretaceous sediments, derived largely from the newly elevated highlands, were deposited in a series of inland basins that stretched from Alaska to Southern California.   Some of the basins, connected by straits with the open ocean to the west, were broken up by islands or projecting headlands.   These areas of deposition originated at the time of the Nevadian orogeny and several of them persisted into the Tertiary. The Great Valley of California, one of these troughs, still continues as an important area of deposition and subsidence.

The sediments consist of arkose sandstones, conglomerates, sandy shales, and a few thin beds of impure limestone.   There was comparatively little volcanic activity.   The sediments show great lateral variations in lithology within short distances, indicating highly variable and shifting conditions of deposition in the different basins.   Correlation of the various units is difficult because fossils are often absent or very scarce.   The Cretaceous throughout the

Coast Ranges may be divided into two units with a definite physical break between them, and in several places three divisions are recognizable.   The total thickness of the Cretaceous rocks is over 50,000 feet.   The Shastan series, of Lower Cretaceous age, is more than 20,000 feet thick in the northern Coast Ranges.   Farther north, Late Cretaceous rocks reach a thickness of 5,000 feet on Vancouver Island, and 11,000 feet in the Queen Charlotte Islands.

THE CRETACEOUS OF EUROPE

For a distance of many miles, chalk (Fig. 213) belonging to the Upper Cretaceous stands exposed along the English Channel,

Fig. 213.—Cretaceous chalk exposed along the eastern coast of England at Selwick's Bay, Flamborough, Yorkshire.   (*Photographed by Geological Survey of Great Britain.*)

both in France and in England.   The deposit is regularly bedded, and some of it is composed largely of Foraminifera.   At certain horizons these chalk beds contain many flint nodules, which were mined extensively by men during the Old Stone Age and used for making weapons and implements.   It is a remarkable fact that most of the chalk found in the geologic column was deposited during this period.

Much of the sand that is found in The Sahara of northern Africa has been derived from the weathering of Cretaceous sandstones.

THE LARAMIDE REVOLUTION

The Mesozoic Era was brought to a close by vast mountain-making upheavals that affected great areas of the earth's surface. The sediments in the Rocky Mountain geosyncline were subjected to tremendous compressive stresses from the west that folded and faulted the rocks in the trough into a great system of mountains extending a distance of 3,000 miles from Mexico to Alaska and reaching a maximum width of about 500 miles in the United States.

Fig. 214.—Little Chief Mountain in Glacier National Park, Montana. Big Chief and Little Chief Mountains are outliers of the great Lewis thrust sheet. (*Photographed by Hileman. Courtesy of the Great Northern Railway.*)

When such vast areas containing many different kinds of rocks that vary greatly in thickness and strength are subjected to orogenic forces that are themselves highly variable, many diverse structural features will be produced in different parts of the disturbed region. This is true of the mountains that were formed during the Laramide revolution.

The Northern Rockies.   There was thrust faulting on a tremendous scale in the Rocky Mountains from Montana and Idaho southward into Utah.

Proterozoic rocks in Glacier National Park, Montana, were pushed eastward many miles along the flat Lewis thrust plane and brought to rest upon rocks of Cretaceous and Paleocene (Fort

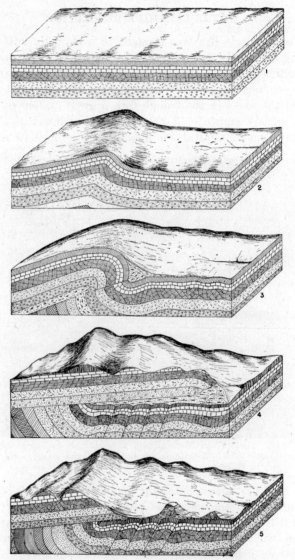

Fig. 215.—How Big Chief and Little Chief Mountains were formed. 1. Sediments were first deposited in a geosyncline that covered much of the present Rocky Mountain region. 2. Compressive forces from the west folded these sediments during the Laramide revolution. The fold overturned toward the east. 3. The fold developed into a thrust fault with displacement toward the east. 4. The thrust reached its maximum extent and Pre-Cambrian rocks then rested upon those of Cretaceous age. 5. Erosion removed most of the overthrust mass leaving two remnants or outliers that are now called Big Chief and Little Chief Mountains.

Union) age. Big Chief and Little Chief Mountains (Fig. 214) are prominent outliers from this great thrust sheet (Fig. 215). The Lewis fault line may be traced for 4 miles along the north wall of Lower Swiftcurrent Canyon in Glacier Park.

The Heart Mountain overthrust lies several miles east of Yellowstone National Park, in the northwestern part of Wyoming. Here Paleozoic rocks of the Absaroka Range, which were thrust eastward at least 25 miles, now overlie Cretaceous and Eocene formations. Some of the isolated peaks in the Big Horn Basin of Wyoming have beds of Mississippian (Madison) limestone resting upon Eocene (Wasatch) rocks as a result of this great movement.

The Bannock thrust has been traced from the Snake River Plains in southeastern Idaho southward more than 200 miles into Utah. Erosion has cut deeply into the thrust sheets, forming Fenster (German for windows), which expose the overridden rocks below.

The Southern Rockies. Broad arched structures, formed in the Southern Rockies, may still be recognized in the Front Range of Wyoming and Colorado, as well as in the Park and Sawatch ranges farther west. Broad synclinal areas, which originated at the same time between the ranges, are represented today by such open areas as North, Middle, and South Parks (Figs. 239 and 240) in Colorado and the great San Luis Valley, which lies west of the Sangre de Cristo Range. These synclines became receiving basins for enormous quantities of continental sediments that were washed down from the near-by mountains, especially during the early part of the Tertiary.

The Big Horn Mountains of Wyoming and the Black Hills farther east, in Wyoming and South Dakota, were formed during the Laramide revolution. Erosion has clearly revealed their enormous dome-like structures.

Igneous Activity. There was much volcanic activity throughout the West during the Laramide revolution, and igneous materials are common in many places. The Boulder batholith in southwestern Montana—a great mass of granitic rock more than 100 miles long and 75 miles wide—was intruded at this time. The copper deposits of the famous Butte mining district are associated with this intrusion. The Idaho batholith, in the west central part of the state, covers an area of about 16,000 square miles.

Thin layers of bentonite are found interbedded with Upper Cretaceous chalk and shale formations in many parts of the Western Interior region, and some of the ash beds cover many hundreds of square miles. Such deposits are very valuable for correlation purposes, because all parts of each layer were deposited at essentially the same time. Thick accumulations of volcanic ash occur in the Upper Cretaceous rocks through Wyoming, Montana, and Colorado.

The Age of the Laramide Orogeny. The widespread orogenic movements that produced the first generation of Rocky Mountains did not begin at the same time in all parts of the Cordilleran region. In some places upheavals started even before the Cretaceous sea had retreated from the land, and islands were formed in a number of localities. Coarse, detrital sediments derived from these local *land* areas accumulated in the near-by sea; and in other places, from which the marine waters had withdrawn, deposition of Late Cretaceous materials continued in basins between the rising ranges.

Long after the mountain-building forces of the Laramide revolution had reached their climax, movements still continued along some of the larger thrust *planes* and did not stop until after the Oligocene epoch of the Tertiary.

The Andes Mountains. During the Paleozoic and Mesozoic eras, the great Andean geosyncline lay along the western side of South America and received several thousand feet of sediment derived from a highland area to the west. These sediments were upheaved in the latter part of the Cretaceous period into a chain of mountains that extended for nearly 5,000 miles from one end of the continent to the other.

CRETACEOUS MINERAL DEPOSITS

Coal. As the Upper Cretaceous sea slowly retreated from the Western Interior region of North America, vast lowland areas became fresh-water swamps in which widespread coal beds were formed over about 100,000 square miles in the Rocky Mountain region. These coal deposits accumulated in the Late Cretaceous and in the Early Cenozoic (Fort Union). The reserves are estimated at about 900,000,000,000 tons. The coal over the Great Plains region, where the rocks are undisturbed, is lignite or sub-bituminous, but in the mountains, where the formations have been subjected to great compression, the coal is of a much higher grade and ranges from bituminous to anthracite.

Petroleum. Cretaceous rocks have produced immense quantities of oil in a number of localities. Production in the famous east Texas and Mexican fields, as well as in the great Salt Creek field of Wyoming, comes from formations of this period.

Metals. The intense igneous activity that accompanied the Laramide revolution was indirectly responsible for the deposition of many valuable metal deposits in the Rocky Mountain region. The most famous of these is the copper deposit at Butte, Montana; but this district also produces gold, silver, lead, and zinc.

CRETACEOUS CLIMATES

Several lines of evidence show that the climatic conditions during most of the Cretaceous period were mild and uniform, even in the high latitudes. The existence of breadfruit, cinnamon, laurel, and fig trees on the western coast of Greenland during this period indicates a milder climate than prevails there at present, but it was not necessarily tropical or even subtropical. It is possible that these trees had adapted themselves to temperate conditions in the Cretaceous, even though their modern relatives live only within the mild temperate or subtropical regions. Some warm oceanic current may have greatly modified the area where the trees were growing, while colder conditions prevailed in other lands of the same latitude. However, it is certain that Greenland was not covered by a great ice sheet at this time.

Huge dinosaurs lived in Mongolia and in Alberta, Canada, during the Cretaceous, although such animals could not live in those regions today.

The uplift in the western part of North America that accompanied the Nevadian disturbance caused a lowering of the annual temperature within the disturbed area, and the climate of the early Cretaceous was probably somewhat diversified in the western part of our continent. When marine waters spread widely over the western portion of North America in the latter half of the period, there was probably a return to the more equable oceanic type of climate.

Glaciers that formed over the high plateau region of eastern Australia during a part of Early Cretaceous time flowed westward to the interior sea, where icebergs floated away and carried glaciated stones and even large boulders, which were dropped as the ice melted. The stones were then buried in the accumulating marine sediment. Some of these erratics, 6 feet in diameter, have been found scattered through outcrops for a distance of about 600 miles.

The Laramide revolution resulted in widespread uplifts over the western part of North America, and this undoubtedly caused a much cooler climate within the disturbed regions.

LIFE OF THE CRETACEOUS

Angiosperms. The angiosperms, or modern types of flowering plants, appeared in great abundance during the Lower Cretaceous. Very little is known about the evolutionary history of this remarkable flora, but it must extend far back into the Jurassic period.

FIG. 216.—Cretaceous leaves. 1, *Magnolia elliptica;* 2, *Quercus primordialis;* 3, *Laurus nebrascensis;* 4, *Ficus laurophylla;* 5, *Sassafras cretaceum;* 6, *Populites cyclophylla.* *(After Lesquereux and Newberry.)*

Forests of the Middle Cretaceous contained such familiar types of trees (Fig. 216) as maple, oak, birch, walnut, poplar, beech, fig, sassafras, ebony, magnolia, plane, and breadfruit. Many varieties of evergreens were also present, although they were now reduced to a secondary position. The sequoias, which are found today only in a few areas along the Pacific Coast, grew in a great many places throughout the northern hemisphere during the Cretaceous.

A great variety of shrubs that bore seeds and fruit appeared at this time, as well as grasses, cereals, and many of the modern types of vegetables. The appearance of the angiosperms was an event of the greatest evolutionary significance, for both the plant and the animal world. Not only are the flowering plants the dominant forms in the flora today, but they have furnished most of the food eaten by the vast hordes of mammals that have lived in all parts of the world since the Cenozoic era began. It seems highly probable that the presence of this inexhaustible food supply has had an important controlling influence upon the development and spread of mammalian life since the Cretaceous period.

The angiosperms have been able to adapt themselves to a wide range of environmental conditions, from moist lowlands to dry and arid uplands, with many aquatic forms living in both fresh and salt water. Plants of this group grow luxuriantly throughout the tropics and some hardy varieties live in the Arctic.

One reason for the great success of the angiosperms is their habit of forming seeds rapidly and in enormous numbers. When the seeds are ripe and after the leaves have fallen, the plants enjoy a resting stage, which is an adaptation either to a recurring dry season or the periodic cold of winter. This very common habit suggests that angiosperms may have originated in some highland areas, where seasonal changes doubtless occurred; but the record of this great evolutionary advance is lost because such elevated regions were subjected to erosion and any fossil record that might originally have been preserved has since been destroyed. By the Cretaceous period, according to this theory, these plants had reached lowland areas, where sediments were accumulating, and since that time fossil remains of angiosperms have been common.

The first appearance of modern types of plants in the eastern part of North America is recorded in the lower Cretaceous (Arundel formation) of Maryland. The Dakota sandstone has preserved a remarkable record of about 500 species of angiosperms.

Invertebrates. Foraminifera increased greatly in numbers and varieties during the Cretaceous, and their remains are common in some of the chalk beds and other calcareous formations. Siliceous and calcareous sponges occur in the chalk deposits of England, but they are not commonly found in the Cretaceous rocks of the United States. Corals, which were locally abundant in Europe, were rare in this country.

Brachiopods were not very common during this period, and their shells are numerous only in restricted localities. Pelecypods were

Fig. 217.—Characteristic and abundant Cretaceous pelecypods. *Right*, *Ostrea congesta* from the Niobrara limestone; *left*, *Inoceramus labiatus* from the Greenhorn limestone. (*Courtesy of U.S. Geological Survey.*)

Fig. 218.—Cretaceous pelecypods. 1, *Exogyra ponderosa;* 2, *Exogyra costata.* (*Courtesy of U.S. Geological Survey.*)

very abundant. Certain forms, such as oysters (Fig. 217) and the related genera *Gryphaea* and *Exogyra* (Fig. 218) lived in great numbers. Bioherms were built in the Cretaceous seas by bizarre

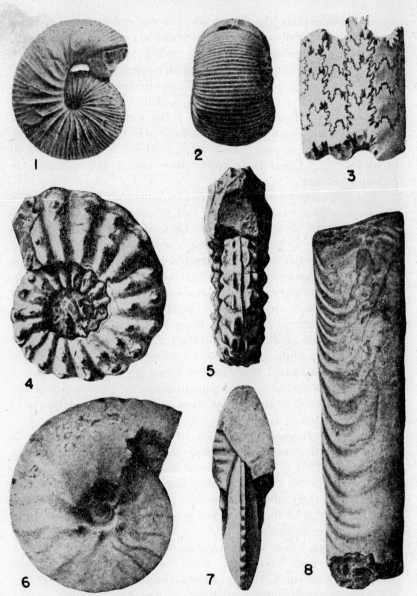

FIG. 219.—Cretaceous cephalopods. 1, 2, *Scaphites ventricosus;* 3, *Baculites ovatus,* showing complex sutures; 4, 5, *Mortoniceras shoshonense;* 6, 7, *Placenticeras planum;* 8, *Baculites ovatus,* showing exterior of shell. (*Courtesy of U.S. Geological Survey.*)

forms of pelecypods like *Chama* and the rudistids. Some of these shells assumed conical shapes that strikingly resemble cup corals. Mound-shaped bioherms, commonly called "tepee buttes," which are found in the Pierre shale of Colorado, contain enormous numbers of the small pelecypod, *Lucina*. These bioherms average about 15 feet in diameter and consist of a roughly circular core of limestone entirely surrounded by shale. For some unknown reason, clams and other marine organisms were able to live upon a very restricted area of the sea bottom while mud was being deposited all around them. Gastropods were quite varied and common in certain localities.

The echinoderms are represented by numerous heart urchins in the Lower Cretaceous of Texas; and great numbers of the free-floating crinoid, *Uintacrinus*, have been collected in the Niobrara of Kansas.

Crabs were particularly characteristic representatives of the crustaceans. Ammonites (Fig. 219) still flourished in the Cretaceous seas, although the group was on the decline. The shells of these cephalopods are frequently highly ornamented with strong ribs, spines, and nodes, while many of them assumed strange shapes. Some built their shells in the form of a spiral, like those of the gastropods, while the shells of others were twisted without any semblance of pattern. Such bizarre forms usually appear when a group is on the decline. The ammonites became extinct during the Cretaceous period. Belemnites were still important elements in the marine fauna.

Fossil insects are not common in Cretaceous rocks, but it is quite certain that most of the modern types were in existence at that time. With the appearance of flowering plants, the flower-visiting insects became abundant; they doubtless carried pollen very much as their modern descendants do. The social wasps were present, and one of their nests has recently been discovered in the Upper Cretaceous rocks of Utah.

Vertebrates. *Fish and Amphibians.* Modern types of fish, or the teleosts, were abundant. Some of these, like *Xiphactinus* (*Portheus*) from the Late Cretaceous, reached a length of 15 feet and were fierce, predatory creatures. Amphibian remains are not common, but a few specimens of salamanders have been found and they are very much like the modern forms.

Reptiles. Crocodiles were very common and widely distributed in the warm, quiet waters of Cretaceous rivers and bayous. The giant marine turtle *Archelon* (Fig. 220) was 11 feet long and 12 feet wide across the front flippers. The shell was comparatively soft and light in weight.

Ichthyosaurs still lived in the Cretaceous seas, but they were few in number. The plesiosaurs surpassed those of the Jurassic only in size. *Elasmosaurus*, from the Cretaceous of Kansas, was over 40 feet long and had a slender, snake-like neck that measured 22 feet in length.

Mosasaurs. The seas of this period were dominated by a fierce, fast-swimming group of reptiles called the mosasaurs (Fig. 221).

Fig. 220.—The giant marine turtle *Archelon* from the Pierre shale of Wyoming. (*Drawn by John Jesse Hayes.*)

These "sea serpents" had long, slender bodies, and the four limbs were modified into flippers. The skin was covered with scales similar to those on the body of a snake, and the animal propelled itself through the water by means of undulating movements of the body, assisted by the powerful tail. An extra joint in each half of the lower jaw, near the middle, enabled the mosasaurs to swallow animals larger in diameter than themselves. The sharp, recurved teeth were fitted for seizing and tearing rather than for chewing. The largest known mosasaur reached a length of about 35 feet. The group is known only from rocks of the Cretaceous period.

Pterosaurs. Of the pterosaurs, which were still numerous, some forms reached gigantic size and were highly specialized. *Pteranodon*

Fig. 221.—*Platecarpus*, one of the mosasaurs, and the giant turtle *Archelon* from the Cretaceous period. *Pteranodon*, largest of the flying reptiles, is in the air. (*From a painting by Charles R. Knight, courtesy of Chicago Natural History Museum.*)

(Frontispiece), from the Niobrara of western Kansas, had a wing spread of 22 feet in the largest forms and is the greatest flying vertebrate that has ever been discovered. Its thin-walled, hollow bones and small body reduced the animal's weight to about 30 pounds. The narrow head reached a length of 4 feet in some individuals and there was a backward extension of the skull that acted as a counterbalance to the extended front part, probably serving also as a rudder. The powerful and flexible neck was equipped with some special articulations that made it possible for this pterosaur to deliver very powerful thrusts with its beak. The jaws of *Pteranodon* were toothless and resembled those of a modern

Fig. 222.—*Hesperornis regalis*, an aquatic bird from the Niobrara chalk of Kansas. (*After Gleeson.*)

bird. The hind limbs were so slender and relatively weak that they were probably not used to any extent for walking purposes. While at rest, the animal could cling to trees and rocky cliffs after the manner of a bat. This remarkable flying reptile probably launched itself in flight from the edge of a cliff, as it could hardly have "taken off" from the ground in still air. A throat pouch, similar to that of a pelican, was part of its equipment. *Pteranodon* ruled the air during a portion of the Cretaceous period.

Birds. Two types of birds have been found in the Niobrara chalk of Kansas. *Ichthyornis*, a small form, very much like a sea gull in general appearance, had strong wings, indicating well-developed powers of flight. The sharp, recurved teeth are reptilian in character.

Hesperornis (Fig. 222), from the Cretaceous of Kansas, was a powerful swimming and diving bird that reached a length of nearly 6 feet. The wings were vestigial and the hind legs were used to propel the animal through the water. The neck was long and flexible and the slender jaws were set with sharp teeth. The bony tail, several inches long, probably served as a rudder when the bird was diving. It is very doubtful whether *Hesperornis* could walk or even stand upon its legs, since they stood out nearly at right angles to the body.

Many other types of birds must have lived during the Cretaceous, but the delicacy of the skeletons that are characteristic of this group in general made their bones difficult to preserve as fossils. The lower jaw of a toothless bird has recently been discovered in Late Cretaceous continental deposits of Alberta, Canada.

Dinosaurs. The remarkable and highly successful tribe of dinosaurs continued to dominate the lands until the end of the Mesozoic era. Although the sauropods were declining, their remains have been found in the Cretaceous rocks of Maryland, Montana, Utah, Texas, and South America.

A large number of giant sauropod tracks has recently been found in the Glen Rose formation of Lower Cretaceous age in Texas. Some of the hind footprints, measuring 38 inches long and 26 inches wide, show clearly the impressions of four claws, but there were no claws on the front feet. The length of the stride was 10 or 12 feet. There was no impression of the long, slender tail associated with one series of tracks, so the individual that made these footprints was probably wading in the comparatively shallow water of some lagoon, with the tail floating instead of dragging on the bottom. Following alongside these tracks were the three-toed footprints of some great flesh-eating dinosaur, which may have been stalking or even attacking the huge sauropod.

The discovery of these dinosaur tracks in Texas shows that the mild climate and favorable environment of the Jurassic period persisted, at least in this region, until well toward the end of the Mesozoic, making it possible for the sauropods to survive here long after they had become extinct in other places.

Tyrannosaurus rex (Fig. 224), the climax of the carnivorous dinosaurs in both size and strength, was a magnificent but frightful example of destructive power built of flesh and bone. This huge reptile was 45 feet long and nearly 20 feet high. The head was 4 feet long and 3 feet wide, and the jaws were armed with sharp teeth from 3 to 6 inches in length. *Tyrannosaurus* (Fig. 224) walked on his massive hind legs, the front pair being greatly reduced in size. Long claws on the hind feet were used for holding his prey while the teeth tore away the flesh. The only dinosaurs that might have been able to compete with this monster were other members of his own tribe.

Ornithomimus (Fig. 225) was a bipedal, carnivorous dinosaur that resembled an ostrich in general appearance. This remarkable reptile was about 6 feet tall, with a small head and a toothless bill that was probably horny like that of a bird. The three-fingered hands were useful for grasping, and the powerful hind legs indicate that the animal was a swift runner. *Ornithomimus* probably fed upon eggs and crustaceans.

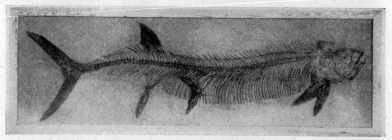

Fig. 223.—Skeleton of the great marine fish, Xiphactinus (Portheus), from the Cretaceous rocks of Kansas. This specimen is over 10 feet long.

Triceratops (Fig. 224) looked somewhat like a rhinoceros. This heavy-bodied dinosaur reached a length of 25 feet. Several of the skulls that have been found are 9 feet long. There was a long, sharp horn over each eye and a single one on the nose. Such structures must have served as efficient weapons for both defense and offense. *Triceratops* had a beak like that of a turtle and teeth that were adapted for eating plant food. A heavy bony structure extended backward from the skull, expanding into a great protective shield over the neck. These reptiles fought with others of their own kind and were often forced to defend themselves against the fierce *Tyrannosaurus*, who was always hungry. Several skulls of *Triceratops* have been found with horns that were broken and healed during life, while the bony shields often show perforations that must have been made by the horns of other individuals in the course of terrific combat. These animals frequented the banks of rivers and swampy places, where there was an abundance of lush vegetation.

Several skeletons and some eggs of *Protoceratops* have been

FIG. 224.—*Triceratops* (left) prepares to defend itself against an attack by the great carnivorous dinosaur *Tyrannosaurus rex.* (*Courtesy of Sinclair Refining Company.*)

found in the Gobi Desert of Mongolia, and a few fragments of dinosaur eggshells were discovered in the Lance beds of Upper Cretaceous age, near Powell, Wyoming.

Iguanodon was a very common type of herbivorous dinosaur in Europe. Many an individual reached a length of 30 feet and stood 15 feet high. There were three toes on each hind foot and five digits on each hand, while the thumb was long and shaped like a spike. At least 17 of these creatures fell into an open fissure in the

Fig. 225.—*Ornithomimus*, the carnivorous, ostrich-like dinosaur. (*Drawn by John Jesse Hayes.*)

Carboniferous rocks of Belgium, and their skeletons were recovered in a remarkably fine state of preservation. The *Iguanodon* normally walked on its hind legs, but occasionally came down on all fours to rest or to feed. The footprints look like those of giant birds.

The trachodonts (Fig. 226) or duck-billed dinosaurs, were especially numerous in the Cretaceous period. These animals walked on their hind legs, although they often assumed the all-fours posture when feeding. Some individuals had as many as 2,000 teeth in their jaws. The trachodonts probably ate highly siliceous types of plants, such as the horsetail rushes, which were abundant in the Cretaceous.   The bony, duck-like beaks are distinctive features of this group.

Many well-preserved impressions of *Trachodon* skins have been found, and two very remarkable specimens show imprints of almost the entire bodies.   The skin was covered with tubercles of different sizes and shapes, and the color patterns were probably variable.

These dinosaurs, which frequented rivers and swamps in search of food, were doubtless good swimmers.

Fig. 226.— *Trachodon*, the duck-billed dinosaur.   (*Drawn by John Jesse Hayes.*)

Hadrosaurus, a relative of *Trachodon*, has been found in Cretaceous marl beds of New Jersey.

Racial Extinction.   The rise and fall of many great animal dynasties is clearly recorded in the geologic record.   Certain groups of vertebrates and invertebrates that once lived in vast numbers all over the earth have completely disappeared.   These cases of extinction are difficult to explain, especially those that were world-wide in their scope and that affected families whose members lived under many different kinds of environmental conditions.   Our perspective is frequently foreshortened by the incompleteness of the geologic record, so that cases of racial extinction that appear to have been quite sudden, geologically speaking, were probably very gradual. It is true that a certain form might disappear from one locality and continue to live in another place for a long time, but ultimate extinction at last would overtake the group.

Extinction of the Dinosaurs. This truly remarkable group of reptiles must be considered highly successful, because it spread over almost the entire world and retained its supremacy for more than 100,000,000 years. It seems incredible that such animals could ever have disappeared; yet not a single individual has been found in rocks above the Mesozoic. There was probably no single factor that brought about the downfall of the dinosaurs. Disease may have played an important part in their extinction. It has been suggested, also, that their eggs were either eaten or destroyed by mammals like the rodents. Gnawing animals were abundant in the Cretaceous, but some of the dinosaurs lived in the water, where their young were born alive; therefore, the mammals could have had nothing to do with the extinction of such forms.

The most plausible explanation of the dramatic racial death is based upon the obvious fact that the dinosaurs had become highly specialized, even overspecialized, animals. Most of them had adjusted themselves to definite and rather narrow ranges of environmental conditions. Some ate only certain kinds of plants, while the diet of others was restricted to a few types of animals. Water was absolutely essential to the giant sauropods. When the environmental conditions began to change, the dinosaurs could not alter their old habits to meet the new conditions.

The Laramide revolution in the latter part of the Cretaceous caused a widespread uplift in the western part of North America. This brought about a cooler climate, which in turn must have caused many changes in the plant life within the uplifted regions. Large areas became semiarid, swamps and lakes were drained or dried up, and the herbivorous dinosaurs began to disappear. This, in turn, affected the flesh eaters and finally the entire race disappeared from the face of the earth.

Mammals. From the Upper Jurassic until late in the Cretaceous, the fossil remains of mammals are rare and their evolutionary history is difficult to trace. The Pantotheria became extinct in the Jurassic, but they left two very important groups of descendants in the Cretaceous. These are the marsupials, or pouch-bearing mammals, and the insectivores, which are the most primitive of all the known placental mammals.

The earliest marsupial, *Eodelphis*, which comes from the Belly River beds of Canada, belongs to the opossum family. A large variety of teeth have been found in the Lance formation of Wyoming. These are also referred to the opossum group, which had become greatly diversified by the Upper Cretaceous. The insectivores are known from the Lance beds of North America and the Djadochta of Mongolia (Fig. 227), where several well-preserved

 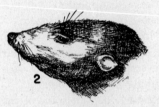

FIG. 227.—1, *Zalambdatestes lechei;* 2, *Deltatheridium pretrituberculare.* Insectivores from the Cretaceous of Mongolia. These animals were similar to the modern shrews. (*After Gregory.*)

skulls have been found. These animals were all small creatures and resembled the modern hedgehog and shrew.

As the powerful group of reptiles decreased in numbers and varieties during the latter part of the Cretaceous, the rapidly evolving mammals quickly took their places and soon spread widely over the earth. The Age of Mammals was approaching.

Reading References

BALL, O. M.: A Dicotyledonous Florule from the Trinity Group of Texas, *Jour. Geology,* vol. 45, pp. 528–537, 1937.

BIRD, ROLAND T.: A Dinosaur Walks into the Museum, *Natural History,* Vol. 47, No. 2, pp. 74–82, February, 1941.

BROWN, BARNUM: The Last Dinosaurs, *Natural History,* Vol. 48, No. 5, pp. 290–295, December, 1941.

CLARK, WILLIAM B., ARTHUR B. BIBBINS, and EDWARD W. BERRY: "The Lower Cretaceous Deposits of Maryland," *Maryland Geol. Survey,* pp. 23–88, The Johns Hopkins Press, Baltimore, 1911.

———: "The Upper Cretaceous Deposits of Maryland," *Maryland Geol. Survey,* pp. 23–109, The Johns Hopkins Press, Baltimore, 1916.

COLBERT, EDWIN H.: A Fossil Comes to Life, *Natural History,* Vol. 53, No. 5, pp. 280–283, May, 1939.

DORF, ERLING: Relationship between Floras of Type Lance and Fort Union Formations, *Geol. Soc. America Bull.,* vol. 51, pp. 213–236, 1940.

JEPSEN, G. L.: Dinosaur Shell Fragments from Montana, *Science*, pp. 12–13, Jan. 2, 1931.

LULL, R. S., and NELDA E.: WRIGHT, Hadrosaurian Dinosaurs of North America, *Geol. Soc. America Special Papers* 40, pp. 29–46, Aug. 31, 1942.

SCHLAIKJER, ERICH M.: The Rise of the Dinosaurs, *Natural History*, Vol. 48, No. 5, pp. 284–287 and 303, December, 1941.

CHAPTER XVIII

THE CENOZOIC ERA

THE TERTIARY PERIOD

The Cenozoic era is the last great division of geologic time. A study of radioactive materials indicates that its length is about 60,000,000 years, which is a short stretch of time compared with the other eras. Nearly all the important features of the earth's surface with which we are familiar today were shaped during this time. Most of the ancient stocks of reptiles had disappeared by the end of the Mesozoic and the mammals ruled in their place until finally, almost at the very end of the era, modern types of men appeared.

The Cenozoic has witnessed widespread orogenic disturbances that still continue in many parts of the world. Movements along some of the great thrust-fault lines that began with the Laramide revolution continued well into the Cenozoic, and mountain-making forces that became active in the latter part of the era are still at work. Earthquakes and volcanic eruptions are still common around the borders of the Pacific Ocean. These reveal a great deal of crustal unrest that will continue far into the future. As a result of comparatively recent mountain-building and regional uplifts, the continents stand unusually high at the present time. Climatic zones are more sharply defined than they were during most of the Cenozoic, and the distribution of plants and animals over the earth no longer has the cosmopolitan aspect that characterized many of the past geologic periods.

The Cenozoic era is commonly divided into two periods, called the "Tertiary" and the "Quaternary." Neither of these terms is very appropriate, partly because the original meaning is entirely lost. There is certainly no valid reason for retaining the Quaternary, which has only a single division called the "Pleistocene." It is therefore abandoned. This last epoch includes the events of the Ice Age, and the world has not yet emerged from the effects of the great continental glaciers that formed at that time. The Cenozoic is divided into six epochs, which are generally recognized. They are the Paleocene, Eocene, Oligocene, Miocene, Pliocene, and Pleistocene epochs. These divisions are sometimes regarded as periods.

326

North America has not been invaded by any extensive body of marine water since the Cretaceous sea disappeared, and by far the most important part of the Cenozoic record is written in the great series of continental deposits that are found throughout the western part of our country.

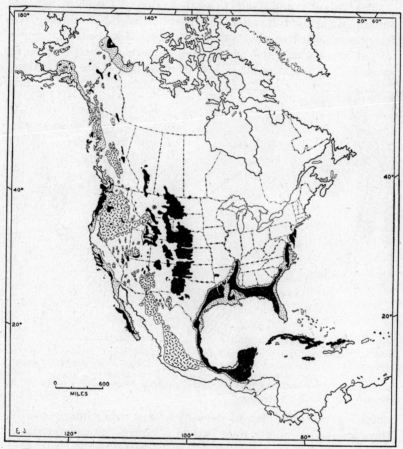

Fig. 228.—North America during the Cenozoic era. The stippled areas along the coasts show the inferred extent of the seas. Outcrops are in black. The deposits in the Western Interior region are nonmarine (continental). Areas of igneous rocks in the west are shown by dashes. (*Modified from Branson and Tarr.*)

CENOZOIC MARINE DEPOSITS OF NORTH AMERICA

The Interior Region. The Cannonball beds (Fig. 229), covering a small area in the Dakotas, represent the only known marine deposits of Cenozoic age in the interior of North America. These sediments were formerly considered as late Cretaceous, but they are now placed at the base of the Paleocene as a part of the Fort Union formation. The connection between this local interior basin of marine deposition and the ocean was probably by way of some narrow arm of the sea that came in from the Gulf of Mexico, but the position of the channel is unknown.

The Atlantic and Gulf Coastal Regions. Cenozoic deposits outcrop in narrow belts along the Atlantic Coastal Plain from New Jersey southward to the Gulf of Mexico. The beds dip gently toward the sea and the overlapping deposits of each succeeding epoch do not reach as far inland as those of the preceding time,

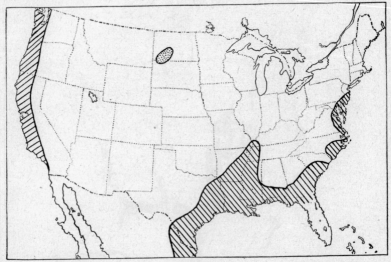

Fig. 229.—The dotted area in North Dakota and South Dakota shows the position of the Cannonball member of the Fort Union formation with respect to the nearest known areas of Tertiary marine sediments along the Pacific coast and in the embayment from the Gulf of Mexico. (*After Stanton and Vaughan, U.S. Geological Survey.*)

indicating that the area of deposition was rising intermittently. These successive uplifts were part of a larger regional movement that domed up the old Appalachian Mountain region and tilted the coastal-plain area gently eastward. Since the movements began very early in the Cenozoic and continued at intervals throughout the era, the older Tertiary deposits are inclined at progressively steeper angles than the younger beds.

Cenozoic sediments outcrop in a broad band around the Gulf Coastal Plain, and the Eocene deposits extend up the Mississippi Valley region to southern Illinois. As the water over the northern end of this embayment was very shallow, extensive lagoons with coastal-plain swamps developed over the flat lands. The Eocene sediments at the upper end of the Gulf embayment, which are largely of continental origin, contain beds of lignite.

Nature of the Deposits. Cenozoic sediments of the east consist mostly of unconsolidated sands, calcareous shales, clays, and marls. The sands are often silty and lenticular, with frequent lateral gradations into shale. Some of the limestones are moderately hard and in Florida there are loosely cemented masses of shell fragments, called "coquina." Glauconite, or greensand, is prominent in some of the marine Tertiary deposits. Several of the Cenozoic beds in the east are famous for their enormous numbers of beautifully preserved marine fossils, especially pelecypods and gastropods.

Tertiary rocks vary greatly in thickness from place to place. Over large areas of the Atlantic Coastal Plain region they are only a few hundred feet thick. Florida has an unusually complete section of Tertiary beds, including deposits made during all the epochs. The maximum thickness is more than 5,000 feet, indicating that much of the state was a slowly subsiding area during the Cenozoic. Limestones predominate in the section until the Miocene epoch, when sands began to accumulate along the eastern side of the region.

A modern geosyncline lies along the northern border of the Gulf of Mexico. In the southern part of Louisiana deep oil wells have penetrated 13,000 feet of Cenozoic materials. Soundings made by means of the seismograph in the same area show a total thickness of at least 20,000 feet, while recent estimates made in the southwestern part of Louisiana indicate that the Tertiary beds there may be 30,000 feet thick. This trough, which runs in an east-and-west direction, is called the "Barton" geosyncline.

The subsidence that formed the Gulf of Mexico must have begun at least by the Cretaceous period, because rocks of that time are found on the coastal plain around the Gulf. Continued depression during the Cenozoic has resulted in the present great depth of this Gulf, as well as that of the Caribbean Sea to the east.

The Pacific Coast Region. Tertiary rocks of both marine and continental origin are found in many places along the Pacific Coastal region of North America, but instead of occurring in more or less continuous belts, as they do in the eastern part of the United States, the Cenozoic formations of the Far West are found in disconnected areas. Two adjoining regions may have strata that differ greatly in thickness and in character of material. Marine and continental sediments often formed at the same time in near-by places. While sedimentation was proceeding in one locality, erosion was active in another area not far away; still later, the conditions in the two places might be reversed. The deposits are frequently lens-like in shape and the character of the sediments often changes rapidly both horizontally and vertically.

These highly variable Cenozoic formations were deposited in a series of fault troughs that formed bays and inlets along the narrow coastal region. The Tertiary basins followed much the same patterns as the Cretaceous basins that had originated at the time of the Nevadian disturbance. Each of these intermittently subsiding areas was largely independent of the others, and sediments came from bordering highlands. As some of the regions subsided more rapidly and to greater depths than others, they consequently received thicker deposits. The sea often persisted in the middle of the basins after it had disappeared along the margins, and this resulted in unconformities around the edges but not in the center. There is evidence that folding was occurring in some of these down-faulted areas during deposition, because in places the lower beds stand at steeper angles than those in the upper parts of the sections. The Great Valley of California is one of these troughs that is still subsiding and receiving great quantities of continental sediments today from the Sierra Nevada and Coast Ranges.

Marine waters spread widely over the Pacific border during the Miocene epoch. The deposits of this time reach a thickness of 12,000 feet in Southern California. The Monterey group consists chiefly of shales, and some beds are made up largely of the siliceous skeletons of minute plants, called "diatoms." The source of the petroleum of the Monterey, which is one of the most important oil-producing horizons in California, may have been the diatoms.

Certain marine invertebrates found in the Eocene rocks of California are very much like some of those that occur in the Paris Basin. This similarity indicates a waterway between the two regions, possibly across the present Central American area. The larvae of mollusks are often carried (rafted) across great stretches of the ocean on floating seaweeds, and these Tertiary forms might have been distributed in a similar manner.

Two miles of brackish and fresh-water sediments, including several beds of coal, were deposited in the Puget Sound area during the Tertiary.

CONTINENTAL DEPOSITS

The Central Interior Region. Vast lowland plains covered the great Central Interior region of North America during the entire

Cenozoic era.   Many parts of this plain were heavily wooded, and sediments accumulated chiefly in the beds of rivers and over extensive flood plains.   In the Pleistocene epoch, important deposits were made over portions of this region by great continental glaciers and by streams that flowed away from the melting ice.

The Western Interior Region.   *The Great Plains.*   The Great Plains (Fig. 230) were built up along the eastern side of the Rocky Mountains during Cenozoic time, largely by streams that meandered widely across the gently sloping country.   Sands and gravels accumulated in the river beds, while silt and clay were spread over the flood plains.   The changing velocities of the streams, together

Fig. 230.—The Great Plains in western Kansas.   (*Photographed by Oren Bingham, Kansas Geological Survey.*)

with their highly variable volumes of water and constantly shifting channels, resulted in a heterogeneous accumulation of sediments that vary greatly in character and thickness from place to place.

THE PALEOCENE EPOCH

The Fort Union formation is widely distributed through Wyoming, North and South Dakota, Montana, and Alberta.   The sediments, varying in thickness from 2,000 to 5,000 feet, consist largely of soft sandstones and shales with extensive beds of coal. The Fort Union was deposited by sluggish, meandering streams, and in temporary lakes that formed over the flat country during flood stages of the rivers.   The thick deposits of vegetation that accumulated in extensive bogs and swamps furnished the material that formed the coal.

The Cannonball member is a marine deposit found at the base of the Fort Union in North and South Dakota. It contains a fauna consisting chiefly of Foraminifera and mollusks (Fig. 231), among which oysters are particularly abundant in places. This deposit was formerly correlated with the Lance formation of Late Cretaceous age, but recent studies of the Foraminifera and the associated land plants show that the Cannonball probably belongs to the Paleocene.

Several hundred species of plants have been described from the Fort Union sediments. These include such common types of forest trees as maples, oaks, elms, sycamores, hickories, poplars, and

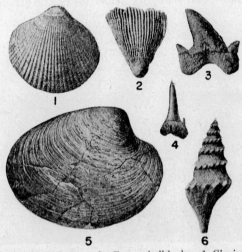

FIG. 231.—Marine fossils from the Cannonball beds. 1, *Glycimeris subimbricata;* 2, *Paracyathus thomi;* 3, *Otodus obliquus,* a shark tooth; 4, *Lamna cuspidata,* a shark tooth; 5, *Arctica ovata;* 6, *Turricula bacata.* (*After T. W. Stanton and T. W. Vaughan, U.S. Geological Survey.*)

birches. The beds contain a very characteristic mammalian fauna in the Big Horn Basin of Wyoming, but vertebrate remains are not common in other localities.

THE EOCENE EPOCH

Eocene nonmarine formations are found mostly in Wyoming, Colorado, Utah, and New Mexico. The sediments, which were deposited chiefly in basins between the Laramide ranges, are largely the work of rivers and wind, although some of the materials were laid down in lakes. Each of the basins was an independent area of deposition, but the wide distribution of certain forms of mammals makes it possible to correlate the deposits in some of the different areas. Thick conglomerates found in several places represent alluvial fans that were built at the mouths of gullies by torrential rivers, which flowed chiefly during the occasional heavy rains.

The Wasatch group includes a number of members from the Lower Eocene. It is typically developed in the Big Horn Basin of Northern Wyoming and Montana. Here the sediments are about 2,000 feet thick and were formed mostly by rivers. The Wasatch beds have given up a large number of Tertiary mammals—among them, the famous *Eohippus* (dawn horse).

Fig. 232.—Bryce Canyon in southern Utah. (*Courtesy of Union Pacific Railroad.*)

Deep erosion of Wasatch rocks has made Bryce Canyon (Fig. 232), in Southern Utah, one of the greatest scenic spectacles in the entire world. In this remarkable canyon, which is 3 miles long and 2 miles wide, the brilliantly colored rocks have been carved into a great number of slender spires and pinnacles that produce some magnificent and startling effects.

The Green River Basin lies chiefly in the southwestern part of Wyoming and in northwestern Colorado. During the middle part of the Eocene epoch this region was partly occupied by a large but shallow lake, in which about 2,000 feet of finely laminated and evenly stratified shales were deposited as the basin slowly subsided. Most of the laminae are about as thick as a sheet of coarse paper, and the layers are supposed to be seasonal accumulations. If this is true, it required about 6,500,000 years to deposit the Green River sediments. These shales contain vast quantities of carbonaceous material and great numbers of well-preserved fishes, insects, and impressions of leaves, but very few mammals. There is a large area of the shales south of the Uinta Mountains that was formed in an extension of the lake from the main Green River Basin.

The Bridger beds are best developed in southwestern Wyoming and northeastern Utah, where they consist mostly of sandy and shaly materials that are largely of fluviatile origin. These soft and friable sediments have been eroded into extensive badlands.

The Uinta beds form the top of the Eocene section in the Western Interior region. These sediments, which are found along the south side of the Uinta Mountains in Utah and Colorado, are very much like the Bridger beds, upon which they rest with apparent conformity.

THE OLIGOCENE EPOCH

The nonmarine Oligocene deposits are found widely distributed through Montana, Wyoming, North and South Dakota, Nebraska and Colorado.

The White River beds cover large areas in South Dakota, Nebraska, Wyoming, and Colorado. These deposits vary in thickness from 200 to 600 feet and consist largely of clay and silt, with a great deal of volcanic ash. Here and there at various levels crossbedded sandstones are found. These mark the courses of ancient stream channels. The fine sediments were deposited on broad flood plains and in temporary lakes or playas. The region was covered with an abundance of vegetation, which supported large numbers of mammals whose bones have been preserved in the soft sediments. The Big Badlands (Fig. 234) of South Dakota have been eroded out of the White River beds.

THE MIOCENE EPOCH

The Arikaree group includes a number of formations that are widely distributed over the Great Plains. Sands and gravels, which are especially common, were deposited by streams flowing from the Rocky Mountain region. Fine-grained sandstones near Agate, Nebraska, contain an enormous number of bones, belonging mostly to a form of rhinoceros called *Diceratherium*. The disarticulated skeletons of thousands of animals that perished in the original quicksands at this locality occur as a bone conglomerate.

A particularly interesting occurrence of Miocene beds is found

FIG. 233.—Scotts Bluff seen from the North Platte River in western Nebraska. The rocks belong to the Oligocene, Miocene, and Pliocene epochs. (*Photographed by Charles Downey.*)

FIG. 234.—The Big Bad Lands of South Dakota. (*Bell Photo, Rapid City, South Dakota.*)

near the village of Florissant (Fig. 235) in Colorado.   Here a great
deal of volcanic ash and dust, derived from small explosive volcanoes in the neighborhood, settled to the bottom of a lake, burying
thousands of insects and leaves, which are preserved with remark-

Fig. 235.—The Florissant Lake Basin at Florissant, Colorado. (*Photographed
by T. S. Lovering and M. F. Van Tuyl, U.S. Geological Survey.*)

able fidelity as impressions on the fine-grained paper shales (Fig.
236).   A few fishes and birds have also been found at this locality.

THE PLIOCENE EPOCH

Pliocene deposits are scattered over the Great Plains from
Nebraska to Texas.   Other areas of these rocks are found in Arizona, New Mexico, Nevada, Idaho, and southeastern California.
The Ogallala group consists of slightly consolidated sand, gravel, silt,
and clay, having a maximum thickness of about 500 feet.

CENOZOIC HISTORY OF THE APPALACHIAN MOUNTAINS

After the upheaval of the Appalachian Mountains in the Permian
period, they were gradually eroded and, long before the Cenozoic,
most of this mountainous region had been reduced to a peneplain.
In the northern part of the disturbed area, the White Mountains of
New Hampshire and the Adirondacks of New York, together with
several more or less isolated peaks such as Mt. Katahdin and
Cadillac Mountain in Maine, rose as monadnocks above the monot-

onous level of the plain.   In the southern Appalachian region, the Great Smokies were high erosion remnants, standing from 2,000 to 3,000 feet above the surrounding country.   In other parts of the Appalachian region there are numerous remnants of a once wide-spread erosion surface that bevels hard and soft rocks alike.   Remnants may still be seen in the even crest line over the folded belt of

Fig. 236.—Beds of Miocene volcanic ash at Florissant, Colorado.

the Appalachians.   This great, flat surface is called the "Schooley peneplain" (Fig. 238).   If the Upper Cretaceous sea ever invaded any part of the peneplaned Appalachian area, the sediments left by this sea have either been removed by erosion or have not been discovered.

Several great rivers in the eastern part of the United States, such as the Potomac and the Susquehanna, had established themselves upon the surface of the Schooley peneplain and were flowing

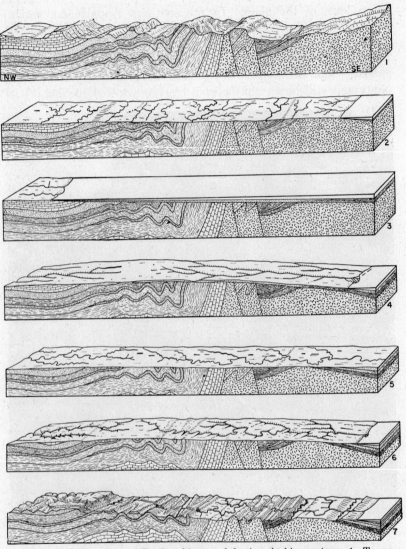

FIG. 237.- Mesozoic and Tertiary history of the Appalachian region. 1. Topography in Early Jurassic time produced by dissection of the Appalachian area. 2. The area was peneplaned by the Early Cretaceous. 3. The Cretaceous sea invaded the region and deposited thin Coastal Plain beds. 4. Near end of the Cretaceous the region was uplifted and arched. Southeastward-flowing consequent streams were established. 5. Erosion produced the Schooley peneplain by Early Tertiary. 6. About Mid-Tertiary the Schooley peneplain was arched and streams were intrenched. 7. Further uplifts and erosion produced the Harrisburg surface and the present topography. (*From D. W. Johnson, "Stream Sculpture on the Atlantic Slope," by permission of Columbia University Press. Drawn by Glenn Tague.*)

slowly in meandering courses toward the southeast. At some undetermined time in the Cenozoic era, a series of uplifts began that gently arched up the plain along the central northeast-southwest axis. The first of these movements elevated the region a few hundred feet, and the rejuvenated rivers began to intrench themselves in their old meandering courses, which they had long followed transverse to the strike of the beds and across both hard and soft rocks. Tributary streams were developed along the belts of less resistant rocks, and the softer portions of the peneplain were eroded faster than the harder parts, producing, eventually, the present rough topography of the Appalachian Mountains.

Fig. 238.—Moccasin Bend of the Tennessee River as seen from the top of Lookout Mountain. The Schooley peneplain is in the distance.

The lowland that was formed as a result of the first period of uplift and rejuvenation is called the "Harrisburg surface." Still later the region was again upwarped and the Harrisburg surface was dissected, but the lowlands formed at that time were more local in their extent. The periodic uplifts continued and the Schooley peneplain was eventually upheaved to a maximum height of about 4,000 feet along the central axis of the arch, while the main streams cut their valleys deeper.

The essential events in the Appalachian history are summarized as follows: The original mountains were formed in the Permian by crustal movements that folded and faulted thousands of feet of sediments in the Appalachian geosyncline. These mountains were peneplaned during the Mesozoic era, and the present relief has been the result of differential erosion over the broad, upwarped surface of the peneplain.

CENOZOIC HISTORY OF THE ROCKY MOUNTAINS

The Laramide revolution produced a number of downwarped basins, which lay between the ranges of the original Rocky Mountains. Two of these intermontane areas in Colorado are represented, in part, by North Park and South Park (Fig. 240). The Uinta Basin lies in Utah and Colorado, while the large Green River Basin is in southwestern Wyoming. In the northern part of the state there is the Big Horn Basin.

When sediments from the surrounding highlands poured down into the subsiding areas, the coarser materials were deposited around the margins as a series of alluvial fans, while finer sands and muds settled over the relatively flat basin floors. This deposition continued with great vigor during the early part of the Tertiary, while the mountains were high and the agents of weathering and erosion retained their maximum power. By the Miocene epoch, most of the basins had been completely filled, portions of the mountain ranges themselves were buried under the accumulating debris, and the mountains as a whole were so greatly reduced in height that the entire area was essentially a peneplain (Fig. 241) that was the product of both degradation and aggradation. The general elevation of the plain was between 2,000 and 3,000 feet above sea level, while some of the higher parts of the ranges stood a few thousand feet above the surrounding country and other low monadnocks were scattered here and there over the entire area.

Uplift and Canyon Cutting. About Pliocene time, a series of broad uplifts began in the Rocky Mountain area, continuing at intervals until late in the Pleistocene epoch. This resulted in a broad arching-up of the entire peneplain, with numerous peaks and ridges along the continental divide reaching elevations of from 12,000 to 14,000 feet. The rivers, rejuvenated as a result of the regional upwarping, began to cut their channels deeper and to remove the sediments from the intermontane basins. The buried portions of the hills were gradually uncovered, and differential erosion finally produced the present rough topography of the Rocky Mountains.

Some of the streams in the southern Rockies of Wyoming and Colorado find their way out of the mountains through steep-walled gorges that have been cut to depths of a thousand feet or more. These canyons lie transverse to the ranges, and the courses of the

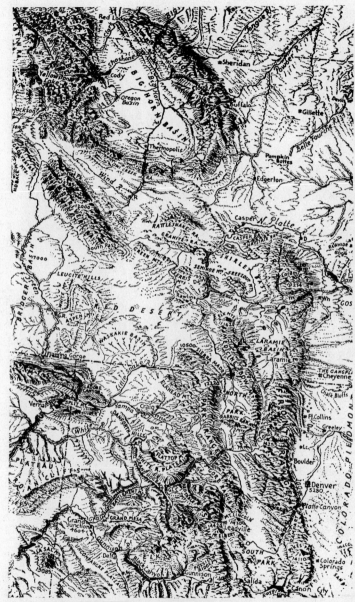

Fig. 239.—Map of the Southern Rocky Mountains showing basins, parks, and rivers flowing through the ranges in prominent gorges. (*From a map by Erwin Raisz to accompany Atwood's "Physiographic Provinces of North America." Courtesy of Ginn and Company.*)

FIG. 240.—The southern end of South Park, north of Salida, Colorado, looking west. This view shows the basin-like depression that was once largely filled with Tertiary sediments. (*Photographed by M. V. Denny.*)

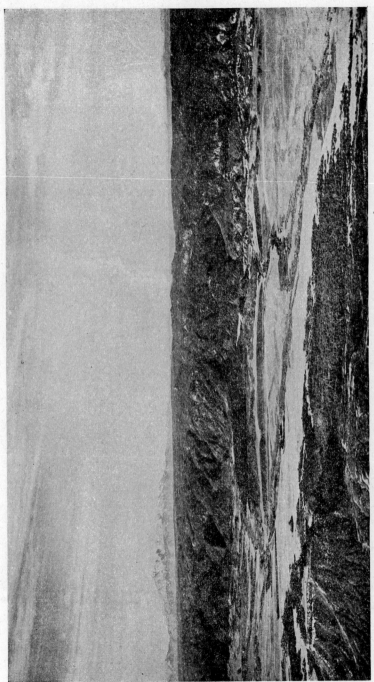

FIG. 241.—The region southwest of Castle Rock, Colorado. The Overland Mountain erosion surface runs entirely across the picture. (Photographed by T. S. Lovering and F. M. Van Tuyl, U.S. Geological Survey.)

rivers run so counter to the present topography that they can be understood only by reconstructing their history.   These rivers were

Fig. 242.—The Royal Gorge of the Arkansas River west of Cañon City, Colorado.
(Photo by Mitchell and Egbers.)

originally flowing in graded courses across both sediment-filled valleys and buried ranges.   When the streams were rejuvenated as a result of regional upwarping, they began to deepen their channels and soon reached the buried parts of the ranges, where they continued their downward cutting until the present gorges were produced.

The following are a few striking examples among 25 or more canyons or water gaps that have been cut by superimposed streams throughout the middle and southern parts of the Rockies. The Colorado crosses the Gore and Sawatch ranges in three gorges. The Arkansas River follows an easy southerly course for several miles along the western side of South Park and then, instead of continuing in that direction, it turns directly eastward and crosses the Front Range through the impressive Royal Gorge (Fig. 242), which is over 1,600 feet deep in places. The Laramie River flows northward for about 50 miles across the Laramie Basin, west of the range. Its course should apparently have continued in that direction across comparatively low country until it joined the Platte. Instead, the river turns eastward and cuts through the Laramie Range in a gorge that is over 1,000 feet deep. The Black Canyon of the Gunnison in Colorado and the gorge of the Shoshone near Cody, Wyoming, are further examples of the canyon-cutting stage in the history of the modern Rockies.

THE COLORADO PLATEAU

The Colorado Plateau is a vast region of comparatively horizontal sedimentary rocks lying between the southern Rockies and the Great Basin in Utah, Arizona, New Mexico, and southwestern Colorado. This entire area has been very resistant to mountain-making deformation, but broad regional uplifts have affected most of the plateau and lifted it to elevations that range from 5,000 to 11,000 feet. A considerable amount of warping has occurred in places, while several monoclinal bends and normal faults have varied the general structure. The western side of the region is particularly characterized by a series of flat-topped plateaus and spectacular vertical cliffs that rise stepwise toward the east. One who travels north from the Grand Canyon into southern Utah will see several of these great walls, bearing such names as Vermilion Cliffs, White Cliffs, and Pink Cliffs. The slow recession of these escarpments shows that an enormous amount of erosion has affected the region since uplifts began in the early Cenozoic.

A final important uplift in the Pleistocene rejuvenated the rivers within the plateau area and was largely responsible for several magnificent canyons, particularly Zion and the Grand Canyon.

The Colorado River system was started at that time and the course of the stream itself was probably changed. The excavation of the Grand Canyon has not required so great a length of time, and as the river, together with its numerous major and minor tributaries, continues to dissect the plateau, a later period in the erosion cycle will produce an intricate series of steep-walled buttes and headlands similar to those that are found in the canyon at present.

THE BASIN AND RANGE PROVINCE

The Basin and Range Province lies mostly in Nevada and the western part of Utah, between the Colorado Plateau and the Rocky

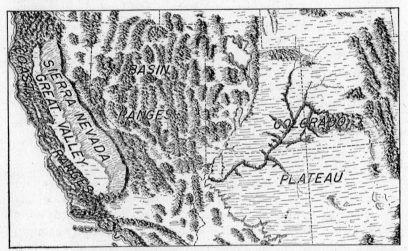

Fig. 243.—Relief map of the southwestern portion of the United States showing certain physiographic provinces. The Sierra Nevada is a huge tilted earth block with a steep fault scarp facing eastward. The Great Valley is a geosyncline where sediments have accumulated to a depth of several thousand feet.

Mountains on the east and the Sierra Nevada and Coast Ranges on the west. This region had a mountainous relief after the Laramide revolution, and the almost complete absence of early Tertiary deposits shows that sediments were being carried beyond the area. By the Miocene epoch, erosion had greatly reduced the general elevation of the province, but portions of the region still stood about 3,000 feet above the surrounding country. During a long period of faulting that began about the middle of the Tertiary, great earth blocks were tilted to form the present Basin Ranges (Fig. 243). The height of some of these ranges is not entirely due to block faulting but has been inherited from a previous surface, whose relief was mature or submature.

As the fault blocks were elevated, erosion grew more vigorous, and late Tertiary sediments in many places reach such great thicknesses that some of the mountains are partly buried beneath debris which they themselves furnished. Clays and silts are found in a number of places, but there are particularly heavy beds of conglomerates made of angular and subangular rock fragments that were deposited as alluvial fans by torrential streams running down from highlands of considerable elevation. These coarse sediments reach a thickness of about 3,000 feet in several places through southern Nevada, where they rest with an angular unconformity upon Paleozoic and early Mesozoic rocks. The clays and silts, with their interbedded layers of gypsum and borax, were deposited under arid conditions in basins of interior drainage that were very much like the Great Salt Lake area of today.

Block faulting in the Basin and Range Province has continued intermittently down to the present, and fault scarps may be seen along which very recent movements have taken place. The tilted and truncated Miocene beds may be seen in places overlain unconformably by Pliocene sediments.

THE SIERRA NEVADA

The region of the modern Sierra Nevada was part of an extensive area that was folded and faulted into a great mountain range during the Nevadian revolution, in the latter part of the Jurassic period. These older mountains had been largely peneplaned by the Miocene epoch and the deep-seated batholiths lay exposed. A period of faulting began about that time that tilted the great Sierra earth block westward and lifted the eastern front (Fig. 244) to a height of about 13,000 feet, while the depressed part formed the great California trough. The modern Sierra Nevada Mountains have been eroded out of this enormous tilted block, which is about 400 miles long and 100 miles wide.

Before the strong uplifts began in the Sierra region, some of the main streams in the area were flowing in broad valleys many miles wide. The first period of uplift and rejuvenation resulted in the cutting of mountain valleys to depths of 1,000 feet or more below the original level and, during later uplifts, probably in the Pleistocene, the present impressive canyons were eroded in the older valley floors. Yosemite National Park lies in the midst of the Sierra Nevada. The magnificent Yosemite Valley was shaped largely by the action of mountain glaciers during the Pleistocene.

Fig. 244.—The steep eastern side of the Sierra Nevada Mountains seen from Owens Valley, California.   The great alluvial fans are 2,000 feet thick in places. Old Camp Independence in foreground.   (*Courtesy of Spence Air Photos.*)

Mt. Whitney (14,555 feet), the highest peak in the United States, lies toward the southern end of the Sierras.

THE MID-TERTIARY DISTURBANCE

About the middle of the Tertiary period, during the Miocene epoch, there was widespread and intense mountain building through central and western Wyoming, southern Idaho, Nevada, and southeastern California.   The disturbances throughout these areas are not clearly related either to the closing phases of the Laramide revolution or the early part of the Coast Range revolution.   Many details of the Mid-Tertiary disturbance have not yet been determined.

THE COAST RANGES REVOLUTION

The first movements of a great revolution that is still in progress along the Pacific Coast region of the United States began in the Middle Miocene and reached their maximum about the middle of the Pleistocene, with a somewhat lesser period of intensity in the Upper Pliocene.   The Coast Ranges in general were folded and thrust-faulted, while certain areas with a rigid crystalline bedrock were affected chiefly by faulting.   As the crustal movements continued, the basins of deposition were further broken up into smaller areas, and while folding was progressing in one part of a trough the conditions might be comparatively static in another part only a few miles away. Many complications of structure have been introduced by the different vertical and horizontal crustal movements as they varied in amount and intensity from place to place.

The Late Pliocene and Early Pleistocene sedimentation was brought to a close in the Middle Pleistocene by very intense and widespread diastrophism that strongly accentuated the Pliocene folds and faults of the Coast Ranges as a whole and also affected the Sierra Nevada. The ranges were not only further uplifted, but they were widened, as well, while new faults and folds were formed. Diastrophism still continues in many places along the Pacific Coast of North America, and California is a laboratory where the various processes that are involved in the building of mountain ranges may be studied.

Widespread regional uplifts occurred in North America and other continents during the Late Pliocene and Pleistocene epochs. The dissection of these uplifted areas has produced most of our present prominent topographic features. In the western part of North America, the modern Rockies, Sierra Nevada, the Cascades, and other ranges of varying extent were formed. In the East, the present Appalachians, the Great Smokies, the Adirondacks, the Taconic Mountains, the Green Mountains and the White Mountains in the New England region, all were formed very much as they are today. In the south central part of North America, the Ozark Mountains of Missouri, Arkansas, and Oklahoma; the Ouachitas of Arkansas and Oklahoma; the Arbuckle Mountains and the Wichita Mountains of Oklahoma and Texas, all came into existence. It is also likely that the Huron Mountains and the Porcupine Mountains in the Upper Peninsula of Michigan were elevated to their present height. Uplifts and dissection in the northeastern part of North America produced the highlands of eastern Quebec, the coastal mountains of Labrador, and the mountains of Baffin Land. Thus, nearly all of our present hills and mountains have been sculptured out of areas that were uplifted during very late geologic times, and the uplifts and dissection are still continuing in many places.

TERTIARY VOLCANISM

Very few periods in the geologic history of North America have witnessed such intense and prolonged volcanic activity as that which occurred throughout the western part of our continent during the Cenozoic.

In some places chains of explosive volcanoes (Fig. 245) spread ash widely over the country, while in other regions successive lava flows poured from fractures in the earth's crust and spread over thousands of square miles. Some of the most beautiful and famous mountains in the West are, in reality, extinct or dormant volcanoes. Among these are Mt. Shasta (14,380 feet) (Fig. 246) in northern California, Mt. Hood (11,225 feet) (Fig. 247), a beautiful composite cone in northwestern Oregon, Mt. St. Helens (9,671 feet), and Mt. Rainier (14,408 feet) (Fig. 248) in southwestern Washington. Lassen Volcanic National Park, at the southern end of the Cascades in California, is famous for Mt. Lassen (10,437 feet) (Fig. 249). This mountain began to erupt in May, 1914, after lying dormant for an unknown length of time, and has been intermittently active ever since.

The San Francisco Mountains near Flagstaff, Arizona, are a group of very impressive recent volcanoes that have been built up above the level surface of the Colorado Plateau by a long series of eruptions. Sunset Crater, a few miles from Flagstaff, Arizona, is a strikingly beautiful dormant volcano with a bright orange-colored crater rim.

Crater Lake, in Oregon, occupies a great caldera, which is 6 miles long and 4 miles wide. Most of the original volcanic mountain disappeared long ago, when the top of the cone collapsed into the crater and was engulfed as the lava column subsided. The name "Mt. Mazama" has been given to this ancient volcano, which was active until late in the Pleistocene. Glacial deposits have been found interbedded with volcanic materials on the slopes of the mountain, proving that between the great eruptions there were long periods during which glaciers were able to form.

The picturesque San Juan Mountains in southwestern Colorado are largely of volcanic origin. The Spanish Peaks (13,623 feet), northwest of Trinidad, Colorado, are two mountains that have been eroded out of Eocene sediments and intrusive rocks. The most remarkable features of these mountains are the great radiating dikes that extend for miles across the plains.

Volcanism continued for a long time in the Yellowstone National Park region, while lava flows of rhyolite and basalt built up an extensive plateau in the area. The numerous hot springs and geysers are evidence that there is still uncooled lava at no great depth below the surface. Yellowstone Canyon (Fig. 252) is a brilliantly

FIG. 245.—Amboy Crater, a recent cinder cone, near Amboy, California.   (*Courtesy of Spence Air Photos.*)

FIG. 246.—Mt. Shasta, a dormant volcano in Northern California.   (*Courtesy the Redding, California, Chamber of Commerce.*)

FIG. 247.—Mt. Hood in northwestern Oregon is an extinct volcano. (*Courtesy of U. S. Forest Service.*)

FIG. 248.—Mt. Rainier, an extinct volcano in southwestern Washington, and the Nisqually Glacier. (*Photographed by Asahel Curtis.*)

Fig. 249.—Lassen Peak from the northeast showing the devastated area after the blast of May 22, 1915. Photograph taken on July 22, 1915. (*Photographed by Arthur L. Day. Courtesy of The Carnegie Institution of Washington and the Geophysical Laboratory.*)

Fig. 250.—El Parícutin, an active volcano, 200 miles west of Mexico City. Eruptions started Feb. 20, 1943. (*Photographed by Kenneth McMurray. University of Michigan Parícutin expeditions sponsored by Major O. O. Fisher.*)

colored, V-shaped gorge, cut to a depth of 1,200 feet in volcanic material. In the northeastern part of the park there are 17 successive forests, each one buried beneath ash and lava after it had grown. These remarkable petrified trees, which are exposed upon the slopes of Amethyst Mountain, extend through a vertical thickness of 2,000 feet. Many of the stumps are still rooted in the original soils and some of the trunks reach a diameter of 10 feet.

The John Day beds in north central Oregon consist almost entirely of volcanic ash and tuff derived from explosive volcanoes of Oligocene age that were located somewhere in the Cascade Moun-

Fig. 251.—A lava flow issuing from North Crater in Craters of the Moon National Monument, Idaho. (*Photograph from United States Department of the Interior.*)

tains. These deposits are mostly covered by the Columbia River lava flows and can be seen only where streams have cut deep canyons. The extent of these beds is unknown, but their thickness varies from 2,000 to 3,000 feet. The middle part of the John Day section contains a very rich mammalian fauna.

Columbia River Lava Flows. The vast Columbia River Plateau (Fig. 253) in the northwestern part of the United States, covering about 200,000 square miles, is one of the greatest lava fields (Fig. 254) ever formed. The plateau was built up during a long period of time by a succession of eruptions that reached great intensity about the Miocene epoch. The lava is mostly basalt, and the individual flows vary in thickness from 10 to more than 200 feet.

The molten rock issued chiefly from fissures in the earth's crust, although in the Snake River region and several other places the eruptions were from local centers. No single flow covered the entire region, and the intervals of eruption were sometimes followed by relatively quiet times, during which the igneous rocks

Fig. 252.—Grand Canyon of the Yellowstone River.

weathered to form a thick covering of soil. These soils, as well as deposits made by streams and in lakes, are found interbedded with the flows.

The old land surface over which the Columbia River lavas flowed was quite irregular, even mountainous in places. Some of these buried mountains have been exposed in Idaho, where deep gorges have been eroded in the basaltic rock. The canyon of the

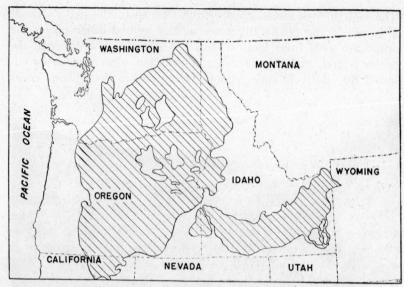

FIG. 253.—Map showing the area covered by the Columbia River basaltic lava flows of the Tertiary.

FIG. 254.—Columbia River lava plains, Dry Falls State Park, Washington.   (*Courtesy of Spence Air Photos.*)

Snake River in western Idaho has exposed over 4,000 feet of basalt flows.   Here the original thickness was at least a mile.

Craters of the Moon.   In southern Idaho there is a very interesting district called "Craters of the Moon National Monument" (Fig. 251) where the spectacular results of very late Cenozoic volcanic activity may be clearly seen.   Some of the igneous rocks are so fresh that they appear to have been molten only a short time ago, and the rough surface of the scoriaceous lava shows no signs of weathering.

THE CENOZOIC ON OTHER CONTINENTS

The Andes Mountains were upheaved along the western side of South America in the latter part of the Mesozoic.   These ranges were extensively peneplaned during the early Cenozoic, and widespread regional uplifts in the Pliocene and Pleistocene epochs lifted the plain to great heights, while weathering and differential erosion produced much of the present rough topography.

During the Mesozoic era a great geosyncline stretched across southern Europe and eastward beyond the present site of the Himalaya Mountains.   The first orogenic movements in the Alpine section of this trough came in Jurassic times, when a few low folds were lifted above the sea.   Uplift was renewed during the Cretaceous; then in the Eocene came the first thrusting.   However, it was not until the Oligocene that tremendous compressive forces from the south began to drive the great recumbent folds northward in a series of flat thrusts that overlap like shingles.   Further thrusting and regional uplifts in the Pliocene and Pleistocene lifted the mountains to their present height.   Some of the pressure that brought the Alps into existence was transmitted to a belt of horizontal sediments that lay to the northwest, and these rocks were folded into the Jura Mountains.   The Carpathians and the vast Himalayan system reached their present height in the late Cenozoic.

The warm waters of the Tethyan sea, which covered northern Africa, southern Europe, and the region of the present Himalaya Mountains during the Eocene and Oligocene epochs, swarmed with large disk-shaped protozoans called Nummulites.   The shells of these Foraminifera built up extensive beds of limestone, and Eocene rocks containing the fossil protozoans are found at elevations of 10,000 feet in the Alps and 20,000 feet in the Himalayas.   This limestone was used by the Egyptians in building the Pyramids.

There was intense volcanic activity in Mexico, Central America, and the Andes region during the Cenozoic.   Great flows of basalt

are found in northern Ireland, where they form the celebrated
Giant's Causeway. Similar rocks are found in the northwestern
part of Scotland, in Iceland, and in eastern Greenland. The lands
bordering the Pacific Ocean are still areas of great seismic and
volcanic activity.

Eocene rocks in the Paris Basin are famous for the great number of well-preserved invertebrate fossils that they contain. Cuvier
(1769–1832) used a great amount of vertebrate material from these
rocks in his epoch-making studies on comparative anatomy.

CLIMATE OF THE CENOZOIC

Many different kinds of plants and animals are excellent barom-
eters of climatic conditions. The trees of today apparently live
under much the same environmental conditions that their early
Tertiary ancestors preferred. The plants of the rain tropics are
distinct from those found in deserts, and the Arctic has its own
peculiar types of vegetation. Extensive floras have been found
in the Green River shales of Colorado and Wyoming, the Wilcox
group of the Gulf Coastal region, and the Eocene of Greenland.
These plants show that the climate was warmer and more uniform
over larger areas of the earth's surface than it is today. The
climate of Greenland was about like that of Virginia or the
Carolinas at present, and there were no ice sheets within the Arctic
regions.

There were palm trees in Minnesota during the early part of the
Tertiary, and large crocodiles lived there. The presence of these
reptiles so far north of their present range is proof that the year-
round climate was at least subtropical. Forests that today are
characteristic of moist, temperate zones grew in Spitzbergen,
Alaska, and Greenland during the Eocene and Oligocene epochs.
The presence of figs and magnolias in Alaska is especially significant.
Mild climatic conditions continued during the Oligocene along the
coastal regions, but the disappearance of palms and large crocodiles
from the northern interior portion of the United States indicates a
cooling of the climate. However, the change from the Eocene was
not very great, for small alligators still lived in South Dakota.
Plants found in the Miocene volcanic ash deposits of Florissant,
Colorado, are similar to those of the present Gulf States, and small
alligators lived in Nebraska during the Middle Miocene. This
shows that the winters were mild.

As the mountains in the extreme western part of the United
States rose higher, local arid regions began to appear on the lee

sides of the hills. Miocene formations in southern Nevada contain beds of salt. The present widespread aridity in the West began largely in the Pliocene and Pleistocene, when by regional uplift the Cordilleran ranges rose to their present height.

The first generation of San Juan Mountains, in southwestern Colorado, had been upheaved to great heights during the late Cretaceous and early Tertiary, with the result that mountain glaciers developed and the Ridgeway tillite was deposited. These glacial conditions, which were local, disappeared as the mountains were gradually lowered by erosion. The age of the Ridgeway tillite cannot be determined precisely, but it lies above Cretaceous rocks and below volcanic tuff that was formed during the Eocene. The climate slowly grew colder during the Pliocene as the first glacial epoch of the Pleistocene approached.

CENOZOIC ECONOMIC PRODUCTS

Salt Domes and Petroleum. Tertiary sediments in the Coastal Plain region of Texas, Louisiana, and Mexico have been intruded by tremendous cylindrical masses of salt, which in some cases reach a diameter of a mile and extend down to unknown depths. In many cases the salt plug was pushed up through the overlying sediments. These sedimentary rocks are now turned up at their contact with the salt, and they have also been truncated. The sediments are important sources of oil in some places.

Miocene and Pliocene rocks in California produce great quantities of petroleum. The Green River shales in northwestern Colorado and adjoining parts of Utah and Wyoming contain a great potential supply of oil that will doubtless be recovered by distillation at some future time when other sources of petroleum have been exhausted. The oil that comes from the great Baku field of Russia, in the eastern part of the Caucasus, is found in Oligocene, Miocene, and Pliocene rocks. Other important localities in which the petroleum occurs in Tertiary formations are found in Iraq, Iran, the Dutch East Indies, Rumania, and Venezuela.

Coal. The Fort Union group of the Paleocene epoch contains important coal deposits in Wyoming and Montana. Tertiary coal beds are scattered over considerable areas in Washington and Oregon. The various fields are of limited extent, but their output is of considerable importance in the Pacific Coast region. The coal is mainly lignitic, although in some places folding stresses have changed it into a subbituminous variety.

Diatomaceous Earth.   The Miocene rocks of California contain thick beds of diatomaceous earth.   Near Lompoc, in Santa Barbara County, the deposits are interbedded with volcanic ash, while in other places they occur with limestones.   Similar beds are found in Virginia and Maryland.   Diatomaceous earth is used in making polishing powders, as an insulating material, and as a filtering medium.

Placer Gold.   The gold-bearing quartz veins of the Mother Lode region in California were originally buried beneath great thicknesses of sediments.   This covering was eroded during the Cretaceous and early Tertiary.   Finally, the veins themselves were uncovered and attacked by weathering.   The gold particles were released from the surrounding quartz, and concentrated in stream-deposited gravels, from which they are recovered by hydraulic mining and dredging operations.   In some places, where the auriferous gravels have been covered by lava flows, a tunnel is run to the gold-bearing part of the bed and the gravel is hauled to the outside, where it is washed.   The placer deposits of California were discovered in 1848, and in 1849 occurred the famous historic rush to the gold fields.   More than $1,200,000,000 worth of gold has been taken from these Tertiary gravels.

Famous Mining Camps.   Many of the celebrated mining properties of the West have been developed in ore deposits of Cenozoic age. The Cripple Creek district in Colorado has been producing gold since 1890 from veins that are associated with Tertiary volcanics.

The famous Comstock Lode near Virginia City, Nevada, discovered in 1858, has produced a great quantity of silver, as well as gold.   Very high temperatures were encountered in some of the lower workings.   In 1863 a part of the mine was flooded with water that had a temperature of 170°F.   The mining towns of Telluride, Ouray, and Creede are located in the San Juan region of southwestern Colorado.   Tremendous volcanic activity occurred in this district during the Tertiary period, and the gold, silver, and lead deposits were formed at that time.   The Bingham Canyon area of Utah is one of the leading copper-producing regions in the United States.   The source of the ore is a great mass of igneous rock that was intruded into Carboniferous quartzites and limestones during the later Mesozoic or the early Tertiary.

Reading References

ASHLEY, GEORGE N.: Studies in Appalachian Mountains Sculpture, *Geol. Soc. America Bull.*, vol. 46, pp. 1395–1436, Sept. 30, 1935.

CAMPBELL, N. M., and OTHERS: Guide Book of the Western United States, *U. S. Geol. Survey Bulls.* 611–614, 1915.

CHANEY, RALPH W.: Tertiary Forests and Continental History, *Geol. Soc. America Bull.*, vol. 51, pp. 469–488, 1940.

FENNEMAN, N. M.: "Physiography of the Western United States," 534 pp., McGraw-Hill Book Company, Inc., New York, 1931.

O'HARRA, C. C.: "The White River Badlands," *South Dakota School of Mines Bull.* 13, 181 pp., 1920.

SCOTT, WILLIAM B.: "A History of Land Mammals in the Western Hemisphere," rev. ed., pp. 97–122, The Macmillan Company, New York, 1937.

TALIAFERRO, N. L.: Geologic History and Structure of the Central Coast Ranges of California, State of California, Dept. Natural Resources, Division of Mines, *Bull.* 118, Part 2, pp. 119–163.

YARD, R. S.: "The Book of the National Parks," 420 pp., Charles Scribner's Sons, New York, 1919.

CHAPTER XIX

THE CENOZOIC ERA

THE PLEISTOCENE EPOCH

The spread of great continental glaciers over vast areas of the earth's surface is one of the most significant and spectacular events in the Pleistocene epoch. Such tremendous masses of ice had profound effects not only upon the glaciated regions themselves but in places beyond the reach of the ice. Climatic zones in the Northern Hemisphere were shifted southward and Arctic conditions prevailed in the northern part of the United States. All forms of life disappeared within the ice-covered areas and living conditions became very severe for many animals and plants that lived outside the glaciated regions. The Pleistocene is of special interest because it was during this epoch that man rose to a dominant position. Since the glacial age began, the various races of human beings have spread to all parts of the world.

Fig. 255.—Frank Leverett (1859–1943). A leader in the study of Pleistocene glacial geology.

BEGINNING OF THE GREAT GLACIERS

Centers of Glaciation (Fig. 256). Some geologists believe that the North American ice sheets radiated from two main areas in Canada. The Labrador center was located on the low plateau east of Hudson Bay and the ice moved in all directions from this region. At the time of its maximum extent, the glacier front reached 1,600 miles southwestward into the Ohio and Mississippi valleys. The Keewatin center was situated to the northwest of Hudson Bay over a lowland region and the ice moved westward to the piedmont

area of the Rocky Mountains and north to the Arctic Circle, while
the southern border followed roughly the Missouri River as far as
St. Louis. The ice from these two great centers probably united
at some time during their maximum extent, forming a continuous
sheet that covered almost 4,000,000 square miles of the continent.
The Patrician center in northwestern Ontario was one of the minor
places of accumulation. Ice from this region merged with the
greater glaciers of the Labrador and Keewatin areas. The line

Fig. 256.—Map of North America showing the extent of the Laurentide ice sheet
at the time of its maximum development during the Pleistocene glaciation. The
Driftless Area is shown in black.

joining the two chief centers of glaciation extended in a northwest-
southeast direction, following the course of the isotherms as they
are at present. This fact, which is significant, indicates that the
temperature relations between the eastern and western sides of
North America were about the same during the Pleistocene as they
are today, although the average annual temperature must have
been several degrees lower during the glacial phases than it is at
present.

Great valley glaciers formed in the Cordilleran region (Fig. 256)
of Canada. Some of these spread eastward beyond the mountains

as piedmont ice sheets and joined the glacier from the Keewatin field. The Yukon region and Alaska were not covered by a continental glacier during the Pleistocene, largely because winds from the Pacific lost their moisture content over the lofty mountains that border the coast. Much of the Alaskan area still receives comparatively little snowfall for the same reason. There was a separate center of ice accumulation in Greenland and this great land mass was completely buried beneath the glacier.

Some authors reject the theory that the Pleistocene continental glaciers of North America originated chiefly in the Keewatin and Labrador centers. There is considerable evidence to show that the Laurentide ice sheet of Wisconsin age, and perhaps all the preceding ones, originated as mountain glaciers in the highlands of Baffin Land, Labrador, and Quebec. As the ice in the mountains increased in thickness, it buried the ranges, expanded into piedmont glaciers and spread westward over the whole of Canada to the Cordillera and southward to the Ohio and Missouri rivers. This vast Laurentide glacier was nourished by moist air that came from the Pacific, the Atlantic, and the Gulf of Mexico. The moisture from these sources was responsible for the great extension of the ice sheets toward the west and south.

The snowfall was not uniform around the entire margin of the glacier. In certain areas where the precipitation was unusually heavy—as in the Keewatin, Labrador, and other centers—low, broad domes were formed, which shifted their positions following the shifting areas of maximum snowfall. The ice flowing radially from these dome-like centers produced the striations that are found on the bedrock in many places. The striae that are preserved today must have been made during very late Wisconsin time; the older ones have been scoured away.

Small glaciers are still found in the mountains of Labrador and large ones persist on Baffin Island and Ellesmere Island. The northeastern part of Canada has practically no warm summer season even now and, if the annual temperature of this part of North America should drop only a few degrees, glaciers might once more increase in size, eventually assuming continental proportions.

The Driftless Area. In Wisconsin there is a district covering about 10,000 square miles that is called the "Driftless Area" (Fig. 257) because it was not covered by glaciers at any time during the Pleistocene. Several factors combined to cause this interesting situation. The area lies south of Lake Superior and west of Lake Michigan, while to the north there are remnants of some very

FIG. 257.—Castle Rock in the Driftless Area of Wisconsin. Such unstable erosion remnants would have been largely destroyed if the glacier had advanced over the region. The rock is of Cambrian age. (*Photographed by A. E. Luckenbill.*)

ancient mountain ranges, some of which still rise 2,000 feet above sea level. The flow of ice from the Keewatin and Labrador regions was deflected around the Driftless Area by these highlands and by the deep troughs of Lake Superior and Lake Michigan. There is no proof that the region was ever completely surrounded by ice at any one time. During the Wisconsin stage of glaciation there was a broad opening toward the south, but one of the earlier ice sheets may have walled the area in on all sides, although this is doubtful.

There is no way to determine accurately the thickness of the ice at either of the two main dome-like centers. The glacier moved southward from the Labrador region, covering the White Mountains of New Hampshire—and these highlands rise to elevations of 5,000 feet. The Adirondacks, which reach elevations of more than 4,000 feet, were probably completely buried. It seems quite probable that the ice was at least 2 miles thick at the Labrador center and equally thick in other places of heavy snowfall.

The approximate locations of the dome-like centers of Wisconsin time have been determined by plotting the glacial striations that are found on the bedrock and observing the areas toward which these striae converge. The actual direction of ice movement can be told wherever chatter marks and staple grooves occur. Certain kinds of rocks that outcrop only in limited areas, such as the jasper conglomerate of the Georgian Bay region, have sometimes been moved from their places of origin. Wherever these rocks are found, they show the approximate direction of ice movement.

GLACIAL AND INTERGLACIAL STAGES

For a long time after the existence of continental glaciers in North America had been clearly established, geologists believed that there had been a single glacial stage, followed by a retreat of the ice. Later studies, however, demonstrated that there were at least four glacial stages and that each advance of the ice was followed by a widespread retreat. The evidence of multiple glaciation during the Pleistocene is now generally accepted. When the glaciers advanced southward from the chief centers in Canada, great quantities of sand, gravel, and clay, called "glacial drift," were carried by the ice and deposited widely over the land when the climate grew warmer and the ice melted.

Plants and animals gradually returned to the glaciated regions as they became habitable. Remains of such life are found buried in the deposits of bogs and swamps that formed when the ice had retreated. After a long interval, during which the exposed glacial material was subjected to weathering and erosion, another invasion of the ice brought more drift, which was deposited unconformably upon the weathered surface of the older glacial debris. Buried soils and swamp deposits containing the fossil remains of temperate-climate plants and animals are thus found buried between typical accumulations of till or boulder clay. These present evidence of relatively mild interglacial stages, some of which were much warmer than the climate of the present.

There is no way to tell, at present, whether we are living in an interglacial period or whether the ice is in its final retreating stage. In general, the glaciers all over the world have been getting smaller since the last Pleistocene ice began to melt, and even though eventually the present may prove to be an interglacial stage, the climate will continue to grow warmer for several thousand years before the next great ice sheets begin to form. It is true that the Ice Age has not yet ended, because Greenland and Antarctica are still buried beneath continental glaciers several thousand feet thick.

The Coming of the Glaciers. Snow and ice doubtless existed on high mountains many times during past geologic history, even though the climate of the lowlands may have been very warm. The vast ranges of the Himalayas are only a comparatively short distance north of India, with its extremely hot climate; yet these mountains are heavily blanketed with permanent snow fields, and great glaciers descend from higher levels into the valleys.

The Nebraskan Drift. The exact position of the center from which this oldest ice sheet radiated is uncertain. Some geologists have placed it about 300 miles northwest of Hudson Bay, but there is a possibility that it may have been much farther south. The limits of the till sheet are difficult to trace because it is covered in most places by the Kansan drift, but the deeply weathered surface of this old glacial material has been recognized in Nebraska, Minnesota, Iowa, northern Missouri, and Kansas. The original extent of the Nebraskan ice must have been far greater than the known distribution of its drift sheet.

When this glacier moved southward, it apparently encountered great forests of conifers, which were leveled and destroyed as the ice passed along. The evidence for this is found in numerous splintered slabs of wood that are mixed with the Nebraskan boulder clay.

The problem of the snow supply for the Nebraskan ice is a difficult one. The cold North Atlantic was far distant from the glacial center, and mountains along the coast probably prevented any great quantity of snow from reaching the interior. The fact that the ice sheet was greatly extended toward the south is an indication that the supply of moisture came chiefly from the Gulf of Mexico region. The Nebraskan ice front reached latitude 38°N., which is not far from St. Louis, before the loss from melting was able to balance the forward movement. The climatic conditions around the margin of the glacier must have been very much like those in Greenland today. Terrific blizzards blew down from the ice during the long winter, and in summer great quantities of water from the melting ice flowed southward, while the Mississippi River must have been a raging torrent with water spreading widely over the low, flat lands along either side.

The Aftonian Interglacial Stage. The upper part of the Nebraskan till was subjected to a long period of weathering during the Aftonian interval, during which the soluble carbonates were leached away and a very sticky clay, called "gumbotil," was formed. In some places at the top of the Nebraskan drift, this reaches a thickness of nearly 8 feet.

The climate during the Aftonian stage was at least as mild as that of the present, and there was an abundance of rainfall that supported a luxuriant vegetation. Pollen from interglacial peat beds of Iowa, which have been studied recently, indicate that during the early part of the Aftonian the forests of Iowa were coniferous. This phase was followed by a great spread of grasslands, but, toward the end of the interglacial stage, oaks appeared, and as the climate grew colder conifers returned.

The Mississippi Valley was inhabited by great numbers of mammals, which included several varieties of wild horses, ground sloths, bears, deer, beaver, six species of elephants, bison, and camels. The large numbers of herbivorous animals that are known to have lived at this time prove that there was plenty of plant food available and that the mammals had apparently suffered very little as a result of the Nebraskan glaciation.

The Kansan Drift. When the Keewatin ice sheet reached its maximum development during the Kansan glacial stage, the front of the glacier reached south to Kansas City and St. Louis. The till sheet, which extends beyond that of the Nebraskan, has a distribution farther to the southwest than that of the later drift deposits. The Kansan till is exposed in Missouri, Kansas, Iowa, and Nebraska; and in Montana it probably extended to longitude 110°W. The northward extent is but imperfectly known. Kansan ice from the Labrador center reached into southern Illinois.

The till deposited during this stage of glaciation has been deeply weathered, and in many places erosion has removed the material, so that its original extent is difficult to determine.

Before the coming of the Kansan ice sheet the headwaters of the Missouri River are thought to have drained northward in the direction of the Nelson River and Hudson Bay. When this outlet was blocked by ice, the Missouri changed its course and became a tributary of the Mississippi, making that river a much larger body of water.

The trunks of trees are frequently found embedded in the base of the Kansan boulder clay, showing that the glacier overwhelmed forests during its advance.

The Yarmouth Interglacial Stage. The Kansan ice finally disappeared, leaving the till deposits exposed to prolonged weathering, and 11 feet of gumbotil were formed during the exceptionally long Yarmouth interval. The climate was mild and moist during the early part of this interglacial period, but later it became dry and great quantities of loess were carried by the wind from the arid western plains and deposited extensively over the surface of the Kansan drift.

Unquestioned Yarmouth peat beds, some of them 15 feet thick, have been found in Iowa, while similar deposits that occur in neighboring states are probably of the same age as the Iowa beds, although this is not certain. Most of the plants found in these swamp deposits belong to types that still grow in the same regions. The vertebrates include giant ground sloths, giant beavers, tapirs, peccaries, horses, elephants, deer, bison, hares, skunks, and wolves.

The Illinoian Drift. The Illinoian drift was deposited by a great glacier that radiated from the Labrador center and extended southwestward to the Ohio River, and across the Mississippi into Iowa and Missouri. One of the largest of all the Pleistocene ice sheets, it covered nearly all of the northeastern part of our continent, including the extreme northern part of Pennsylvania, a portion of New Jersey, Long Island, nearly all of New York, and the states that lie to the northeast. The important mountain barriers encountered by the Illinoian ice over the New England region and in New York were in part responsible for the great extension of this glacier toward the southwest. It is uncertain whether ice formed at this time over the Keewatin center west of Hudson Bay.

A lobe of the Illinoian ice that pushed into Iowa from the Keewatin area forced the Mississippi River to flow in a new channel, several miles west of its present position.

Fig. 258.—Recessional moraine of the Wisconsin stage of glaciation east of Ann Arbor, Michigan. (Photographed by M. V. Denny.)

The Sangamon Interglacial Stage. There was prolonged weathering of the Illinoian drift during the Sangamon interval, when gumbotil formed to a depth of 4 to 6 feet. Muck and peat deposits 20 feet thick accumulated in many places, indicating a temperate climate, and extensive deposits of loess cover the Illinoian till.

Great numbers of insects lived in the bogs and swamps. The wing cases of beetles are especially common. Although the fragmental remains of *Elephas primigenius* have been found in the Sangamon deposits, skeletons of vertebrates are very rare. These

Fig. 259.—Sand and gravel deposited by water from the melting Wisconsin glacier. The Campus, University of Michigan.

animals were apparently intelligent enough to avoid the marshy places, where their bones might have been preserved as fossils.

The Wisconsin Drift. The Wisconsin drift is exposed at the surface over several hundred thousand square miles in Canada and the United States, where it is largely responsible for the present topography (Fig. 258). Only a few thousand years have elapsed since the retreat of the last glacier, and the till deposits present a remarkably fresh appearance. A comparatively thin soil has formed on top of the drift, reaching down to a depth of only 2 or 3 feet. Swamps and undrained areas are still common throughout the area of this last glaciation and extensive deposits of peat have formed in many places.

Both the Labrador and Keewatin regions were centers of radiation during the Wisconsin glacial stage. Ice from both of these great areas reached into the upper part of the Mississippi Valley. All the different types of glacial deposits are still preserved in the Wisconsin drift and they have been studied in great detail. A system of concentric recessional moraines marks successive steps in the retreat of the ice. Kame hills made of poorly stratified and assorted gravels and sands are found in many places, and eskers mark the courses of subglacial streams. Drumlins are distributed fanwise over the ground moraines in a number of localities.

FIG. 260.—Glaciated surface of Pre-Cambrian granite (rôches moutonnées), south of Kalador, Ontario. (*Courtesy of Geological Survey of Canada.*)

Extensive outwash plains of sand and gravel (Fig. 259) were formed in front of the recessional moraines by streams from the melting ice.

Ice from the Keewatin center moved westward across the Great Plains, depositing boulders from the Hudson Bay region upon the piedmont area of the Rocky Mountains. Many of these stones weighing several tons each are now resting 3,000 feet above their place of origin. The ice of continental glaciers is the only agent capable of moving such heavy objects uphill.

A study of pollen grains found in swamps that formed after the retreat of the Wisconsin ice shows that the climate of the United States was comparatively warm and dry for several thousand years after the glacier had disappeared. The pollen shows that mild-climate trees were able to live at that time much farther north than their present limits. Later, the climate grew cooler and more moist, and this condition still exists.

Mantle rock and soil were carried by the moving ice from great areas of the Canadian shield (Fig. 260), leaving vast expanses of bed-rock either bare or covered with thin soil and a very sparse growth of vegetation. Some of the original soil that had slowly formed through countless ages of weathering preceding the Pleistocene was deposited over the Upper Mississippi Valley region, where it makes very rich farm lands.

FLUCTUATIONS OF SEA LEVEL

Enormous volumes of water were evaporated from the oceans during the formation of the Pleistocene continental glaciers, and there were important fluctuations of sea level as the ice first accumulated and then melted. When the greatest of these ice sheets reached its climax, the ocean level dropped at least 250 feet and extensive areas of the present continental shelves became dry land. During such times the British Isles were joined to the mainland, while forests and grasslands covered what is now the region of the North Sea. Java, Borneo, and Sumatra were part of the Asiatic continent, and a land bridge stretched from Siberia to Alaska.

During interglacial periods the level of the oceans stood at approximately the present height. When all the ice on the Antarctic continent and in Greenland has melted, the sea level will stand about 100 feet higher than it does today. This will submerge considerable areas along the Atlantic and Gulf Coastal Plains.

DEPRESSION OF THE LAND

The tremendous weight of the ice depressed the crust of the earth over large portions of the glaciated area, in some places to a position several hundred feet below its preglacial level. The maximum amount of depression was about a thousand feet. Since the melting of the glacier, however, this load of ice has been removed and the down-warped areas are slowly rising. The upward movement has been greatest toward the north, and one of the glacial Lake Algonquin (Fig. 262) beaches now stands 900 feet higher at its northern than at its southern end. The hinge line, north of which this tilting movement has occurred, runs in a northwest-southeast direction through the north central part of southern Michigan and southeastern Ontario.

The St. Lawrence Valley was depressed so much by the weight of the Wisconsin ice that when the glacier melted marine water spread into the Champlain Valley and probably as far as the basin of Lake Ontario, forming the Champlain Sea. The sediment that was deposited in this body of water contains a subarctic fauna consisting largely of mollusks. The presence of whale bones in post-glacial deposits of Southern Michigan shows that there was an easy migration way from the ocean into the Great Lakes region.

Changes in Drainage. The advancing ice sheets obliterated all the old drainage channels within the glaciated areas, and even after the retreat of the glaciers most of the former river valleys were filled with drift. Northward-flowing streams, turned aside by the ice sheets, were forced to flow along the front of the glacier until they found a course toward the south. Near Warrensburg, New York, the Hudson River was deflected westward by a lobe of the ice; and farther south, at Corinth, New York, a moraine forced the river to flow eastward. Several different streams united their waters to form the Ohio River, while the Missouri was shifted southwestward from its preglacial channel. Many streams, like the Illinois and Minnesota, because of the tremendous increase in the volume of water when the ice began to melt, cut wide valleys, which are much too large for the present rivers.

HISTORY OF THE GREAT LAKES

The basins of the modern Great Lakes were broad lowlands, long before the Pleistocene, and, when the glaciers moved over these areas, they were scoured to greater depths. As the climate grew warmer, the southern border of the Wisconsin glacier began to melt, the front of the great ice sheet retreating northward. Those portions of the glacier that filled the deep valleys were extremely thick and became great lobes when the thinner ice to either side melted. While the front receded unevenly, meltwater collected in the valleys as they were gradually uncovered. Thus, the Great Lakes slowly came into existence. Lake Duluth occupied the western end of the Superior Basin and Lake Chicago, the southern end of the Michigan Basin. A complicated succession of change-able lakes developed in the Huron and Erie basins (Fig. 261). The early history of these bodies of water shows a complex series of drainage changes as the ice melted and uncovered new outlets at lower levels. While ice still blocked the St. Lawrence region, the lakes drained into the Mississippi through the Wabash and Illinois Rivers. The Atlantic drainage began when the Mohawk Valley in eastern New York was uncovered. This valley stood at a lower level than the spillways into the Mississippi, and for a while the

water drained into the Hudson River. Finally the ice disappeared
from the St. Lawrence Valley—the route that still serves as a
drainage channel for the Great Lakes.

Lake Algonquin. The ice continued its general northeastward
retreat, sometimes halting temporarily, even advancing for a short
time. Finally the basins of Superior, Michigan, and Huron were
uncovered. The magnificent sheet of water that filled these
depressions has been called "Lake Algonquin" (Fig. 262). This
vast lake, covering an area of a hundred thousand square miles, was
more than 1,500 feet deep in several places.

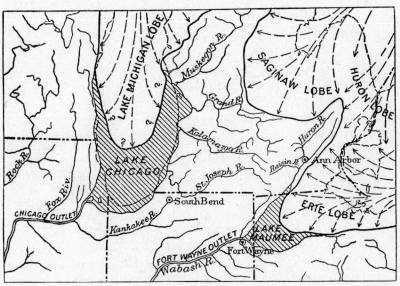

Fig. 261.—Beginning of the Great Lakes following the retreat of the Wisconsin
glacier. (*After Leverett, U.S. Geological Survey.*)

Changing Outlets. Lake Algonquin probably drained first
through the Chicago outlet into the Mississippi and then past Port
Huron and down the Niagara River. A little later, the retreating
ice uncovered a lower outlet near Kirkfield, on the eastern side of
Georgian Bay, and the water then flowed through the valley of the
Trent River into the Ontario Basin, finally reaching the Atlantic.
The Kirkfield outlet was not a permanent drainage channel.
The glacier continued its retreat and, after the great load of ice
was removed, the land rose and Kirkfield was lifted to approximately
the same level as Chicago and Port Huron, with the result that two
or three outlets were brought into action for a while. This stage
of Lake Algonquin lasted for several thousand years, and the Wis-

consin ice front was apparently stabilized because of a somewhat cooler climate. When the ice began to retreat once more, the land resumed its rise. The Kirkfield outlet was abandoned when it rose above those at Port Huron and Chicago. Finally only the Port Huron outlet was left to drain Lake Algonquin, because it was able to cut down its channel faster than did the stream that flowed through the Chicago outlet.

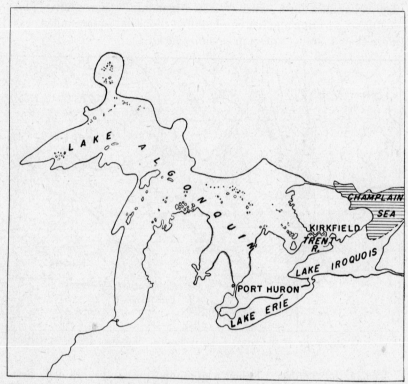

FIG. 262.—Lake Algonquin. (*After Leverett.*)

The beaches along the southern shore of Lake Algonquin, which have been mapped in great detail, are almost as distinct as those of many modern lakes. In many places, the old shore is not far back from the present strand lines; it is horizontal around the southern end of Lake Michigan and the lower portions of Lake Huron and Saginaw Bay. The Algonquin beach rises north of the hinge line, standing more than 400 feet higher near Sault Sainte Marie than it does in the region of horizontality.

Climate and Life during Algonquin Times. The country immediately south of the ice front was undoubtedly barren, but this was not the condition a few hundred miles farther away from the glacier. The heavy shells of clams (unios) have been found in the Algonquin Beach near Chicago. These pelecypods are characteristic Mississippi River species, which could never have lived under Arctic conditions. Even when the ice stood near the middle of the Lake Michigan Basin, oak trees and spruce were able to live in the Chicago area. Vertebrate life was certainly abundant, but the remains are few. *Elephas columbi*, red deer, and diving mergansers were present, indicating that the climate was not especially severe. An ancient Algonquin log jam near Michipicoten,

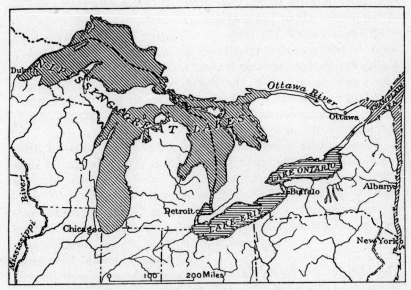

FIG. 263.—The Nipissing Great Lakes. (*After Leverett.*)

Ontario, contains spruce, pine, balsam, cedar, and poplar, just like those growing in the region today. The flora and fauna suggest that the climate was no colder than the average annual temperature along the north shore of Lake Superior today. There is a possibility that the stagnant edge of the Wisconsin ice was covered by morainic material upon which extensive forests grew, like those of the present Malaspina glacier in Alaska.

The Nipissing Lakes. When the ice front finally retreated from the northeastern shore of Lake Algonquin and the watershed toward James Bay lay open, a new outlet was uncovered, lower than that through the St. Clair River (Port Huron outlet). This channel led to the east through the North Bay outlet into the Ottawa

Valley, which was then under the waters of the Champlain sea. The level of Lake Algonquin was soon lowered, and the Nipissing Great Lakes began. No glacial ice bordered the shores of this huge body of water.

The Nipissing Lakes (Fig. 263) drained eastward through the Ottawa River by an outlet that starts at North Bay. The land above the hinge line continued its intermittent rise, and after a time the Port Huron drainage channel was brought into action, giving the Nipissing Lakes two outlets. This stage lasted for a long time, but finally, about three thousand years ago, the discharge was shifted entirely to the St. Clair River. This marks the beginning of the present Great Lakes system.

Niagara Falls. The section at Niagara Falls includes a thick series of easily eroded Silurian shales and sandstones, capped by the hard, resistant Lockport dolomite. The rocks dip gently southward and, long before the Pleistocene, the northward-facing Niagaran escarpment came into existence. It may still be traced for many miles westward, past Lewiston, Ontario, into the Upper Peninsula of Michigan.

Niagara Falls came into existence during the time of Lake Algonquin, when the retreating ice of the Wisconsin glacial stage uncovered the escarpment, permitting water to tumble over the edge of the cliff. The falling water undermines the soft rocks at the base of the scarp and leaves the hard dolomite on top projecting without any support. As the undermining proceeds, great blocks of the cap rock break off. By this process the falls have gradually receded, leaving the great gorge to mark their path. The history of Niagara Falls is not so simple as it once seemed, because the volume of water falling over the escarpment has varied greatly from time to time. It was especially small when Lake Algonquin drained down the Trent River past Kirkfield, and when the Nipissing Lakes emptied through the North Bay outlet. The problem is further complicated by the fact that a part of the gorge, including the whirlpool portion, was cut by some earlier interglacial Niagara Falls. This part of the gorge was later filled with glacial debris and reexcavated by the present falls, which began late in the Wisconsin glacial stage.

Lake Agassiz. This enormous body of water, which came into existence at about the time that Lake Algonquin was formed, covered about 110,000 square miles in North Dakota, Minnesota, Manitoba, and Saskatchewan. The silt and clay that were deposited on the floor of this shallow lake now make some of the richest wheatlands in the entire Middle West. Lakes Winnipeg and Winnipegosis, in Manitoba, are the largest existing remnants of Lake Agassiz.

Lake Bonneville. Greatly increased precipitation during a portion of the Pleistocene caused the formation of Lake Bonneville, in Utah. This body of fresh water covered about 20,000 square miles, was 1,000 feet deep in places, and drained northward through Red Rock Pass into the Snake River. When the climate grew more arid, the water level dropped below the outlet through the pass, and Great Salt Lake gradually came into existence. This shrunken remnant of Lake Bonneville covers less than 2,000 square miles, has an average depth of not more than 20 feet, and contains one part of common salt to five parts of water.

GLACIERS OF THE PLEISTOCENE

In the Cordilleran Region. Glaciers developed on a grand scale in the mountains of western Canada and the United States (Fig. 264). The ice reached a thickness of between 6,000 and 7,000 feet in some of the valleys of the Rockies and Coast Ranges of British Columbia, so that only the higher peaks and ridges stood as nunataks above the glaciers. Ice trapped in some of the deeper valleys became stagnant in its lower portions, while only the upper parts flowed away through main outlet valleys, one of which led southwestward into the Puget Sound area of Washington, another southeastward toward Montana, and a third into the Yukon Valley in the northwest. The Cordilleran glacier at the time of its maximum extent was about 1,200 miles long and 400 miles wide, with the main gathering grounds for the snow between latitudes 55° and 59°N.

There is comparatively little evidence of glacial erosion in the valleys, because movements of the Cordilleran ice were restricted by mountain barriers and in several places unconsolidated preglacial river gravels were not disturbed.

Farther up the mountain slopes, however, at elevations of between 7,000 and 8,000 feet, there are many erratics as well as deposits of till, and the rock surfaces are grooved and striated. The outlet valleys to the north and south, which were subjected to considerable scouring action, are now broadly U shaped. Glaciers formed in the mountains of Alaska, in the Rocky Mountains of Canada and the United States, and in the Cascade Ranges as far south as Arizona and California. Great glaciers still exist in Alaska, while shrunken remnants of the ice fields may be seen in Glacier

National Park, Montana, and upon the slopes of Mt. Rainier in
Washington.

The Greenland Glacier.   A great continental glacier still covers
700,000 square miles of Greenland.   It is still 8,000 feet thick in
places.   There are two centers of ice accumulation, one in the north
and the other toward the south.   The front of this great continental
glacier is now almost stationary except locally, where tongues of
ice move down between mountain peaks into the sea and float away

FIG. 264.—The broad Yosemite Valley was shaped largely by great mountain
glaciers during the Pleistocene.   El Capitan on the left.   Bridal Veil Falls, on the
right, tumbling out of a hanging valley.   (*Courtesy the Merced, California, Chamber
of Commerce and the Yosemite Park and Curry Company.*)

as icebergs.   The conditions in Greenland today are quite like
those that existed in the glaciated regions of North America during
portions of the Pleistocene.

Other Continental Glaciers.   *In Europe and Asia.*   A great ice
sheet, centering in the Scandinavian region, spread eastward across
Russia and beyond the Ural Mountains.   The ice also moved
southward into northern Germany and covered all the British Isles
except the extreme southern part of England.   Another glacier
formed in Siberia, but its extent has not been accurately determined.
There were four advances of the European glaciers, each one followed by a warmer epoch.

The mountain glaciers in the Alps, Pyrenees, Apennines, and Himalayas were much larger than they are at present.

The Antarctic Glacier. The glacier in the Antarctic region developed during the Pleistocene, and 5,000,000 square miles of the

Fig. 265.—Glacial cirques and U-shaped valleys in the mountains west of Salida, Colorado. These cirques and valleys were occupied by mountain glaciers in the Late Pleistocene.

south polar continent are now buried beneath an ice sheet that is still larger than any of the Pleistocene glaciers in North America.

DURATION OF THE PLEISTOCENE

No accurate method has yet been developed for measuring the duration of the entire Pleistocene epoch, but the duration of portions of the Ice Age may be measured with a fair degree of accuracy. Further discoveries may, of course, lead to a solution of the problem.

St. Anthony Falls moved upstream about 7 miles from the original position near Ft. Snelling, Minnesota, to the present location on the Mississippi River at Minneapolis, the recession having been accomplished in about 15,000 years. This event occurred in postglacial times, after the ice front had retreated to a position north of the Great Lakes.

In an attempt to determine the length of the interglacial stages, geologists have studied the depths to which the leaching of calcium carbonate has reached in certain upland gravels. Since the late Wisconsin ice sheet retreated from Iowa, upland gravels belonging to the Mankato drift have been leached to a depth of about two and one-half feet. This has been accomplished, according to some writers, in about 25,000 years, and is the standard used in estimating the length of time required to leach other glacial gravels during interglacial stages. This method gives the following results for Iowa: the Aftonian, 200,000 years; the Yarmouth, 300,000 years; the Sangamon, 120,000 years.

It is now reasonably certain that the total length of the warm interglacial stages of the Pleistocene was considerably greater than the duration of the glacial stages. Consequently, the climate during most of the so-called "Ice Age" was not colder than that of today, while large portions of the Pleistocene were much warmer than the present.

Varve Clays and Silts. One of the more accurate methods for measuring the rate of ice recession was discovered several years ago by De Geer, the Swedish geologist, while studying the clays and silts deposited in lakes that formed along the ice front during a period of recession. Such deposits, which are called "varve clays," occur in alternate light and dark bands. The light-colored silt was deposited during summers when the ice was melting, and the finer darker colored clays settled slowly to the lake bottom in the winters, when there was no meltwater coming from the glacier and when the lake water was perfectly quiet. Thus, each pair of layers repersent a year's accumulation of sediment; therefore, by counting the varves, the time required for their deposition can be accurately determined.

De Geer plotted and correlated the varves in a number of different sections, from southern Sweden to central Norway. He discovered that it had required 13,500 years for the glacier to retreat from the southern part of Sweden to the present small icecaps in the north central part of the country.

Recent studies show that the climax of the last glacial period in Europe was reached about 35,000 years ago. Antevs has counted several thousand varves in New York, New England, and Canada, but it has not been possible to correlate the various sections and make a continuous record. The best estimates available at the present time indicate that the Wisconsin ice sheet began to retreat 25,000 to 30,000 years ago.

CAUSES OF CONTINENTAL GLACIERS

Continental glaciers have developed over different parts of the earth's surface several times during the long course of geologic history, but the exact causes of these ice ages still remain an unsolved problem. Although several hypotheses have been proposed to account for these great ice sheets, they are not generally acceptable.

It is highly probable that periods of continental glaciation are not the result of any one cause, but rather a combination of conditions that has occurred only occasionally throughout the history of the earth.

The Elevation Hypothesis. Mountain glaciers have long been familiar objects and their causes are well known, so it was quite natural that one of the early attempts to explain the Pleistocene continental ice sheets should involve an elevation of the glaciated regions. This hypothesis encounters serious difficulties in explaining the succession of four glacial and three interglacial stages, because these require alternate elevation and depression of great areas of the earth's surface through several thousand feet within a comparatively short time. However, it is true that periods of continental glaciation have followed or accompanied times of extensive mountain building. The upheaval of a great mountain range inevitably alters the air circulation and has an important effect upon the distribution of rainfall and snowfall. It seems likely that such orogenic disturbances may have been a factor in continental glaciation. Certainly, it is no coincidence that the greatest continental glaciations of the past have occurred during those times when lofty mountain ranges were formed over great areas and when continents in general stood well above the sea.

The Atmospheric Hypothesis. Dust and volcanic ash may be held suspended in the earth's atmosphere for several years, and during that period they would tend to shut out some of the radiant energy that comes from the sun. If such a condition could last for a great many years, the annual temperature of the earth might be lowered sufficiently to cause continental glaciers over certain areas. While it is true that volcanoes were unusually active during portions of the Pleistocene, it is equally true that there were several tremendous periods of volcanism in the Cenozoic era, when the climate remained very mild.

Carbon dioxide in the air has a blanketing effect, tending to retard the escape of heat from the earth. A decrease in the quantity of this gas in the atmosphere would permit increased radiation of heat from the earth and lower the annual temperature of certain regions so much that glaciers might form. According to this hypothesis, an increased quantity of carbon dioxide in the atmosphere should cause higher annual temperatures.

Carbon dioxide might be removed from the air in a number of ways. Green plants, while they are growing, remove the gas. Cold water absorbs it in considerable quantities. Extensive plant growths and cold oceans might thus be important factors in reducing the carbon dioxide content of the atmosphere and this, in turn, would tend to lower the annual temperature at the earth's surface.

When the continents are elevated above the seas and large land areas lie exposed to weathering, great quantities of carbon dioxide are consumed during the decomposition of rocks.

Water vapor in the atmosphere is a very important factor in climatic control. A desert may be exceedingly hot during the day but extremely cold at night, because there is very little water vapor in the air to retard the escape of heat after sunset. During times of continental elevation, epeiric seas are absent or are restricted in size and evaporation is decreased, thus reducing the amount of water vapor in the air.

Astronomic Hypothesis. The orbit of the earth is an ellipse, and for this reason our planet is closer to the sun at some points in its path than at others. The time of closest approach, or perihelion, now comes in December, while the earth is farthest from the sun in June. Because of this condition, the Northern Hemisphere has somewhat milder winters and its summers tend to be a little bit cooler than those in the Southern Hemisphere.

Seasonal changes are caused by the fact that the earth's axis of rotation is inclined to the plane of its orbit, and that for half of the year the Northern Hemisphere is turned toward the sun, while the Southern Hemisphere is turned away, these conditions being reversed during the second half of the year. Each hemisphere has its summer when it is inclined toward the sun, because then the heat rays are most direct and the days are longest. Opposite conditions prevail during the winters.

At the present time, summer temperatures in the Northern Hemisphere are high enough to melt all the snow and ice that accumulate during the winters, but a drop of a few degrees might reverse this situation and cause glaciers to form once more in Canada. Such a lowering of the summer temperature might be brought about by changes in the direction of the earth's axis and in its orbital movement. The axis of the earth is changing its position very slowly, and its behavior is somewhat like that of a spinning top. This very slow axial motion, which is called "precession," requires about 26,000 years to complete the cycle. Because of this motion, the Northern and Southern hemispheres are alternately turned toward the sun approximately every 13,000 years.

The eccentricity of the earth's orbit is slowly changing, and at certain times this great path is considerably more elongated than it is at present. Any one of the above causes might not be sufficient to bring about an ice age, but let us assume that the orbit of the earth has reached its maximum eccentricity and that the summer seasons in the Northern Hemisphere occur when our planet is farthest from the sun. Then, if the inclination of the earth's axis happened to be somewhat smaller than it is at present, the summer temperatures in the Northern Hemisphere would be especially low and continental glaciers might begin to develop once more in the Canadian region.

Reading References

COLEMAN, A. P.: "Ice Ages Recent and Ancient," 296 pp., The Macmillan Company, New York, 1926.

———: "The Last Million Years," 216 pp., The University of Toronto Press, Toronto, Canada, 1941.

DALY, R. A.: "The Changing World of the Ice Age," 271 pp., Yale University Press, New Haven, 1934.

FLINT, R. F.: Growth of North American Ice Sheet during the Wisconsin Age, *Geol. Soc. America Bull.*, vol. 54, No. 3, pp. 325–362, Mar. 1, 1943.

KAY, G. F.: Classification and Duration of the Pleistocene Period, *Geol. Soc. America Bull.*, vol. 42, No. 1, pp. 425–466, March, 1931.

LEVERETT, FRANK, and F. B. TAYLOR: "The Pleistocene of Indiana and Michigan," *U.S. Geol. Survey Mon.* 53, 529 pp., 1915.

WRIGHT, W. B.: "The Quaternary Ice Age," 2d ed., 478 pp., Macmillan & Company, Ltd., London, 1937.

CHAPTER XX

LIFE OF THE CENOZOIC

The widespread forests of the early Cenozoic contained nearly all the main types of hardwood trees that are in existence today, and the world must have presented a very modern aspect. By the Miocene epoch, the grassy plains were spreading widely over the lands and, with the food supply thus made available, grazing

Fig. 266.—Tertiary insects and a spider. 1, *Paladicella eruptionis*, from the Florissant, Colorado, Lake beds; 2, *Plecia pealei*, from Twin Creek, Wyoming; 3, *Prinecphora balteata*, showing color markings; 4, *Segestria secessa*, a spider from Florissant. (*After Scudder.*)

mammals began their remarkable development. Several species of grasses have recently been found in the Miocene and Pliocene formations of the Great Plains.

INVERTEBRATES

Foraminifera. Prodigious numbers of large, coin-shaped Foraminifera, called "nummulites," lived in the warm, clear Tethys sea that covered northern Africa, southern Europe, and southwestern Asia during the Eocene and Oligocene epochs. The shells of these organisms built up thick beds of nummulitic limestone, which was

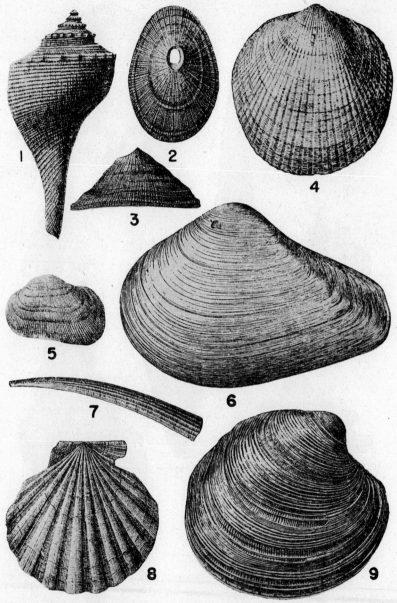

FIG. 267.—Tertiary mollusks. 1, *Fulgur canaliculatum;* 2, 3, *Fissuridea mary-landica;* 4, *Glycimeris parilis;* 5, *Arca centenaria;* 6, *Crassatellites marylandicus;* 7, *Dentalium attenuatum;* 8, *Pecten jeffersonius;* 9, *Venus campechiensis.* (*From Mary-land Geological Survey.*)

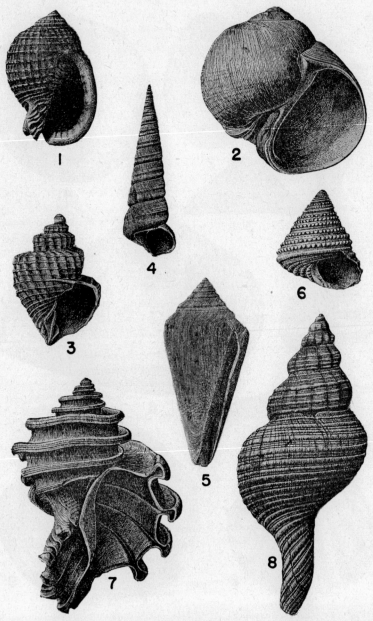

FIG. 268.—Tertiary gastropods. 1, *Cassis caelata;* 2, *Polynices heros;* 3, *Cancellaria prunicola;* 4, *Turritella aequistriata;* 5, *Conus diluvianus;* 6, *Calliostoma philanthropus;* 7, *Ecphora quadricostata;* 8, *Siphonalia marylandica.* (*Maryland Geological Survey.*)

quarried by the ancient Egyptians and used in constructing the great Pyramids of Gizeh, while the Sphinx was carved from a huge residual mass of this rock. Nummulitic limestone is found today at elevations of 20,000 feet in the Himalaya Mountains and up to heights of more than 10,000 feet in the Alps. These characteristic Foraminifera also occur in the Gulf area of the United States and in the Caribbean region.

Incredible numbers of protozoans, belonging to many different types, occur in Cenozoic rocks and are very important in identifying and correlating Tertiary horizons in the oil fields along the Pacific Coast and in the Gulf of Mexico region.

Echinoderms. The crinoid group is still a vigorous one. About 650 species of these invertebrates are known today. Most of them belong to the free-moving, stemless varieties.

Bryozoa. The members of this phylum are common in Tertiary rocks and are still very abundant in many parts of the seas, while some forms are found in fresh water.

Brachiopods. Of these invertebrates, which are not important elements in the marine faunas of the Cenozoic, only about 225 species still live in the seas. Most of these are found in warm, shallow waters, but a few have been dredged from depths as great as 18,000 feet.

Mollusca. Pelecypods and gastropods are exceedingly numerous in many Cenozoic deposits. Thousands of species have been described, and these forms are still common in the seas and fresh water. Tertiary cephalopods are represented chiefly by the nautiloids. There are three species of *Nautilus* still living in the ocean between the Philippines and the Fiji Islands. Squids, octopuses, and crustaceans are extremely abundant in certain localities.

VERTEBRATES

Fish. Teleosts, which were the dominant forms of fish during the Tertiary, vastly outnumbered all other forms, just as they do today. The Green River beds in southwestern Wyoming are famous for the large numbers of wonderfully preserved fish (Fig. 269) that they contain.

Sharks were common during the Cenozoic. A very large form, *Carcharodon*, had teeth 6 inches long and probably reached a length of over 60 feet.

Amphibia. Tertiary amphibia are closely related to modern forms. Such types as frogs, toads, and salamanders were abundant.

Reptiles. Most of the reptiles that had ruled the Mesozoic world for many millions of years were gone, by the Tertiary. The only groups that lived throughout the Cenozoic and that still survive are the snakes, turtles, crocodiles, lizards, and one representative of the ancient Rhynchocephalia, called *Sphenodon*, which is found in the New Zealand region.

Birds. Toothless birds lived in the Eocene epoch, and most of them were like modern forms. One of the most interesting phases of Cenozoic bird life was the presence of giant species with vestigial wings like the living cassowaries and ostriches. *Diatryma* (Fig.

FIG. 269.—The well-preserved skeleton of a fish from the Green River (Eocene) beds in Wyoming.

270), from the Eocene of Wyoming, stood about 7 feet tall and had a very bulky body. The head was 17 inches long and the beak alone was 9 inches in length and 6 inches high. The massive leg bones, with a tibia about 2 feet long, indicate that the bird was a powerful runner. *Phororhacos*, which lived on the plains of Patagonia during the Miocene epoch, was taller than *Diatryma*. The legs were long and comparatively slender, and the massive skull was 23 inches in length and 6 inches high. The upper jaw terminated in a powerful hooked beak that must have been a very formidable weapon.

Huge moas, living in New Zealand until historic times, were finally exterminated by the Maoris, who killed them for food. One locality has yielded the bones of about 800 of these birds. *Dinornis maximus*, the largest of the moas, reached a height of 10 feet.

The head was small and the wing bones had completely disappeared. The legs were longer than those of a horse, and *Dinornis* must have been a very swift runner. *Aepyornis*, of Madagascar, was a little smaller than *Dinornis*, but it laid eggs that reached the amazing length of 13 inches, with a diameter of 9 inches. Such an egg would have the enormous capacity of 2 gallons. The legend of the giant bird called the "roc," in the stories of Sinbad the Sailor, may have originated from the discovery of such eggs.

Fig. 270.—*Diatryma*, from the Eocene (Wasatch formation) of Wyoming was about seven feet tall. The wings had become vestigial and the powerful legs indicate that the bird could run swiftly. (*Drawn by John Jesse Hayes.*)

The most famous of all Cenozoic birds was *Didus ineptus*, commonly called the "dodo." This grotesque-looking animal had a large, heavy body, with short, stout legs. A full-grown individual might have weighed 50 pounds. The dodoes lived on the island of Mauritius, east of Madagascar, until about the year 1700, when they were finally exterminated by sailors in search of food and water.

THE AGE OF MAMMALS

The endless procession of mammals that evolved and spread to all parts of the earth during the Cenozoic rivals in interest and variety those vast hordes of reptiles that lived throughout the

Mesozoic and made it so vivid an era in geologic history. Mammals must have been abundant during the latter part of the Mesozoic, yet their remains are exceedingly rare. This scarcity is difficult to explain. It may be due partly to the fact that mammals, being intelligent animals, were able to avoid most of the traps that caught the reptiles; or it may be because they lived chiefly in the higher altitudes, where preservation was difficult. With the complete disappearance of the dinosaurs, as well as many other groups of reptiles, toward the end of the Cretaceous period, the mammals were freed from the competition of their most powerful enemies.

Fig. 271.—William Berryman Scott (1858–1947). A pioneer and leader in the study of Tertiary mammals. An inspiring teacher.

The mammalian dynasties have ruled the world since the very beginning of the Cenozoic.

The mammals have the great advantage of warm blood and a protective covering of hair, which enables them to live in both warm and cold regions and maintain their activities throughout the year. They have thus proved superior to the reptiles in many ways, but chiefly in their ability to adapt themselves to a very wide range of environmental conditions. This remarkable group of animals is found from sea level to the highest mountains and plateaus. They are equally at home in the tropical forests or the open plains, and even the severe climate of the arctic regions is no barrier to some of the hardier forms. A few have gone underground and become burrowing mammals, one group learned to fly, and many make their homes in the trees. The lakes, the rivers, and the seas are all inhabited by some representatives of the mammals.

The presence of plant food in abundance was one of the extremely significant factors enabling the mammals to spread so widely over the earth. Plants are the ultimate source of food for most animals, and even carnivores depend upon them indirectly.

Factors in Survival. The two prime essentials in life for every animal are food and safety; the structures most directly concerned with attaining these objectives are teeth and the organs of locomotion.

Teeth. The great majority of mammals have several different types of teeth in their jaws. The chisel-shaped incisors in front serve a number of purposes, which include grazing, browsing, and gnawing. The canines are used for seizing and tearing. The premolars may function as grinders, and in some of the carnivores they have been modified into shearing devices that operate like the blades of a pair of scissors. Herbivorous mammals that feed upon tough, harsh grasses on the open plains have developed long-crowned, powerful, grinding teeth, which continue to grow as fast as they are worn down. Certain animals, like man and most of the bears, are omnivorous in their food habits. Their teeth have remained generalized, in keeping with the varied requirements of their diet.

Changes in Foot Posture. Some mammals, such as the raccoons, bears, and man, possess a primitive type of foot posture, called "plantigrade," in which the palms of the hands and the soles of the feet rest upon the ground. The first modification of this position was probably the result of need for greater speed. In this modified posture, called "digitigrade," the animal runs or walks upon its toes. A great many mammals, including agile, running forms like the dog, have developed this type of foot. An extreme variety of foot posture, called "unguligrade," is found in certain mammals, such as the horse, in which the nail has been modified into a hoof. Animals that have evolved this type of foot commonly lose their lateral digits and retain either the middle pair, or, in some cases, only the central one on each foot.

The Brain. One of the most important factors in enabling the mammals to attain their dominant position in the world is undoubtedly the brain. This structure not only increased in size from the earliest mammals to later types, but those parts that are concerned with the higher faculties, such as memory and thinking, gradually became more important, reaching their highest development in the great cerebrum of man.

Archaic Mammals. The seven orders of mammals known from Paleocene rocks all belong to archaic families that have left very few descendants. The marsupials had a much wider distribution during the early Tertiary than they have at present, and the group survives today chiefly in Australia. The American opossum is a very primitive type of marsupial, which has persisted almost unchanged down to the present. It is similar to the original stem from which the group evolved.

The Condylarthra were very primitive ungulates, or hoofed mammals, that ranged into the Lower Eocene. The best-known representative of this family is called *Phenacodus*, an animal about the size of a fox, with 44 teeth that were simple in pattern. There were five digits on each front and hind foot, and the foot posture was semiplantigrade.

The Amblypoda were short-footed, hoofed mammals, which appeared in the Paleocene and became extinct during the Upper Eocene. *Coryphodon* had a heavy body and short, powerful limbs.

Fig. 272.—A typical scene in the Bridger Basin region of southwestern Wyoming about the Middle Eocene epoch. The gigantic and fantastic *Uintatherium* was one of the commonest animals of the time. (*Drawn by John Jesse Hayes.*)

The smallest species stood nearly 4 feet high and the largest one was about the size of an ox. As this animal lived in swampy places, it may have been partly aquatic in habit.

The uintatheres (Fig. 272) were the largest mammals of the Eocene. Some individuals reached a height of 7 feet at the shoulder. Uintatheres had three pairs of blunt, bony protuberances on top of the skull and two long, curved tusks in the upper jaw.

The creodonts (Fig. 282) include a varied assemblage of primitive mammals with some carnivorous forms and others that were apparently omnivorous. There were small varieties about the size of a weasel and giants, such as *Andrewsarchus*, from the Eocene of the Gobi Desert. This enormous creature was considerably larger than the Alaskan brown bear, and the skull alone was about 3 feet long. The teeth of the creodonts were not so highly specialized for flesh eating as were those of the later carnivores, and their brains were small and undeveloped in those parts that are concerned with intelligence.

The Modern Types of Mammals. Great changes occurred among the mammals during the Eocene epoch. The archaic groups were gradually eliminated and the modern types firmly established. Among these higher forms there are many groups that were ancestral to such modern mammals as elephants, horses, camels, rodents, whales, true carnivores, and primates. Several of these higher types appeared at about the same time in both North America and Europe, which suggests that their place of origin was some northern land that has since disappeared, from which they migrated to both continents. There is good evidence that the climate of the far north was temperate during much of the Tertiary, with no barren wastes of ice and snow that might have served as barriers to the spread of different groups of mammals.

History of the Carnivores. The carnivores are fierce, predatory creatures that live largely by killing and eating other animals. Hyenas and a few other forms feed upon carrion, while still others, such as the bears and raccoons, depend largely upon vegetation for their food.

The fossil record of the flesh-eating mammals is a comparatively meager one, because their specialized food requirements make it impossible for any one region to support great numbers of such destructive animals. Carnivores are alert, intelligent creatures with keen senses, and they have been able to adapt themselves to a wide variety of environmental conditions. The whales and seals live in the oceans. The raccoon family and some of the cats are partly arboreal, while the badger is a burrowing form. The peculiar specializations of the carnivores are found in their teeth and claws. The long, sharp canines are used for seizing and tearing, while the shearing teeth are for slicing purposes. The claws are useful for both holding and climbing.

The Dogs (Family, Canidae). The dogs are included in the family Canidae, along with wolves and foxes. This group is very widely distributed over the earth, from the cold regions of the Arctic to the hottest parts of the tropics and from high altitudes down to sea level. Some live on semiarid plains, while others range through forests and jungles. The Canidae form a particularly cosmopolitan group, and the various members are usually adaptable creatures. The dogs, built for speed and endurance, are often able to catch their prey by running it down. The first recognizable members of the dog family appeared in the Oligocene epoch. During the Miocene and the Pliocene, huge wolves (*Amphicyon* and *Dinocyon*) as large as the Alaskan brown bear, ranging over the Great Plains, must have been very terrible creatures. The dire wolf (*Canis dirus*) (Fig. 274) had a wide distribution in North America during the Pleistocene, and its remains are exceedingly common in the tar pits of Rancho La Brea, where it is associated with the modern type of gray wolf (*Canis occidentalis*) and the coyote (*Canis ochropus*).

The Bears (Family, Ursidae). The evolutionary history of the bears is but imperfectly known. This group apparently originated in the Old World and the true bears reached North America in the Pleistocene. Skeletons of the black bear and the grizzly have been found in the Rancho La Brea tar pits. A group of very large, short-faced bears, or arctotheres, ranged from Alaska to Argentina during the Pleistocene.

The Cats (Family, Felidae). The cats are among the most highly specialized of all the carnivorous mammals. The carnassial, or slicing, teeth are perfected for shearing purposes and the claws can be retracted or extended at will. Cats are solitary in their habits and always hunt alone. They are not running animals like the dogs, but their prey is usually captured by stealth and a sudden leap from ambush.

The cats probably originated in the Old World. By the Oligocene, several species had reached the United States, where they continued their development until a large number of forms had evolved. The great lion *Felis atrox*, as large as the modern grizzly bear, ranged widely over North America during the Pleistocene. This powerful cat, which came from Asia to North America across the Bering Isthmus, preyed upon herbivorous mammals in many parts of the United States.

Saber-toothed Cats (Fig. 273). The upper canines of the remarkable saber-toothed cats were developed to an extraordinary degree. In the great *Smilodon* of the Pleistocene they reached a length of 6 inches. These flattened, blade-like tusks were recurved, and their edges were serrated. Such weapons must have been very deadly when used for stabbing, and it is difficult to see how they could have been effectively employed for any other purpose. The muscles that served to move the head downward during the stabbing process were extremely powerful, and the neck was very heavy. The massive build of *Smilodon* indicates that, while it was not a swift runner, it probably had great striking power. These cats must have prowled around water holes where they could easily ambush slow-moving herbivorous mammals as they drank. The amazing numbers of *Smilodon* skeletons found at Rancho La Brea (Fig. 274) indicate that the animals frequented this locality. They were doubtless attracted by the cries and struggles of creatures already caught in the sticky tar. *Smilodon* has been found in a

Fig. 273.—The horse, *Equus occidentalis*, and the great saber-toothed cat, *Smilodon*, in California during the Pleistocene. (*Drawn by John Jesse Hayes*.)

number of places from California to Pennsylvania, and it ranged southward into Brazil and Argentina.

Ground Sloths. Giant mammals called "ground sloths" were very conspicuous animals in South America and the southern part of the United States during the Pliocene and Pleistocene. One form *Megalonyx* ranged northward into Alaska. *Megatherium* (Fig. 275), the greatest of these strange animals, was larger than an elephant, some skeletons measuring 20 feet in length. These clumsy creatures walked upon the outer edge of their feet and knuckles, with the long claws bent inward toward the palm of the hand, and must have moved with an awkward, shuffling type of gait. Several remarkable discoveries show that some members of the ground sloth

Fig. 274.—A scene during the Pleistocene at one of the Rancho La-Brea tar pits in California. The animals include wild horses, the saber-toothed cat, *Smilodon californicus*, the carrion-feeding birds, *Teratornis*, and the dire wolf, *Canis dirus* or *Aenocyon*. (*From a painting by Charles R. Knight, courtesy of the Chicago Natural History Museum.*)

FIG. 275.—The giant ground-sloth, *Megatherium* (left). Two armadillo-like mammals on the right, *Doedicurus* in the foreground and *Glyptodon* in the rear. (*From a painting by Charles R. Knight, courtesy of the Chicago Natural History Museum.*)

family lived until recent times. A skeleton of *Nothrotherium* was found in the crater of an extinct volcano in Dona Ana County, New Mexico, with the tendons, claws, and portions of the skin still preserved. This particular individual lived in an arid region, and food that was found associated with the skeleton consisted of typical desert vegetation, including pieces of large roots that the animal must have dug up with its powerful claws.

A large piece of *Mylodon* skin still covered with coarse, yellowish hair was found in a dry cave at Last Hope Inlet, Patagonia. The animal to which this skin belonged had apparently been killed and eaten by Indians.

Glyptodonts. These huge armadillos (Fig. 275) were especially common in South America during the Pliocene and Pleistocene and many of them reached the southern part of the United States. The largest ones were about 14 feet long and 5 feet high. The huge carapace, which resembled that of a turtle, was made of thick bony plates joined firmly together at the edges. The tail was sheathed in bone and, in *Doedicurus*, a cluster of sharp spikes at the end made it a very effective weapon. These animals, like great, walking fortresses, were largely immune from attack.

Camels. Few people think of the camel as a native of the United States. Yet, much of the evolutionary development of this group occurred in our own country. The geologic history of the camel begins in the Upper Eocene with small creatures not more than a foot high. *Protylopus* had front legs that were considerably shorter than the hind ones, and this gave the back a strong forward slope. Each of the front feet had four digits, all of them functional, although the two in the middle were longest. The outside digits on the hind feet were becoming vestigial and bore none of the animal's weight. There were 44 teeth, and the molars had low crowns.

Several complete skeletons of *Poëbrotherium* have been found in the Big Bad Lands of South Dakota. One species, about as tall as a sheep, had a long body and neck and was supplied with two digits on each foot. The general shape of the skull, as well as the narrow facial region, show that this animal belongs in the camel group. *Alticamelus* (Fig. 276) the giraffe-like camel of the Miocene, was a large form with extremely long, slender legs, and a very long neck. This curious camel, which probably browsed on trees, may have had eating habits similar to those of the African giraffe.

Procamelus, from the Upper Miocene, is very close to the common ancestor of the true camels and the llamas. Many varieties of camels lived in the United States during the Pleistocene and then, for some unknown reason, they became extinct. A very few individuals must have persisted until Recent times, because the skull of a *Camelops* was found in a cave near Fillmore, Utah, with some dried skin still clinging to the bone. Two species of camels still live in the Old World, the Arabian dromedary with its single hump, and the two-humped form of central Asia.

Fig. 276.—*Alticamelus*, the gigantic giraffe-camel from the Middle Miocene. A browsing animal with very long neck and legs. (*Drawn by John Jesse Hayes.*)

Rhinoceroses. Many different members of the Rhinoceros family lived in North America during the Tertiary period. The cursorial, or running, forms were agile creatures with three digits on each foot. The middle toes were much the largest and it is quite possible that these animals would eventually have evolved into one-toed types if their development had continued beyond the Oligocene epoch. The remains of *Hyracodon nebrascensis*, a typical running form of rhinoceros, are found in the White River beds.

The amphibious rhinoceroses lived in this country from the Eocene until the middle part of the Oligocene. *Metamynodon planifrons*, the best known member of this group, had short, heavy legs and a massive body.   Its remains are usually found in river gravels, and this is considered evidence of semiaquatic habits.

Many varieties of true rhinoceroses were natives of North America during the Miocene and Pliocene epochs. *Teleoceras fossiger*, from the Upper Miocene and Lower Pliocene of Nebraska, had a huge body and very short legs.   Such an animal must have moved with an awkward, ambling gait.   The remains of a small, running type of rhinoceros, called *Diceratherium cooki*, are found in enormous numbers in a deposit of fine-grained sandstone near Agate, Nebraska.

The most remarkable rhinoceros yet discovered is *Baluchitherium* from the Oligocene and Miocene of Asia.   This immense creature, the largest land mammal that has ever been discovered, stood at least 13 feet high at the shoulder, and its length was about 25 feet.

The woolly rhinoceros (*Coelodonta tichorhinus*) (Fig. 277) lived during the Pleistocene and ranged from southern France to the northeastern part of Siberia.   Complete carcasses of this animal have been found in the permanently frozen tundra of Siberia.   It is difficult to explain why these hardy creatures did not migrate to North America together with the hairy mammoth.

The land bridge that connected Alaska and Siberia during most of the Cenozoic made the intermigration of mammals so easy that it is impossible to determine whether some of the Eocene and Oligocene groups originated in the Old World or the New, but the rhinoceroses probably evolved in Asia.

Giant Pigs.   The entelodonts, or giant pigs, are remotely related to the swine.   Some of them were of great size.   *Dinohyus*, from the Lower Miocene, stood 6 feet high at the shoulder.   Their incisors and canines were the powerful weapons that these savage animals used in fighting.   Their skulls frequently show the marks of fierce combats.   These remarkable creatures had two curious bony processes, one beneath each eye socket, extending laterally and downward; and they also had two knobs on each side of the lower jaw.   If these structures ever had any function, it has never been determined.

Oreodonts (Fig. 278).   These animals formed one of the most abundant and characteristic groups of Tertiary herbivorous mammals in the United States.   There were many different tribes of oreodonts, and most of the individuals were small.   Some of the groups remained conservative throughout their history, developing few marked specializations.   Oreodonts roamed the grassy plains of the West in enormous numbers.   Some of them were amphibious.

Fig. 277.—The woolly rhinoceros in foreground, antelope and mammoth in the background. (From a painting by Charles R. Knight in the American Museum of Natural History, New York, N.Y.)

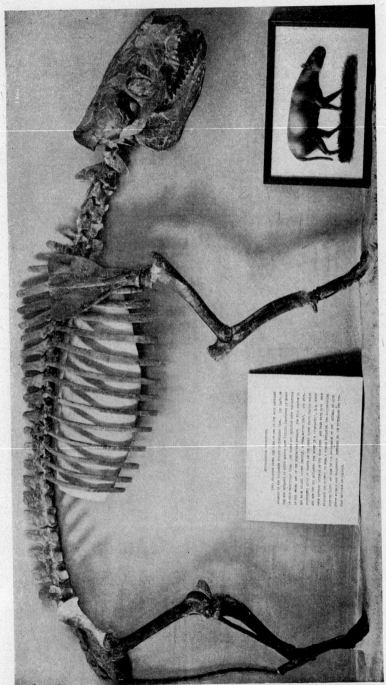

Fig. 278.—*Merycoidodon culbertsoni*, a very common Oligocene oreodont. (*Courtesy of University of Michigan Museum.*)

Syndyoceras (Fig. 279). This strange Lower Miocene mammal belongs to a family whose representatives have been found only in North America; but, in spite of its comparatively brief career, the group evolved many different forms. The front pair of bony outgrowths from the skull curve outward from each other, while the tips of the pair located over the eyes curve inward. These protuberances, like the horns of the giraffe, were probably covered with skin. The hoofs of *Syndyoceras* were similar to those of a deer.

Fig. 279.—*Syndyoceras* in foreground and the gazelle camel *Stenomylus* from the Miocene. Large numbers of *Stenomylus* skeletons have been found in a famous fossil hunting locality in western Nebraska. (*Drawn by John Jesse Hayes.*)

Titanotheres (Fig. 280). These animals first appeared in the United States during the Lower Eocene epoch; yet by the Oligocene they had evolved an amazing number of forms. The larger species had very heavy, bulky bodies, some of them standing nearly 8 feet high. Their teeth remained conservative and low-crowned throughout the history of the group, and the incisors were so small and imperfectly fitted for grazing and browsing purposes that the animal must have had a prehensile lip and a long tongue to assist it in getting its food. The paired nasal horns, which were outgrowths of the skull, varied considerably in size and shape among different genera. Titanotheres have been found in Asia, Europe,

FIG. 280.—*Brontotherium*, a titanothere from the Oligocene of the Big Bad Lands region in South Dakota.   (*Drawn by John Jesse Hayes.*)

FIG. 281.—*Bison crassicornis* from the Pleistocene of Alaska.   This form was similar to *Bison latifrons* which ranged over the Mississippi Valley region.   Both of these animals were gigantic creatures with horns that had a spread of about 6 feet. (*Drawn by John Jesse Hayes.*)

and the western part of the United States. Their remains are very abundant in the Bad Lands of South Dakota.

Bison. Seven distinct species of bison (Fig. 281) lived in North America during the Pleistocene. All of them must have reached this continent from the Old World by way of the Alaskan-Siberian bridge. The remains of these animals have been found in many places, from Florida to Alaska. One species still lives in government-protected herds. *Bison crassicornis* (Fig. 281) was a huge creature, with horns that measured 6 feet from tip to tip. Many skeletons of *Bison antiquus* have been taken from the Rancho La Brea tar pits, some standing 6 feet high. This species ranged as far east as Kentucky.

GEOLOGIC HISTORY OF THE HORSE

Eohippus (Fig. 282). The earliest recognizable member of the horse family appeared in North America during early Eocene times.

Fig. 282.—The primitive horse, *Eohippus*, and the creodont *Oxyaena.* (*Drawn by John Jesse Hayes.*)

This "dawn horse" was a little animal, not more than a foot high, with a long, slender face and a strongly arched back. There were four functional digits on each of the front feet and three on each of the hind feet (Fig. 283), with a hoof-like nail on each toe. The low-crowned teeth indicate that *Eohippus* was a browsing animal.

Mesohippus, which lived during the Oligocene, was about the size of a wolf. Both the front and the hind feet had three functional toes apiece, but the median toes were largest. The teeth were still low crowned, and the animal must have browsed upon comparatively soft vegetation. The brain, which was quite large, had the convolutions of the cerebrum well developed.

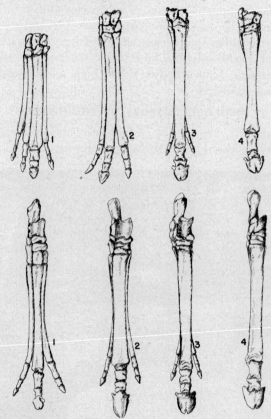

Fig. 283.—Successive stages in the evolution of the feet in the horse group. Right front feet above and right hind feet below. 1, *Eohippus;* 2, *Mesohippus;* 3, *Merychippus;* 4, *Equus.*

Merychippus appeared about the middle of the Miocene and lived until the Lower Pliocene. These animals had three digits on each foot, but the lateral toes were so short that they never touched the ground; thus, *Merychippus* was essentially one-toed. This primitive member of the horse family roamed the open plains. While its milk teeth were still short crowned, the permanent teeth had longer crowns and were better fitted for grinding the tough, harsh grasses that probably formed one of the chief articles of diet. *Merychippus* was about the size of a Shetland pony, and these animals doubtless ran in herds. *Pliohippus*, living during the Pliocene epoch, was a completely one-toed horse with the lateral digits reduced to splints. The high-crowned teeth were set in long jaws, and the animal was a typical grazing form. *Pliohippus* had slender limbs and was about 40 inches high at the shoulder.

Modern types of horses, belonging to the genus *Equus*, were very abundant in North America during most of the Pleistocene. Some of them attained only the size of a small pony (Fig. 273), while others, such as *Equus giganteus*, were larger than the great, heavy-bodied draft horses of today. The skeletons of *Equus occidentalis* are found in the Rancho La Brea tar pits, and *Equus scotti* was common on the Staked Plains (*Llano Estacado*) of Texas. All members of the genus *Equus* are one-toed, with vestiges of the second and fourth digits present as splint bones. The long-crowned teeth of the modern types of horses are set in deep, powerful jaws. These animals are remarkable examples of highly specialized running and grazing types. There were so many species of horses living in the United States during the Pleistocene that it is difficult to see how they could all have evolved from the known Pliocene forms. Some of them may have migrated to this country from Asia.

True wild horses are still found living in the Gobi Desert of Central Asia. These animals are about 4 feet high, with short, upright manes and comparatively large heads. Many pictures of horses were painted on cave walls in France and Spain by Cro-Magnon artists who lived several thousand years ago in the Old Stone Age.

For some unknown reason, horses became extinct in both North and South America in the latter part of the Pleistocene. The cause of this disappearance was apparently not a climatic change brought about by the continental glaciers, but rather some great epidemic that affected the entire group. The wild horses that are found in the western part of North America today are supposed to be the descendants of domestic animals that have escaped from captivity.

GEOLOGIC HISTORY OF THE PROBOSCIDEA

The elephants that are living today in Africa and Asia are only faintly reminiscent of the former grandeur of their race. From the Miocene epoch until the Late Pleistocene many different members of this family roamed in enormous numbers over all the continents except Australia; then, within a comparatively short time, they almost vanished from the face of the earth.

Primitive Representatives. The most primitive member of the proboscidean group yet discovered is *Moeritherium* (Fig. 284), from the Upper Eocene and Lower Oligocene of Egypt. This animal, which was about 3 feet high, had not yet developed either a trunk or tusks, although the second incisors were growing longer. The skull was comparatively long and the 36 teeth were fitted for eating soft vegetation. *Moeritherium* led a semiaquatic existence

Fig. 284.—*Moeritherium* in the swampy environment of the ancient Nile delta during the Eocene epoch. (*Drawn by John Jesse Hayes.*)

upon the swampy regions of the great Nile delta. *Palaeomastodon* lived in the Lower Oligocene of Egypt and was probably ancestral to the true mastodons. The face was long and the second incisors in both the upper and the lower jaws had developed into tusks. The recession of the nasal openings to a position just in front of the orbits indicates the presence of a short proboscis, or trunk. The *Palaeomastodon* skull is considerably higher than that of *Moeritherium* and the animal was more mastodon-like in appearance, although it was probably not much more than 4½ feet tall.

Mastodons. *Gomphotherium* was the first member of the mastodon family to reach North America. It came to this country during the Miocene epoch by way of the Bering Isthmus, and the group was apparently quite numerous. *Trilophodon lulli*, from the Pliocene of Nebraska, had lower jaws that were more than 6 feet long. The most bizarre members of the mastodon family were the "shovel tuskers," whose remains have been found in Mongolia and Nebraska. These animals had flat tusks in their lower jaws that formed digging tools as broad as scoop shovels. *Amebelodon* (Fig. 285) was a characteristic shovel tusker from the Pliocene of Nebraska.

Mammut americanus (Fig. 286) was especially common in the eastern part of the United States. The skeletons and teeth of this

FIG. 285.—*Amebelodon fricki*, "shovel tusker," from the Pliocene epoch of Nebraska. (*Drawn by John Jesse Hayes.*)

animal are frequently found in shallow post-Pleistocene swamps, within the glaciated areas. Some mastodon bones are quite recent and contain traces of the original organic matter. These splendid animals, which reached a height of 9 feet, had a very stocky build. The skull is lower than that of the true elephant and some of the tusks measure more than 9 feet in length. The American mastodon was a browsing form, living chiefly in the forest areas. The Warren mastodon was discovered near Newburgh, New York, in 1845. Some of the undigested contents of the stomach were found between the ribs. This plant food was still identifiable as the twigs of spruce and hemlock trees. The hair which has been reported associated with mastodon remains is probably nothing but filaments of algae, *confervae*, which closely resemble hair. It is not known whether mastodons possessed a dense undercoat of wool, such as served to protect mammoths against the cold of the Ice Age.

At least one South American mastodon, *Cuvieronius*, survived in Equador until comparatively recent times. It was finally killed by natives, who celebrated the event with a great feast. Several fires were built around the carcass and the animal was roasted whole. The skeleton was found in 1929 at the foot of a cliff, where it had been buried beneath a landslide.

FIG. 286.—The American mastodon in Michigan following the retreat of the Wisconsin ice sheet. (*Drawn by John Jesse Hayes.*)

Elephants. The true elephants originated in the Old World. They probably evolved from a Late Miocene mastodon through some intermediate form, such as *Stegodon,* whose remains have been found in southeastern Asia. *Stegodon,* living in the Pliocene, is in some ways transitional between mastodons and elephants. The ridges on the molar teeth were becoming more numerous. These were an adaptation to grazing rather than browsing habits.

Some remarkable changes occurred in the elephant family during its evolutionary history. The proboscis, or trunk, grew longer, while the height of the skull increased out of all proportion to the length and the jaws became so short that they could not accom-

Fig. 287.—The woolly mammoth (*Mammuthus primigenius*) and caribou (*Rangifer tarandus*) in the Pleistocene epoch of Europe. (*Drawn by John Jesse Hayes.*)

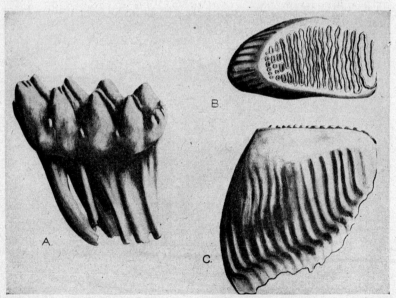

Fig. 288.—*A*, tooth of a mastodon. *B*, grinding surface and *C*, side view of an elephant tooth. (*Drawn by John Jesse Hayes.*)

modate more than eight grinding teeth at one time. As the grinders of the elephant gradually wear out and are finally shed, new ones form in the rear of the jaws and slowly move forward and downward into a functional position. The last molars usually appear between the ages of forty and fifty.

Several species of elephants lived in various parts of North America during the Pleistocene. *Archidiskodon imperator*, the imperial mammoth, was a southern form, which ranged from California and Mexico across the plains of Texas. Some individuals of this species reached a height of 14 feet. *Parelephas jeffersoni* was widely distributed over the Mississippi Valley, and *Mammuthus primigenius* (Fig. 287), the woolly mammoth, was a northern animal that was well fitted for life in cold regions during the glacial period. This remarkable creature ranged from Alaska to New England. Complete carcasses of the woolly mammoth have been found in the frozen tundra of Siberia, and some of the commercial ivory that is used today comes from fossil tusks of these Siberian elephants. Some of the American elephants in their old age developed such enormous tusks that these sometimes crossed at the tips, thus becoming utterly useless for digging purposes and losing most of their efficiency as offensive or defensive weapons. Tusks of the imperial mammoth have been found measuring 13 feet along the curve. These immense incisor teeth must have weighed several hundred pounds each and were undoubtedly a great burden to the animal.

Reading References

DIGBY, BASSETT: "The Mammoth and Mammoth Hunting in North-East Siberia," 224 pp., H. F. and G. Witherby, London, 1926.

COLBERT, E. H.: The Tar Pit Tiger, *Natural History*, vol. 46, No. 5, pp. 284–287, December, 1940.

OSBORN, HENRY F.: Mammals and Birds of the California Tar Pools, *Natural History*, vol. 25, No. 6, pp. 527–543, 1925.

————: Mammoths and Mastodons of North America, *Am. Mus. Nat. Hist. Guide Leaflet*, Series 62, 26 pp., 1926.

SCOTT, WILLIAM B.: "A History of Land Mammals in the Western Hemisphere," rev. ed., 786 pp., The Macmillan Company, New York, 1937.

SIMPSON, G. G.: The Meek Inherit the Earth, *Natural History*, vol. 49, No. 2, pp. 98–103, February, 1942.

————: The Great Animal Invasion, *Natural History*, vol. 49, No. 4, pp. 206–211, April, 1942.

CHAPTER XXI

THE GEOLOGIC HISTORY OF MAN

Thus He dwells in all,
From life's minute beginnings, up at last
To man—the consummation of this scheme
Of being, the completion of this sphere
Of life: whose attributes had here and there
Been scattered o'er the visible world before,
Asking to be combined, dim fragments meant
To be united in some wondrous whole,
Imperfect qualities throughout creation,
Suggesting some one creature yet to make,
Some point where all those scattered rays should meet
Convergent in the faculties of man.
—BROWNING, "Paracelsus"

THE PRIMATES

Characteristics. The primates are a very important group of mammals because they include man as well as the lemurs, monkeys, and great apes. The majority of primates are tree-living or arboreal animals, and this type of life has left its stamp upon every member of the family. Constant climbing around through the trees demands a flexible skeleton and the ability to grasp branches with both hands and feet. The flat nails afford considerable protection to the ends of the fingers and are very useful to man in picking up certain small objects.

Most primates are quadrupeds, but the higher members of the group can walk as bipeds. Although the early forms were largely omnivorous, there has been a decided trend toward the herbivorous type of diet and the teeth are less specialized than in the other mammals. As arboreal life demands keen eyesight, the primates have developed stereoscopic vision. Good vision is a very important factor in the acquisition of information, because it enables an animal to see clearly the various objects that surround him, and a wide acquaintance with his environment becomes possible. The large, well-developed brain is an outstanding primate characteristic and this important structure reaches its highest development in man.

415

Origin. The geologic history of the primates presents many difficulties and much uncertainty, because this group has left very few fossils. There are good reasons why this is true. Primates have always been largely arboreal animals and sediments that might preserve their remains are not commonly deposited in forest areas. When one of these creatures dies today, it falls to the ground, where its flesh quickly disappears and even the bones disintegrate within a short time. The lower primates of today live almost entirely within the tropics and apparently they have always

Fig. 289.—The pentailed shrew of Borneo is a primitive primate. Its probable ancestors have been found in the Cretaceous.

inhabited tropical environments. Most of the Tertiary deposits were formed in subtropical and warm temperate regions, where few, if any, primates lived. Some of the Eocene sediments in North America and Europe were deposited under tropical conditions, and these beds contain the remains of fossil primates.

The insectivores (Fig. 289) are small, primitive mammals whose ancestors appeared for the first time in the Cretaceous period. Some of these animals live on the ground and others are almost entirely arboreal. The brain is simple, a collarbone (clavicle) is present, and both feet and hands usually have five digits each. This group is represented today by the shrews, moles, and hedgehogs. It is possible that some large-brained, generalized, pro-

FIG. 290.—Restoration of the lemur *Notharctus* from the Eocene epoch of Wyoming. (*After Gregory.*)

FIG. 291.— *Tarsius spectrum*, the spectral tarsier, a very small primate from the East Indies and Philippine Islands. (*Drawn by John Jesse Hayes.*)

gressive member of the insectivore group was the ancestor of the primates.

Primate Types. The lemurs are the most primitive of the primates. These animals are found today in the tropical parts of Asia and Africa, but they are especially common on the island of Madagascar. Lemurs (Fig. 290) have been found in the Paleocene and Eocene rocks of the United States and in the Eocene of Europe, but they disappeared from these countries before the Oligocene epoch, probably because the climate was too cool for their tropical natures.

Tarsius (Fig. 291) is considerably higher in the evolutionary scale than are the lemurs. This furry animal is about the size of

a small rat, with a long tail, enormous eyes that are directed forward, a large brain, and five digits on each of the hands and feet. The thumb and the great toe can be opposed to the other digits. The ankle bones are greatly elongated, and the animal hops like a kangaroo. *Tarsius* is an arboreal form that lives in the Indo-Malayan Archipelago. The remains of many *Tarsius*-like animals (Fig.

Fig. 292.—*Anaptomorphus homunculus*, an Eocene tarsioid from the Wasatch beds. (*After Scott.*)

292) have been found in Eocene rocks. In some respects they form a link between the lemurs and the higher primates.

The monkeys represent a very distinct advance upon the lemurs and the tarsioids. These animals live in trees. Although they normally walk upon all fours, many of them habitually assume a sitting posture, which frees the hands for many purposes other than that of locomotion. The brain is large and the eyesight probably is as good as that of man. Monkeys are found in Central and South America and in various parts of the Old World. A jaw and a few fragments of monkey skeletons have been found in Oligocene rocks of the Fayum district in Egypt. Very little is known about the geologic history of the American monkeys.

The Manlike Apes. The gibbon, orang-utan, chimpanzee, and gorilla are the four living members of the anthropoid, or manlike ape, group. While all these animals are large, gorillas reach gigantic size. These great apes have well-developed brains, which, in the gorilla, may reach a maximum of 630 cubic centimeters. Experiments with a chimpanzee show that it has a good memory and that its reasoning powers, although they are only slightly developed, are of the human type. No living member of the anthropoid apes is

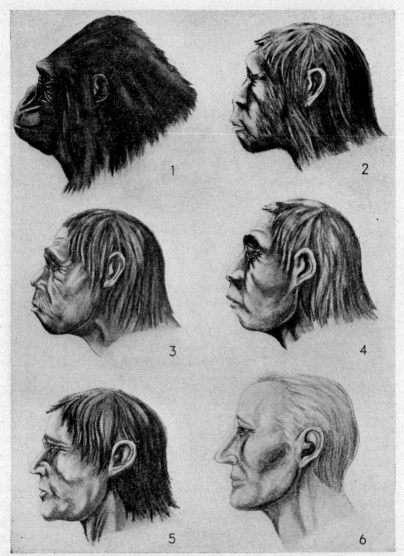

Fig. 293.—1, A gorilla; 2, *Pithecanthropus;* 3, *Eoanthropus*, the Piltdown man; 4, a Neanderthal man; 5, a Cro-Magnon type of man; 6, man of a modern race. (*Drawn by John Jesse Hayes.*)

the ancestor of man, but the human race has descended from some unknown member of the group.

Gibbon-like apes lived in the Old World during the middle Tertiary, and fragmentary remains of large primates called *Dry-opithecus* have been found in the Miocene and Pliocene of India. These fragments consist chiefly of teeth and jaws, and some of them possess characteristics indicating that they may be very close to the ancestral line of man.

Man.   If the anatomy of a modern man (Fig. 294) is compared with that of an ape, we find that they are essentially alike in bony

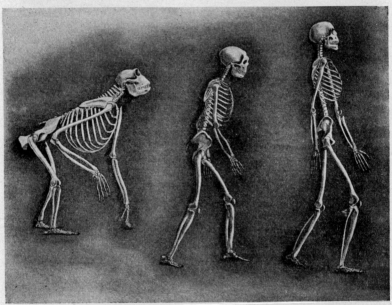

Fig. 294.— Skeleton of a chimpanzee on the left, a Neanderthal man in the center, and a modern type of man on the right.   In order to show all the bones clearly the skeleton of the chimpanzee is drawn to a larger scale than that of the other two.   The skeletal structures of these three forms, as well as those of all the primates, are essentially the same.   (*Drawn by John Jesse Hayes.*)

structure, muscles, and all the organs.   The differences are almost entirely a matter of degree.   Man's legs are longer in proportion to his arms than are those of the apes, and *Homo sapiens* is probably the descendant of some primate that had not developed the excessively long arms and short legs of permanent tree-dwelling forms. Our prehensile hand, with its five fingers and offset thumb, belongs to a primitive type, while our feet have lost their grasping function and are becoming adjusted to man's bipedal gait.   The toes have shortened, and the big toe is no longer offset, like the thumb, but has moved into a position parallel to the other digits, while the heel has lengthened into a prop. The great apes have very prominent muzzles, rounded chins, and projecting canine teeth, while in man the face has shortened, the chin extends forward, and the canines are no longer than the teeth on either side.

The brain is the outstanding characteristic of modern man. The average size ranges from about 1,200 to 1,500 cubic centimeters —two and three times that of the larger apes. Man's physical powers are not great, but his highly developed intelligence and the use of tools have enabled him to reach his present place of dominance over the entire earth and all its other inhabitants.

Primates are all inquisitive animals, possessing a spirit of adventure that is strongly developed and a desire to explore the world about them. Modern man has these same characteristics, which probably played an important part in causing our remote ancestors to leave the comparative safety of the trees and gradually take up life on the ground, where there was more danger but where the possibilities for future development were infinitely greater. Life in the trees is not difficult for small primates like the monkeys, but giant forms like the gorilla find it much easier to live on the ground. Increased size may also have been an important factor in causing our distant primate ancestors to become ground-living forms. Terrestrial life among the primates must have started about the Miocene epoch.

The Use of Weapons and Implements. Long before man learned the use of permanent weapons and implements, he probably picked up sticks or pieces of flint and used them for a few moments, after which they were discarded and forgotten. Finally he learned that a certain implement could be of great assistance to him in a particular situation. This happened after the association centers of the brain were rather well developed, and it gradually led to the use of permanent tools and weapons.

Some doubtful evidence of the existence of toolmaking creatures has been found in Late Pliocene gravels at Foxhall, near the village of Ipswich in Suffolk, England. This locality, which has been the scene of intensive search by archaeologists since 1910, has yielded a number of crude flints, called "eoliths," which show a little evidence of having been made by members of the human family who had acquired the art of crudely chipping flints. Nothing is known about the appearance of these Pliocene flintworkers, because no human remains have been found at any of the localities.

After men began to live in caves and bury their dead, human fossil remains became more numerous. The deposits found on the floors of numerous caverns in Europe contain not only the bones of human beings, but the remains of a great variety of lower animals and vast numbers of chipped flints. Successive layers of cave debris have revealed the progress made by the human race during thousands of years.

THE PILTDOWN SKULL

Piltdown Common is a stretch of moorland lying in the county of Sussex, a few miles south of London. During the early part of the Pleistocene, probably in the first interglacial epoch, the River Ouse covered this area with an extensive sheet of sand and gravel, in which a considerable number of worked flints have been found. One day Charles Dawson, a lawyer and enthusiastic naturalist from the town of Lewes, was walking across the common and stopped to examine a fresh exposure of the gravel. He soon found a fragment of a human skull. Later researches in the same locality resulted in the recovery of other skull parts, as well as the right half of a lower jaw, a lower canine tooth, and the nasal bones. These parts make up the famous Piltdown skull. The race of human beings to which it belongs has been called *Eoanthropus dawsoni* (Fig. 293), in honor of the discoverer. Parts of another skull were found later in the same gravel bed, but about two miles from the first site. After much very careful study, the original skull fragments were placed in their proper positions, with the missing portions restored, and a reconstruction of the head was made. The skull, which probably belonged to a female, shows several remarkable features. The forehead is high and the brow ridges scarcely more prominent than those of modern races. The cranial capacity is about 1,400 cubic centimeters, which is slightly greater than the average for European women of today. The skull bones are unusually thick and the bridge of the nose is broad and low. The protruding (prognathous) jaws and the receding chin are the most ape-like features of the Piltdown race, while the large brain and the slight development of the brow ridges indicate a very advanced stage of evolution. *Eoanthropus* may be an early Pleistocene ancestor of modern man.

PITHECANTHROPUS ERECTUS

The celebrated *Pithecanthropus erectus* (Fig. 293) was discovered in 1891 by Dr. Eugene Dubois, a Dutch army surgeon, during some excavations along the Solo River on the Island of Java. The remains consist of a well-preserved brain case, the left thighbone, pieces of nasal bones, and three teeth. These fragments were not found together but they came from the same horizon in the river gravel and may have belonged originally to one individual, although this is still uncertain. The skull is long, the forehead very low and receding, the brow ridges extremely heavy. The cranial capacity is about 900 cubic centimeters, which exceeds that of the largest modern ape, but still falls about 500 cubic centimeters short of the average among the higher races of today. The head was very unevenly balanced upon the neck, just as is the case among the apes. The chin was rounded, the face protruding, and all reconstructions indicate that *Pithecanthropus* had an ape-like appearance. The femur is straight and quite modern in type and must have belonged to an individual who could walk erect. Three other fragmentary skulls have been discovered recently, of which one shows the basal portion. Parts of both lower and upper jaws, as well as several teeth, have also been found. These show that the canines were not especially long and that the dentition is more human than ape-like. The large mammalian fauna found with the *Pithecanthropus* remains indicates that this race lived during the Middle Pleistocene.

Some recently discovered material has made the origin of man a more difficult problem than it was before, but these discoveries are of the greatest importance.

Pithecanthropus robustus had an unusually massive skull with evidence of a sagittal crest that was beginning to disappear. There was a gap between the canine and the lateral incisor, the palate was wide and smooth, and the second molar was somewhat larger than the first one or the third.

Meganthropus palaeojavanicus is represented by a fragment from the right side of the jawbone, and it must have belonged to an individual with a jaw only slightly smaller than that of a very large male gorilla. In spite of its size, it definitely belongs to a member of the human stock.

Gigantopithecus blacki is represented by three teeth that belonged to an individual who lived in Southern China during the Pleistocene. These teeth are of such immense size that they could only have fitted into a jaw even larger than that of *Meganthropus*, and they undoubtedly belonged to some huge primitive form of man.

THE PEKING RACE

During the middle part of the Pleistocene, a large limestone cavern located in the hills 30 miles south of Peking, China, was inhabited by a remarkable race of ape-men that have been called

Sinanthropus pekingensis. Extensive explorations in this cave since the original discoveries of 1928 and 1929 have resulted in the recovery of many skulls and lower jaws belonging to men, women, and children. A few leg bones have also been found, but for some reason they are not common. Each one of the skulls had been crushed before it was buried. This, together with the scarcity of other skeletal parts, is thought by some authors to indicate cannibalism.

The Peking skulls have low, sharply retreating foreheads, massive brow ridges, protruding jaws, and rounded chins. The cranial

Fig. 295.—Neanderthal men attacking the giant cave bear, *Ursus spelaeus.* (*Drawn by John Jesse Hayes.*)

capacity varies from 850 to 1,220 cubic centimeters, but the average is probably about 1,000 cubic centimeters. The limb bones show that *Sinanthropus* walked erect, although his general appearance was ape-like.

Over 2,000 flint implements belonging to the Chellean cultural stage were found in the cave debris. These are of various types and must have served a number of different purposes. Some of the flints were used for scraping and cutting and others served as awls. Man's interests were varied at that time and he was able to devise special tools for definite purposes. Judging from the large numbers of charred bones found in the cave, the Peking men must have been great hunters and they were acquainted with the uses of fire. In spite of his ape-like appearance, *Sinanthropus* was far ahead of the apes in mental and cultural development and social organization.

Some anthropologists do not regard *Sinanthropus* as a new genus but merely a new species of *Pithecanthropus*, and they believe the name should be *Pithecanthropus pekingensis*.

THE NEANDERTHAL RACE

During the middle portion of the long, warm interval that preceded that last advance of the glacier from the Scandinavian region,

Fig. 296.—A Neanderthal skull from Mt. Circeo in southern Italy.

western Europe was invaded by a remarkable group of savage hunters belonging to the Neanderthal race (Fig. 295). A considerable number of well-preserved skulls and skeletons of these people have been found, so that it is possible to restore *Homo neanderthalensis* as he must have appeared in real life. The original discovery site is a small cave in the Neander Valley, not far from Düsseldorf, Germany. A description of the find, which made a tremendous sensation, was published in 1858; but it was not until several years later that the remains were recognized as belonging to a new and distinct race.

The height of the Neanderthal men was seldom more than 5 feet 5 inches, but they were broad-shouldered and very powerful people. The skull is long (Fig. 296), the forehead low and sharply retreating. The brow ridges are heavy and the chin is retreating in most cases, although a small prominence is present in a few individuals. The

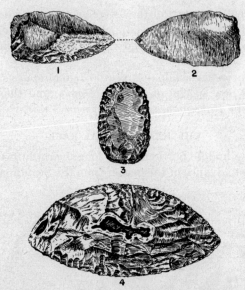

Fig. 297.—Mousterian implements: 1, 2, combined point and scraper; 3, double scraper; 4, a large scraper. (*After de Mortillet.*)

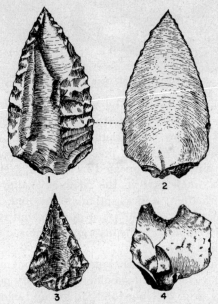

Fig. 298.—1–3, Mousterian points; 4, a scraper used to dress down the shafts of spears.

thighbones have a strong forward curvature, while the shinbones are short. Neanderthal man must have had an awkward, shuffling gait, with the knees bent forward. The cranial capacity is as great as that of modern man, varying from 1,300 to 1,600 cubic centimeters. The brain was larger in the back than in the frontal parts, and it seems quite probable that the higher faculties were not so well developed as they are in the more advanced races of today. The fact that these people occasionally buried their dead and placed

FIG. 299.—The pitfall is used today for capturing large animals and it was probably employed for the same purpose during Paleolithic and Neolithic times. (*Drawn by John Jesse Hayes.*)

food, as well as implements, in the grave suggests a belief in the future life and a developing sense of respect and responsibility toward other members of the tribe.

Neanderthal man made a great variety of specialized tools out of flint (Fig. 297), particularly hand axes, scrapers, and points (Fig. 298). The chief weapons of these men were flint-tipped spears, and yet they managed to kill such large animals as the cave bear, mammoth, reindeer, and bison. They probably set various kinds of traps, and the pitfall (Fig. 299) was probably used for catching larger animals. There is evidence that they had invented a sling or a throwing stick for hurling stones. Such weapons were used against smaller game. The food problem must have been a very difficult one during the long, severe winters that characterized the last advance of the ice, when snows were deep and food animals not too common. However, the intelligence and ingenuity of Neanderthal man enabled him to solve all the difficulties that he encountered during the thousands of years that his race lived in Europe.

Life in the Caves. Neanderthal man lived in caves and under rock shelters, especially during the long glacial winters. These caves are found in limestone bluffs along river valleys, and some of them were occupied as dwellings for a great many hundreds of

Fig. 300.—A Cro-Magnon family in southern France during the latter part of the Old Stone Age. (*Drawn by John Jesse Hayes.*)

years. Only the outer portions of the caverns were used as living places, because of lighting difficulties and the smoke nuisance whenever fires were lighted some distance back from the entrance. Numerous hearths have been found, and charred bones tell us a great deal about the animals that were killed for food. That Neanderthal man made very little attempt to keep the caves free from accumulating debris is a fortunate thing for the anthropologist, because these undisturbed layers of cave material contain a very important record of the Old Stone Age people, which might not have been preserved under any other conditions. There is no direct information about clothing worn by the Neanderthal men and

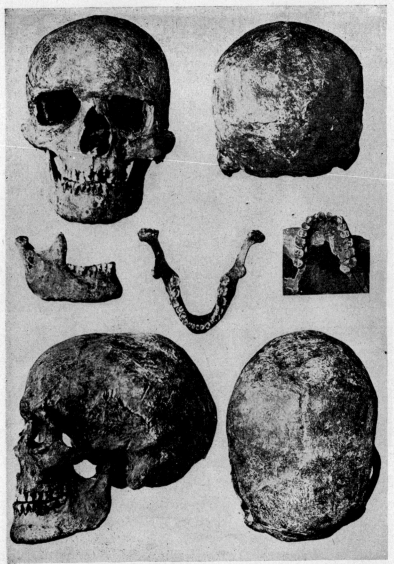

FIG. 301.—Skull and jaws of a Cro-Magnon man from the Grotte des Enfants. (*After Verneau.*)

women, but they must have fashioned garments out of skins, because these were usually available and offered the best protection against severe winter weather.

The great cave bear (Fig. 295) was one of the most powerful animals that lived in Europe during the Pleistocene. These creatures were as large as oxen, standing 5 feet 6 inches high and measuring 10 feet in length. They somehow visited the deepest parts of the caverns, where no ray of light ever penetrated, and they must have found their way around by means of their delicate sense of smell and of touch. When Neanderthal man wanted to secure the use of these caves, which had long been devoted to hibernating purposes by the bears, great conflicts were waged for possession of the shelters. The skull of a cave bear, with a stone axe of the Mousterian type embedded in the right parietal bone, was

Fig. 302.—Cro-Magnon burials. The upper skeleton from the Grotte du Cavillon and the lower from the Grotte des Enfants. (*After Verneau.*)

found in a cavern near the city of Trieste, at the head of the Adriatic Sea. The blow that the bear received must have been struck at close quarters, but the animal was not killed and the bone healed firmly around the axe.

Neanderthal man disappeared from Europe toward the close of the last glacial epoch, when he was forced to leave his old homeland by a group of invaders, the Cro-Magnon race. Many of the Neanderthal people were doubtless killed in battle with these new arrivals, while the rest were driven out and dispersed.

THE CRO-MAGNON RACE

The Cro-Magnon tribes (Fig. 300) began to move slowly into southern Europe during the declining stages of the last glacial epoch and, as living conditions improved, they gradually spread northward, displacing the more primitive Neanderthal people. The Cro-Magnon men were tall, powerful individuals, with massive skulls (Fig. 301) and brains that were just as large and well developed as those of any race living today. They had high foreheads

FIG. 303.—The Grimaldi skeletons. A Paleolithic burial from the Grotte des Enfants. An elderly woman on the left and a boy of about 16 on the right. (*After Verneau.*)

and prominent chins, and in every respect belonged to a thoroughly modern type. Several complete Cro-Magnon skeletons (Fig. 302) have been found, representing people of all ages, from young children to old men. Excellent reconstructions of many individuals have been made. The original discovery site was a grotto near the village of Les Eyzies in southern France, where the skeletons of

five human beings were found.   The female skull bore evidence of a
terrible wound that was probably made by a spear.

Burials.   The dead were often buried in various attitudes of
repose (Fig. 303), with food and flint implements placed beside
the bodies.   One infant had been buried with a large number of

FIG. 304.—Interior of the Font-de-Gaume cavern in the Les Eyzies region of southwestern France.

perforated shells, which must originally have been strung together
to form a shroud.   Another skeleton was found completely
embedded in shells, while others were covered with red ocher.   It is
quite probable that Cro-Magnon men painted their bodies on
certain occasions during life, after the fashion of American Indians.

A remarkable Cro-Magnon village site was uncovered near
Predmost in Moravia.   At this locality a vast accumulation of

Fig. 305.—The prominent rocky headland of Font-de-Gaume on the Beune River in the Les Eyzies region of southwestern France. The entrance to the great cavern is at the extreme right.

Fig. 306.—Polychrome painting of a bison from the cavern of Font-de-Gaume in the Les Eyzies region of southwestern France. (*After Breuil.*)

bones was found, including those of the mammoth, elk, musk ox, bear, wolf, and lion. All the long leg bones had been split open to obtain the marrow, and the skulls were crushed. A remarkable tomb measuring 14 feet long and 10 feet wide was found walled around by shoulder blades and lower jaws of mammoths. The

FIG. 307.—Engravings of wild cattle from the cavern of La Loja in the Cantabrian Mountains of northern Spain. (*After Breuil.*)

FIG 308.—Figure of the woolly mammoth engraved by a Cro-Magnon artist on the wall of the cavern at Combarelles, France. (*After Capitan and Breuil.*)

skeletons of 20 human beings interred in this grave had all been buried with the legs drawn up close to the bodies.

Art and Magic. The walls (Fig. 304) and ceilings of many caverns (Fig. 305) in southern France and northern Spain are covered with hundreds of paintings (Fig. 306) and engravings (Fig. 307) showing animal figures, as well as a great number of curious signs or symbols that doubtless had some magic significance. The chief colors used by the artists were black, yellow, orange, red, and brown. Paint was applied by means of a hair brush or the fingers. Most of the animal figures and curious designs (Fig. 309) are found in remote parts of the caves, which must have been ceremonial chambers where mystic rites were performed upon special occasions. The great seasonal hunts were apparently preceded by elaborate ceremonies, during which spears were hurled at clay models of cer-

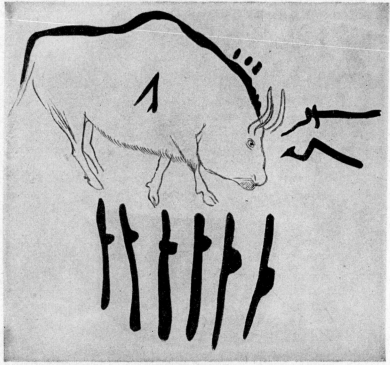

Fig. 309.—Engraving and painting of a bison with a dart embedded in its side. The club-shaped objects below are probably weapons. From the Pindal cavern in northern Spain. (*After Breuil.*)

tain animals, such as the bison. This was supposed to give the hunters good luck. Similar practices are common today among many primitive tribes.

The figures of animals are often painted (Fig. 310) or engraved with considerable attention to details of anatomy, showing that the artists were careful observers, and the artistic ability revealed by some of the paintings and engravings is truly remarkable. The Cro-Magnon medicine men, or witch doctors, wore grotesque masks, which are represented in cartoon fashion on some of the cave walls.

Some of the stone lamps that were used to light the ceremonial chambers have been found still in place on the cave floor, just as they were left after the ceremony had ended.   The ceremonial room in the cavern of La Pasiega in northern Spain has over 250 paintings on the walls, and at one end of the room there is a great throne carved out of solid rock.   This is where the chief of the tribe or the witch doctor sat while the magic rites were being performed.

Nothing is known about the written or spoken language of the Cro-Magnon people, but it is probable that they had both forms of

FIG. 310.—Reindeer painted in colors on a wall of the Font-de-Gaume cavern in southwestern France.

communication.   Many of the signs and symbols that are shown on the cavern walls were undoubtedly intended to convey certain ideas, but the meanings are unknown.

Weapons and Implements.   The bow and arrow (Fig. 311) and the spear thrower (Fig. 312) were the most effective weapons possessed by the Cro-Magnon tribes.   These people had invented a very modern type of harpoon with a barbed edge and a detachable point (Fig. 313).   Bone, reindeer horn, and ivory were used for a variety of purposes.   These materials were easier to work than flints, because they required no chipping, but merely cutting and

grinding.   Clothing was made from skins, and many bone needles
have been found.

Aurignacian Man.   The people who developed the Aurignacian
industry were cave dwellers, but they also built villages in the open.
A number of their camping sites have been found.   The bow and

Fig. 311.—Crude drawings by a Late Paleolithic artist showing use of the bow
and arrow.   (*After Breuil.*)

arrow had apparently been invented by this time, because arrow-
shaft straighteners (Fig. 314) have been discovered, bored to take
shafts of different diameters.   The Aurignacians were great hunters.
Reindeer and wild horses were particularly plentiful.   Near the
village of Solutre in south central France there is a great prehistoric
camp where the bones of several thousand wild horses have been
found piled up in great mounds.   The horses were killed by means

of spears or arrows, or they might even have been driven over the
edge of a great cliff that is near the village site.

Aurignacian man probably entered Europe by way of the
Mediterranean region and gradually migrated northward as the

FIG. 312.—How the spear thrower was used.

climate became less severe.   Scrapers, knife-like blades, and burins
(Fig. 315) were the chief implements of this epoch.   The burin,
a particularly valuable tool, was made in many different types and

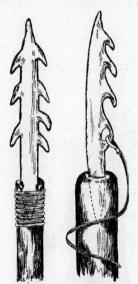
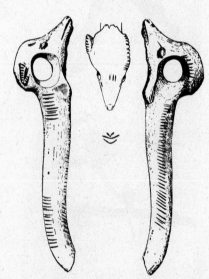

FIG. 313.—How Cro-
Magnon harpoon points
were probably fastened to
the shaft. The point on
the right was detachable
like those used by the
Eskimos.

FIG. 314.—Magdalenian *bâton de
commandement* from the cavern of Font-
de-Gaume in southwestern France. Such
instruments were probably used to
straighten the shafts of spears and
arrows. (*After Breuil.*)

sizes.   It doubtless was used for a variety of purposes, such as
engraving or cutting up hides into various shapes for use as clothing.

Solutrean Man.   The making of flint implements (Fig. 316)
and weapons reached its highest point of development in the

Solutrean epoch. The people who developed this culture were bold hunters who invaded Europe from the east across the more

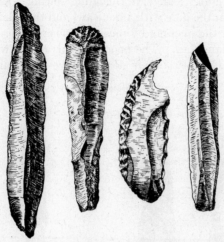

FIG. 315.—Flint knives and engraving tools or burins.

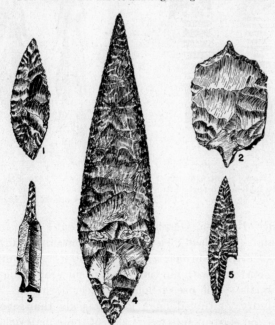

FIG. 316.—Solutrean implements. 1, 4, 5, spear points; 2, a drill or borer; 3, an awl.

open stretches of country. They were apparently a warlike race and had developed unusually fine lance heads, which are like the modern assagai, a spear used by some modern African tribes. These spearheads (Fig. 317) are thin and beautifully shaped, resembling a laurel leaf. At this time sewing was done by first boring a hole in the hide with a bone awl and then drawing a slender sinew through the opening by means of a needle.

Magdalenian Man. The people of this epoch were widely distributed over Europe. Their stations have been found in northern

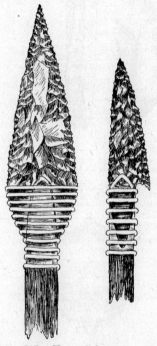

Fig. 317.—How Solutrean spear points were fastened to the shaft.

Fig. 318.—Late Paleolithic harpoons made of stag horn. From western Scotland. (*After Boule.*)

Spain, France, Belgium, Germany, and at Kent's Hole in Devonshire, England. The last Pleistocene glacier was receding and the climate was getting warmer. Reindeer and other animals were migrating northward, with hunting tribes of men following the great herds of animals. The use of bone, reindeer horn (Fig. 318), and mammoth ivory continued on a greater scale than ever before. Arrowheads and spear points were made of these materials. Many of the lance heads were made with one or two rows of barbs (Fig. 319). This was a very important invention, since the barbs would hold firmly any animal that had been speared. The Eskimos use

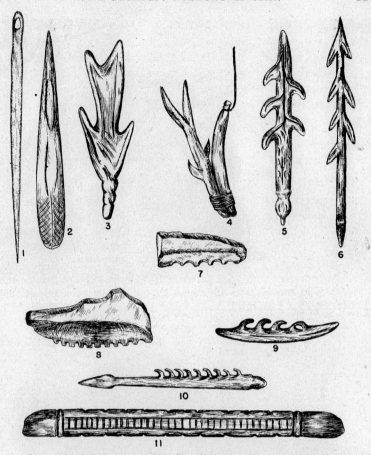

FIG. 319.— Magdalenian weapons and implements. 1, a bone needle; 2, a javelin point of bone—the beveled end was attached to the spear shafts; 3, 4, fishhooks; 5, 6, 9, 10, bone harpoon points; 7, 8, flints with denticulated edges; 11, a chisel.

FIG. 320.— This engraving on a wall of the Font-de-Gaume cavern probably represents a Cro-Magnon tent or hut.

FIG. 321.—Restoration of an Aurignacian hut based upon cave drawings. Skins were stretched over a framework of wood, thus producing a type of shelter that is still used by certain tribes of men. (*Drawn by John Jesse Hayes.*)

FIG. 322.—The line drawings, superimposed upon the body of an animal, probably represent shelters or tents consisting of a wooden framework covered with hides. From the Font-de-Gaume cavern.

harpoons of the same type, today. The Magdalenians had devised a very modern type of bow drill, which could have been used either for boring holes or for making fire by friction.

Prehistoric art reached its highest development during this epoch. Many of the paintings and engravings are excellent, complete even to small anatomical details. Bison, mammoth, and wild boars were all depicted by Magdalenian artists with great fidelity, some of the animals being pictured in lifelike action postures. The people who produced such works were becoming civilized.

Cro-Magnon Dwellings. The old caves of the Neanderthal tribes were still used for dwellings and ceremonial purposes by the Cro-Magnon people, but many houses were built in the open. Several drawings and engravings (Fig. 320) have been found that probably represent different types of huts. The Aurignacians apparently made a tent by first setting up a framework of slender, flexible willow trees or branches and covering this mound-shaped structure with hides (Fig. 321). Later types resemble the wigwams of the American Indians, and some had the sloping roof (Fig. 322) and vertical sidewalls of a modern tent. The art of making a thatched roof from grass or rushes had probably been developed.

The Cro-Magnon stock did not, like that of most of the earlier races, become extinct. It still survives in southern France and other parts of Europe.

CLOSE OF THE PALEOLITHIC AGE

Toward the close of the Old Stone Age, new races began to appear in Europe, while the art that was so characteristic of Magdalenian times declined and finally disappeared. There was also a great decrease in the variety of implements produced from various materials, and most of the instruments that were made exhibit a workmanship greatly inferior to that of earlier times.

During this period of gradual transition to the Neolithic, or New Stone Age, the climate slowly grew warmer, and greatly increased rainfall favored the spread of vast forest areas. Profound changes were taking place in the life of man. He was able to migrate farther to the north and to live in regions that had long been uninhabitable. The most desirable caves were still occupied, but more villages appeared and houses were made of wood and skins. In parts of Italy and Switzerland dwellings were built upon pilings driven into the lake bottoms.

The Cretaceous chalk of southern England contains numerous flint nodules. To secure these, prehistoric men used regular mining methods. First, a shaft was dug; then tunnels or drifts were run in various directions and at different levels along the flint-bearing strata. These mining operations covered hundreds of square miles, and many of the ancient workings may still be followed. Stone lamps were used to light the drifts and certain mining tools were made of staghorn. One of the digging tools was found still clutched in the skeleton hand of a prehistoric miner.

Many smoothed and polished stone implements were in use during the Neolithic Age, and the art of making pottery was discovered. It is difficult to see why the Cro-Magnon people, who made numerous figures out of clay, never learned to make pottery.

Men lived in the valleys of the Nile and the Euphrates during Neolithic times. Evidence of their culture has been found in deep excavations on the sites of such ancient cities as Susa, in the Persian highlands, and Knossos, in Crete.

PREHISTORIC MAN IN NORTH AMERICA

The time of man's first arrival in North America is still a matter of considerable uncertainty, but the migration route that he used must have led from Siberia to Alaska. The time was probably late Pleistocene. In a number of places, flint implements, as well as parts of human skeletons, have been found associated with the remains of animals that are now extinct, such as *Parelephas columbi*, true wild horses, several species of bison, camels of the genus *Camelops*, and giant ground sloths.

Several especially interesting sites have been explored near Vero and Melbourne on the east coast of Florida. The Vero locality has yielded portions of a human pelvis and some foot bones associated with the remains of the ground sloth, wild horses, elephants, and mastodons. Some of the bones belonging to the lower animals bear marks made by flint knives while the flesh was being cut away. Human bones, artifacts, and pieces of pottery have been discovered at Melbourne, associated with a fauna very much like that found at Vero.

A gravel pit located 1 mile north of Frederick, Oklahoma, has yielded several flint implements and the bones of several extinct Pleistocene mammals, including elephants, camels, glyptodonts, ground sloths, and tapirs.

The Folsom Points represent one of the most significant finds yet made in American archaeology. The discovery site is located 15 miles west of Folsom, New Mexico, in a valley called "Dead Horse Gulch." This place had evidently been the scene of a great hunt, because numerous arrow points were found with skeletons of the extinct *Bison taylori*. All the tail bones were missing, which probably indicates that the bison had been skinned and their hides carried away by the Indians. The Lindenmeier site, located 28 miles north of Fort Collins, Colorado, has produced about 2,000 flints of the Folsom variety, including knives, scrapers, drills, hammers, and arrow points. Many of the bison bones found at this locality were burned, the tribe having apparently celebrated their successful hunt with a great feast. No human bones have been discovered at any of the Folsom sites, and the age of the deposits is still in doubt, but they are either Late Pleistocene or early Recent.

The association of human remains and artifacts with the bones of extinct Pleistocene mammals does not prove the great antiquity of man in North America, because some of these extinct animals might have survived until comparatively recent times, but the evidence strongly supports the contention that man lived in North America during the latter part of the Pleistocene epoch and that he may have reached this continent 20,000 years ago.

WHAT OF THE FUTURE?

The geologic processes that have been shaping the surface of the earth for two billion years will doubtless continue their activities indefinitely. Rivers will carry sediments into the oceans, epeiric seas will again invade the continents, and new mountain ranges will rise out of geosynclines that do not even exist at present. The great continental glaciers that cover Greenland and Antarctica will finally melt and important climatic changes will affect large areas of the earth's surface.

Life reaches far back into the dim vistas of Pre-Cambrian time, and living things will continue to inhabit the earth for countless ages. Another group of animals may some day replace the declining race of mammals. Man, as he is at present, is certainly capable of much improvement. The occasional appearance of great individuals who achieve magnificent things may be prophetic of what many future members of the human race will be able to accomplish. Biological progress may be slow, but it has not stopped. Nothing is static forever in nature; change is going on everywhere.

The following lines by Robert Browning give some conception of man's possible destiny.

> The morn has enterprise, deep quiet droops
> With evening, triumph takes the sunset hour,
> Voluptuous transport ripens with the corn
> Beneath a warm moon like a happy face:
> —And this to fill us with regard for man,
> With apprehension of his passing worth,
> Desire to work his proper nature out,
> And ascertain his rank and final place,
> For these things tend still upward, progress is
> The law of life, man is not Man as yet.
> Nor shall I deem his object served, his end

Attained, his genuine strength put fairly forth,
While only here and there a star dispels
The darkness, here and there a towering mind
O'erlooks its prostrate fellows: when the host
Is out at once to the despair of night,
When all mankind alike is perfected,
Equal in full-blown powers—then, not till then,
I say, begins man's general infancy.
For wherefore make account of feverish starts
Of restless members of a dormant whole,
Impatient nerves which quiver while the body
Slumbers as in a grave?   Oh long ago
The brow was twitched, the tremulous lids astir,
The peaceful mouth disturbed; half-uttered speech
Ruffled the lip, and then the teeth were set,
The breath drawn sharp, the strong right-hand clenched stronger,
As it would pluck a lion by the jaw;
The glorious creature laughed out even in sleep!
But when full roused, each giant-limb awake,
Each sinew strung, the great heart pulsing fast,
He shall start up and stand on his own earth,
Then shall his long triumphant march begin,
Thence shall his being date,—thus wholly roused,
What he achieves shall be set down to him.
When all the race is perfected alike
As man, that is; all tended to mankind,
And, man produced, all has its end thus far.
But in completed man begins anew
A tendency to God.

—BROWNING, "Paracelsus"

Reading References

CASTERET, NORBERT: "Ten Years under the Earth," 283 pp., Greystone Press, Inc., New York.

HOOTON, EARNEST A.: "Up from the Ape," 626 pp., The Macmillan Company, New York, 1931.

————: "Apes, Men, and Morons," 307 pp., G. P. Putnam's Sons, New York, 1937.

————: "Twilight of Man," 308 pp., G. P. Putnam's Sons, New York, 1939.

HOWELLS, WILLIAM: "Mankind So Far," 319 pp., Doubleday, Doran & Company, Inc., Garden City, New York, 1944.

MacCURDY, GEORGE G.: "Human Origins," 2 vols., 440 and 516 pp., D. Appleton-Century Company, Inc., New York, 1924.

NEEDHAM, JAMES G.: "About Ourselves," 276 pp., The Jaques Cattell Press, Lancaster, Pa., 1941.

OSBORN, HENRY F.: "Men of the Old Stone Age," 545 pp., Charles Scribner's Sons, New York, 1915.

SOLLAS, W. J.: "Ancient Hunters," 3d ed., 689 pp., The Macmillan Company. New York, 1924.

WEIDENREICH, FRANZ: Man or Ape, *Natural History*, vol. 45, No. 1, pp. 32–37, January, 1940.

INDEX

(Numbers in boldface type refer to pages containing illustrations)

O